THE WAVE MECHANICS OF ELECTRONS IN METALS

FROM THE SERIES IN PHYSICS

General Editors:

J. DE BOER, Professor of Physics, University of Amsterdam
H. BRINKMAN, Professor of Physics, University of Groningen
H. B. G. CASIMIR, Director of the Philips' Laboratories, Eindhoven

Monographs:

B. BAK, Elementary Introduction to Molecular Spectra
H. C. BRINKMAN, Application of Spinor Invariants in Atomic Physics
H. G. VAN BUEREN, Imperfections in Crystals
S. R. DE GROOT, Thermodynamics of Irreversible Processes
E. A. GUGGENHEIM, Thermodynamics
E. A. GUGGENHEIM and J. E. PRUE, Physicochemical Calculations
H. JONES, The Theory of Brillouin Zones and Electronic States in Crystals
H. A. KRAMERS, Quantum Mechanics
H. A. KRAMERS, The Foundations of Quantum Theory
J. G. LINHART, Plasma Physics
J. MCCONNELL, Quantum Particle Dynamics
A. MESSIAH, Quantum Mechanics, Volume I
I. PRIGOGINE, The Molecular Theory of Solutions
E. G. RICHARDSON, Relaxation Spectrometry
P. ROMAN, Theory of Elementary Particles
M. E. ROSE, Internal Conversion Coefficients
J. L. SYNGE, Relativity: The Special Theory
J. L. SYNGE, Relativity: The General Theory
J. L. SYNGE, The Relativistic Gas
H. UMEZAWA, Quantum Field Theory
D. TER HAAR, Elements of Hamiltonian Mechanics
A. VAŠÍČEK, Optics of Thin Films
A. H. WAPSTRA, G. J. NYGH and R. VAN LIESHOUT, Nuclear Spectroscopy Tables

Eatted Volumes:

D. A. BROMLEY and E. W. VOGT (editors), Proceedings of the Intern. Conference on Nuclear Structure (Kingston, 1960)
P. M. ENDT and M. DEMEUR (editors), Nuclear Reactions, Volume I
C. J. GORTER (editor), Progress in Low Temperature Physics, Vol. I–III
G. M. GRAHAM and A. C. HOLLIS HALLETT, Proceedings of the VIIth Intern. Conference on Low Temperature Physics (Toronto, 1960)
G. L. DE HAAS-LORENTZ (editor), H. A. Lorentz, Impressions of his Life and Work
H. J. LIPKIN (editor), Proceedings of the Rehovoth Conference on Nuclear Structure
N. R. NILSSON (editor), Proceedings of the Fourth International Conference on Ionization Phenomena in Gases (Uppsala, 1959)
K. SIEGBAHN (editor), Beta- and Gamma-Ray Spectroscopy
Symposium on Solid State Diffusion (Colloque sur la diffusion à l'état solide, Saclay, 1958)
3e Colloque de Métallurgie, sur la Corrosion (Saclay, 1959)
Turning Points in Physics. A Series of Lectures given at Oxford University in Trinity Term 1958
J. G. WILSON and S. A. WOUTHUYSEN (editors), Progress in Elementary Particle and Cosmic Ray Physics. Volumes I–V
E. WOLF (editor), Progress in Optics, Volume I
BALTH. VAN DER POL, Selected Scientific Papers
P. EHRENFEST, Collected Scientific Papers

THE WAVE MECHANICS OF ELECTRONS IN METALS

BY

STANLEY RAIMES

Reader in Mathematics
Imperial College
University of London

1961

NORTH-HOLLAND PUBLISHING COMPANY – AMSTERDAM
INTERSCIENCE PUBLISHERS INC. – NEW YORK

SOLE DISTRIBUTORS FOR U.S.A.:
INTERSCIENCE PUBLISHERS INC. – NEW YORK

PRINTED IN THE NETHERLANDS
BY N.V. DIJKSTRA'S DRUKKERIJ, V/H BOEKDRUKKERIJ GEBROEDERS HOITSEMA
GRONINGEN

These metaphysics of magicians,
And necromantic books are heavenly;
Lines, circles, scenes, letters, and characters;
Aye, these are those that Faustus most desires.
O, what a world of profit and delight,
Of power, of honour, of omnipotence,
Is promis'd to the studious artizan!

Marlowe's *Dr. Faustus.*

PREFACE

The theory of the solid state has increased greatly in complexity during the past twenty years, many original papers being incomprehensible except to theoretical physicists working in highly specialized fields. As a consequence, experimental physicists, metallurgists and others have often to take theoretical results at their face value, without fully understanding the restrictions imposed by the necessary and unavoidable approximations introduced into the theory. This sometimes leads to an extrapolation of a theory beyond its limits of validity, with results which, if not ludicrous, may draw red herrings across the path of scientific progress.

When he attempts to broaden his theoretical knowledge by reference to text-books, the experimental scientist is faced with further difficulty. Books on the theory of the solid state generally fall into two classes – elementary works which contain little mathematics, and advanced works which presuppose a considerable knowledge both of mathematics and of quantum mechanics. Books of the former kind are very useful to those who are content to have a superficial knowledge of the theory, but do little to prepare the more zealous student for the advanced treatises or for theoretical papers. Furthermore, such elementary treatments rarely, if ever, give an adequate account of the approximations involved in the theory, which require a certain amount of mathematics in their explanation. Indeed, the more advanced works are not entirely blameless in this respect, often erecting huge structures of formal mathematics upon foundations whose flimsiness is, perhaps unwittingly, well concealed.

The present work is a tentative attempt to bridge the gap between the two classes, and at the same time to draw attention to the limitations of the various approximate methods in current use. The treatment is mathematical, but no more mathematics is required than is normally given in undergraduate courses to students of physics, metallurgy and chemistry. Mathematical arguments are presented complete with all intermediate steps, and refresher accounts of certain mathematical topics are given in appendices.

I have thought it useful to make the book self-contained, so that it can be read without either blind acceptance of 'well-known' facts or constant reference to other works. Thus, the necessary wave mechanics is developed from first principles, and applications are given to simple one-electron systems, atoms and molecules, before dealing with the more complex problems of metals and other solids. However, the book does not pretend to be a comprehensive survey of the whole of the electron theory of metals – the theories of conductivity and ferromagnetism, for example, are not treated in detail. The emphasis is upon basic ideas, with the aim of providing a sound foundation for further study in more specialized fields.

Particular attention is paid to the calculation of energies – not only one-electron energies but also the energy of the metallic system as a whole. Here again, however, the emphasis is upon fundamentals, and the many recent techniques used in band structure calculations, which are mainly of interest to specialists, are not described. On the other hand, the thorny problem of the interaction of electrons, which permeates the whole theory, is discussed at length, and there is a chapter on plasma oscillations in metals. Problems relating to every chapter are collected together at the end of the book.

Although the book has been written primarily for graduate students of physics, metallurgy and chemistry, who wish to obtain more than a superficial knowledge of the electron theory of metals and of solid state theory in general, it will be seen that the greater part of the work is suitable for inclusion in undergraduate courses.

In a book of this sort it would be unnecessarily cumbersome always to give references to original papers. This has been done, in fact, only in the case of the more recent papers of particular importance and those which contain the quoted results of experiment or lengthy calculation. When further references are required, they may be found in the works listed in the Bibliography.

The book has not been read by experts, or even discussed with them, before publication, so that any sins of omission or commission are my sole responsibility. Since many of the topics covered have not appeared in textbooks before and the approach to others is somewhat unconventional, it is too much to hope that errors are not present. I shall be grateful to those friends who will point them out to me.

Finally, my best thanks are due to Mr. J. H. Tripp for his help in reading the proofs.

S. RAIMES

Imperial College,
September, 1961

CONTENTS

CHAPTER 1

INTRODUCTION

1.1. Classical Mechanics and Quantum Mechanics

All bulk matter, whether solid, liquid, or gas, is composed of atoms. It is now well known that an atom is not, as was once thought, a particle incapable of further subdivision, but is a complex dynamical system, consisting of negatively charged particles called *electrons* and a positively charged particle called the *nucleus*. Indeed, the nucleus of an atom is itself an extremely complex structure, consisting essentially of positively charged *protons* and uncharged *neutrons*. Fortunately, however, as far as the theory of solids is concerned, it is generally sufficient to regard a nucleus as a particle of negligible size, having a certain positive electric charge and a certain mass, these varying from element to element.

The properties of bulk matter must, in principle at least, be deducible from the properties of the electrons and atomic nuclei of which it is composed. It is found, however, that the observed properties of matter cannot be explained on the assumption that these particles obey the laws of classical mechanics, as formulated by Newton. A new mechanics, called Quantum Mechanics, has had to be constructed, and one particular form of this is called Wave Mechanics. In this book we shall start with the principles of wave mechanics and show how to apply them first to the simplest atomic systems and later to the large and important class of solids known as metals.

It must be understood that these principles of wave mechanics cannot be deduced from classical mechanics. There are, however, several alternative sets of principles, any one of which may be deduced from any other, so that the set which is chosen as fundamental is largely a matter of convenience. Although this applies equally well to the principles of classical mechanics, it is a fact which is often overlooked, owing to the apparently 'self-evident' nature of classical mechanics. For this reason it may be useful to digress briefly on the philosophy of physical theory.

The purpose of theoretical physics is to co-ordinate the known facts of experimental physics, and to predict new ones. A physical theory 'explains' an experimental result if it shows that this result is consistent with other experimental results, which it will do if all the results can be deduced from the basic principles of the theory. As soon as an experimental fact † appears which the theory cannot explain, the theory must be amended. A new theory is set up, or a new principle is established, which accords with the new and unexplained fact. Of course, the new theory must explain all the other experimental facts as well, or it is no improvement on the old theory. It is important to notice, however, that the basic principle of the new theory has no 'explanation', except that deductions from it are in agreement with the experimental facts.

We have, of course, been discussing an idealized situation. Although it is theoretically possible to deduce the result of any experiment from a given set of principles, in practice this may be impossible to do accurately, owing to mathematical difficulties. We shall have many examples of this later in the book. Thus it may not be possible always to verify a theory in a completely satisfactory way. None the less, the theory may be accepted so long as the approximate deductions from it are in reasonable agreement with experiment, and no well-established deduction is completely at variance with any experimental fact.

When we say that a new basic principle itself has no explanation, we do not wish to imply that it never will have. A principle established at one level of experience may have an explanation at a more fundamental level — a macroscopic principle, for example, may have an explanation in terms of atomic motions. However, as we have remarked, at any particular level there may be several alternative sets of principles which lead to the same results. So long as these sets of principles are consistent with each other, they are all equally valid, and it does not matter which is taken to be fundamental. Admittedly, it is aesthetically satisfying to have the basic principles as simple and as few in number as possible, but from a practical point of view this is not important — the most compact set of principles may not be the most tractable. The principles we shall adopt in this work are neither the most compact, nor the most elegant, but are in a form which leads most easily to the results we require.

It may be reassuring to realize that everything we have said is just as

† We use the term 'experimental fact' to denote a *well-founded* experimental result — one which is reproducible; that is, one which can be obtained again and again by repeating a given experiment. This is to overcome the difficulty that the result of a single experiment may conflict with theory simply owing to some chance experimental error.

true of classical mechanics as it is of quantum mechanics. The most elementary formulation of the principles of classical mechanics is contained in Newton's equations of motion — and these are *not* self-evident, but survive only because they correctly predict the motion of macroscopic bodies, such as billiard balls, ballistic missiles, and planets. However, one could equally well take Lagrange's equations, Hamilton's equations, or Hamilton's principle as the fundamental principles of mechanics, since these are all consistent with each other and with Newton's equations. It is true that Newton's equations are the simplest, but, for this very reason, they are suitable only for simple problems; Lagrange's and Hamilton's equations are more useful for complicated dynamical problems.

The situation in quantum mechanics is rather worse. Not only are there many alternative sets of initial postulates, but there are two mathematical formalisms so different that at first sight they appear to be different theories. First, there is *matrix mechanics*, due to Heisenberg, Born and Jordan, and, second, there is *wave mechanics*, due to de Broglie and Schrödinger. The elegant generalization of matrix mechanics, due to Dirac, should also be mentioned. Although matrix mechanics and wave mechanics appear to have little in common, it can be shown that they are, in fact, equivalent, so that we may use whichever is more convenient for a given problem. In this book we shall use only wave mechanics, which is in many ways simpler and makes a more direct appeal to physical intuition, although it may still be worth while to repeat Eddington's † warning that the popularity of wave mechanics may be due to its being 'simple enough to be misunderstood'.

1.2. Basic Experimental Facts

What, then, are the basic experimental facts, which are inexplicable by classical mechanics, and which therefore require a new theory? There is, indeed, a very wide choice of these, since almost the whole of atomic physics, and hence the greater part of modern physics, is quite inexplicable by classical mechanics. In order to avoid mathematical difficulties, however, it is best to start with the simplest and most clear-cut experimental results, and hope that a theory constructed to fit these will also explain the others. We shall begin by considering only two experimental facts: (i) the wave-like behaviour of particles, and (ii) the existence of line spectra.

† *The Nature of the Physical World*, Chap. 10.

1.2.1. WAVES AND PARTICLES

In 1900, Planck proposed, in order to explain the distribution of energy in the spectrum of a black body, that an oscillating electron may not radiate or absorb energy continuously, as required by classical electrodynamics, but only in integral multiples of a fundamental unit called a *quantum*. If ν is the frequency of the radiation, the energy of a quantum is given by

$$E = h\nu, \tag{1.1}$$

where h is a constant of nature, known as *Planck's constant*, which has the value 6.624×10^{-27} erg sec. In 1905, Einstein went further and suggested that light, or electromagnetic radiation in general, might sometimes be regarded as having a corpuscular, or particle-like, nature. The light-particles, or quanta, are called *photons*, and have energy given by (1.1).

Although light had been ascribed a corpuscular nature by Newton, this concept had been shelved owing to the many successes of the wave theory. Einstein's proposal explained very well the photo-electric effect — when a metallic surface is irradiated with ultra-violet light, electrons are emitted with energies which do not depend upon the intensity of the light, but only upon the frequency, in a way which suggests that the light consists of particles each of energy $h\nu$.

According to the theory of relativity, the momentum of a photon must have magnitude p, given by

$$p = \frac{h\nu}{c} = \frac{h}{\lambda}, \tag{1.2}$$

where c is the speed of light and λ is the wavelength. This follows immediately from the equation which is nowadays popularly known as 'the equation of atomic energy', that is,

$$E = mc^2, \tag{1.3}$$

for the energy E of a particle with relativistic mass m. If the speed of the particle is v, the magnitude of its momentum is

$$p = mv = \frac{Ev}{c^2} = \frac{h\nu v}{c^2}, \tag{1.4}$$

using equations (1.1) and (1.3). If we let $v = c$, the speed of a photon, we obtain equation (1.2). This is the only appearance the theory of relativity will make in the present book. In future the mass m will be assumed to be independent of velocity; that is, it will denote the rest mass of the particle. Photons are peculiar in that they travel with the speed of light and have zero rest mass, but we shall not be directly concerned with photons in the following work.

What it is important to notice is that light can be thought of *either* as waves with particle-like properties *or* as particles with wave-like properties. There is no need for us to worry about *how* a thing can be both a particle and a wave; we merely accept that the nature of a given experiment will lead to results which emphasize one aspect or the other, and the relations between the two aspects are those given in equations (1.1) and (1.2).

In 1924, de Broglie generalized this idea, and suggested that *any* moving particle, with mass m and speed v, will in some experiments display wave-like properties, with wavelength

$$\lambda = \frac{h}{p} = \frac{h}{mv}, \tag{1.5}$$

as in equation (1.2). This theoretical suggestion received experimental confirmation in 1927, when Davisson and Germer observed the diffraction of a beam of electrons by a crystal of nickel. Electrons emitted from a hot filament and accelerated through an electric field to a known velocity were allowed to fall upon the surface of a nickel crystal. The reflected beam was found to exhibit directed maxima and minima of intensity, as in the case of X-ray diffraction, which could be accounted for by the assumption that the electron beam consisted of waves with wavelength given by (1.5). Similar results have since been obtained with beams of other kinds of particles, including atoms and molecules.

1.2.2. LINE SPECTRA AND STATIONARY STATES

According to classical electrodynamics, an accelerated electric charge will emit radiation. If we accept Rutherford's model of a hydrogen atom, for instance, as an electron moving in an orbit about a nucleus consisting of a single proton, we should expect a continuous emission of radiation, and hence a continuous loss of energy by the electron. This would result in the orbit getting smaller and smaller until eventually the electron would collide with the proton. It need hardly be said that such a catastrophe is quite contrary to observation.

Neglecting this difficulty, however, another presents itself. According to classical mechanics, a dynamical system can absorb or emit infinitesimal amounts of energy. If the energy of a system, consisting of particles in motion, is increased by a small amount, the velocities and orbits of the particles will simply be changed by small amounts. This means that a classical system could exist with any one of a continuous range of energies. If this were true of atomic systems, we should expect a gas of hydrogen atoms, for example, to absorb and emit light of all frequencies, that is, we should expect a *continuous* spectrum. In fact, the low frequency end of the hydrogen spectrum consists of an infinite series of *discrete* spectral lines. Niels Bohr, in 1913, deduced from this, together with Einstein's photon hypothesis, that an atom can exist in any one of a set of so-called *stationary states*, each with a definite energy, and with a finite energy difference between one and the next. Also, when an atom is in a stationary state it does not radiate, but radiation of frequency ν is emitted when an atom passes from a stationary state with energy E_1 to a stationary state with lower energy E_2, where

$$E_1 - E_2 = h\nu. \tag{1.6}$$

This is called the *Bohr frequency rule*. Clearly, if the atom is in the lower energy state, the absorption of a quantum $h\nu$ will transfer the atom to the higher energy state.

In this book we shall be mainly concerned with calculating the energies of stationary states, or *energy levels*, of atoms and systems of atoms. We shall be particularly interested in the stationary state with lowest energy, or *ground state*, which is the most stable state of an atomic system — the other states are referred to as *excited states*. Of course, we should mention that, as well as the discrete energy levels, there is generally at higher energies a continuum of energy levels, which gives rise to a continuous spectrum. In the hydrogen atom, for instance, this continuous spectrum corresponds to complete ionization — in other words, the case when the electron and proton are no longer bound together, but have become separate free particles.

Bohr himself proposed a theory of atoms, based upon the classical model of planetary electrons circulating about the nucleus, but having the idea of stationary states grafted on to it in a rather artificial way. This theory accounted very well for the line spectrum of hydrogen, but could not be applied directly to more complicated atoms. Thus, although it had several partial successes apart from the hydrogen atom, the utility of the theory was strictly limited, and it soon gave way to quantum mechanics, which represented a more radical, but at the same time more satisfying, break with classical mechanics. We will therefore omit details of the Bohr theory, and proceed directly to a discussion of wave mechanics as applied to the simplest of all dynamical systems — a single particle constrained to move in a straight line.

1.3. Schrödinger's Equation for the One-Dimensional Motion of a Single Particle

Let us consider a particle of mass m moving along a line, which we may take to be the x-axis, under the action of a force F in the positive x-direction. Also let us suppose that the particle has a potential energy $V(x)$, so that, according to classical mechanics, $F = -\mathrm{d}V/\mathrm{d}x$. Such a system, with a potential energy which does not depend explicitly upon the time, is called a *conservative system*, because the total energy is conserved, that is, remains constant. In this book, except for the final chapter, we shall be concerned exclusively with conservative systems.

We now *postulate*, and this will be justified by results, that the state of motion of the particle is in some way represented by a function $\psi(x)$ which satisfies the equation

$$\frac{\mathrm{d}^2\psi}{\mathrm{d}x^2} + \frac{2m}{\hbar^2}[E - V(x)]\psi = 0. \tag{1.7}$$

Here $\hbar = h/2\pi$, and E is the constant total energy of the particle, that is, the sum of its kinetic and potential energies. Equation (1.7) is called Schrödinger's Equation, or Schrödinger's *Wave* Equation, for this system, and the function ψ is called a *wave function*, for reasons which will become apparent. We will leave aside the physical interpretation of ψ for the moment — and indeed one can get a very long way in the theory without interpreting ψ at all — but we will concentrate first upon showing that the Schrödinger equation can provide the sort of result that is required to explain the facts described in § 1.2.

In the first place, if the potential energy V is *constant*, then the kinetic energy T is also constant. We have

$$T = \tfrac{1}{2}mv^2 = E - V, \tag{1.8}$$

where $v = \dot{x}$. Thus, if λ is the de Broglie wavelength, defined in equation (1.5), we find

$$E - V = \frac{h^2}{2m\lambda^2}, \tag{1.9}$$

and equation (1.7) becomes

$$\frac{d^2\psi}{dx^2} + \frac{4\pi^2}{\lambda^2}\psi = 0, \tag{1.10}$$

with λ constant.

The general solution of this equation may be written

$$\psi(x) = A \sin\left(\frac{2\pi}{\lambda}x + \delta\right), \tag{1.11}$$

where A and δ are arbitrary constants, known as the *amplitude* and *phase* respectively. If A and δ are real constants, the graph of ψ is thus the sinusoidal *wave profile*, of wavelength λ, shown in Figure 1.1. The constants A and δ may, of course, be complex numbers, in which case it is preferable to write (1.11) in the alternative form

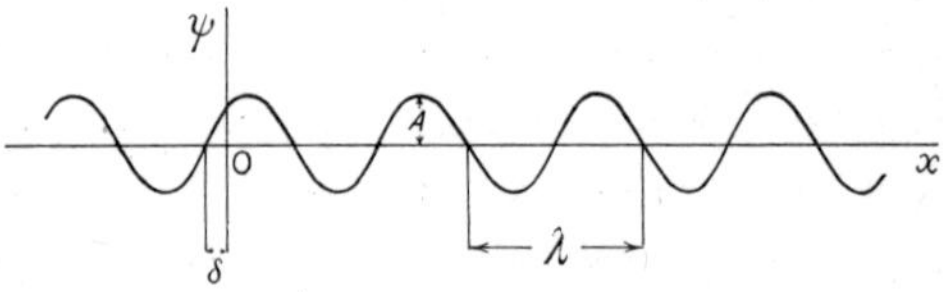

Fig. 1.1. Graph of the function $\psi = A \sin[(2\pi/\lambda)x + \delta]$.

$$\psi(x) = Be^{i2\pi x/\lambda} + Ce^{-i2\pi x/\lambda}. \tag{1.12}$$

Both the real and imaginary parts of ψ are sinusoidal functions like that shown in Figure 1.1.

We have used the term 'wave profile' rather than 'wave' because the latter term generally denotes a *moving* wave profile, or a disturbance which is periodic in time as well as in space. Indeed, another equation can be set up, called the *time-dependent Schrödinger equation*, which, for stationary states, has solutions of the same spatial form as those of equation (1.7), but multiplied by a periodic function of the time. We shall discuss this time-dependent equation in Chapter 11, and shall there see that, so long as we concern ourselves only with stationary states, and not with the mechanism of transitions between one stationary state and another, the time-dependence of the wave functions has no significance. Except in that final chapter, we shall, in fact, confine our discussion to stationary states, and so may ignore the time-dependence.

What we have shown is that the wave function of a free particle, that is, a particle acted upon by no forces ($dV/dx = 0$), has a wavelength which is given by the de Broglie relation (1.5), as required. Furthermore, if in some region of the x-axis $V(x)$ varies only very slightly with x, equation (1.10) will hold approximately in this region and ψ will be very nearly a de Broglie wave profile. Of course, equation (1.7) goes beyond this: it offers a prescription for obtaining ψ even when the de Broglie wavelength can have no meaning, owing to the rapid variation of V with x. Although this generalization is a natural one, its only justification will lie in the results which can be derived from it and compared with experiment. The results in which we shall principally be interested are the energy levels of the system; and this brings us to our second point — that discussed in § 1.2.2.

We deduce from the foregoing work that a free particle can have any energy. Thus, whatever the value of E, there is a corresponding value of λ and a wave function given by equation (1.11). No question of discrete energy levels arises in this case. However, this is not so in the case of a *bound* particle, that is, a particle acted upon by a force which would, according to classical mechanics, confine the particle to a finite region of the x-axis. Such a situation is shown in Figure 1.2. According to classical mechanics, a particle with total energy E and potential energy $V(x)$, as shown, would be confined to the region $a \leqq x \leqq b$, since outside this region the kinetic energy, $T = E - V$, would be negative. On reaching $x = b$, therefore, the particle would be reflected and would travel to $x = a$, where it would again be reflected, and so on. However, classical mechanics permits the energy E to have *any* value lying above the bottom of the potential trough. Wave mechanics presents quite a different picture: we shall see below that the imposition of certain very natural conditions upon the wave function ψ results in a set of discrete energy levels for bound states, and energy values lying in between two adjacent levels are not permitted.

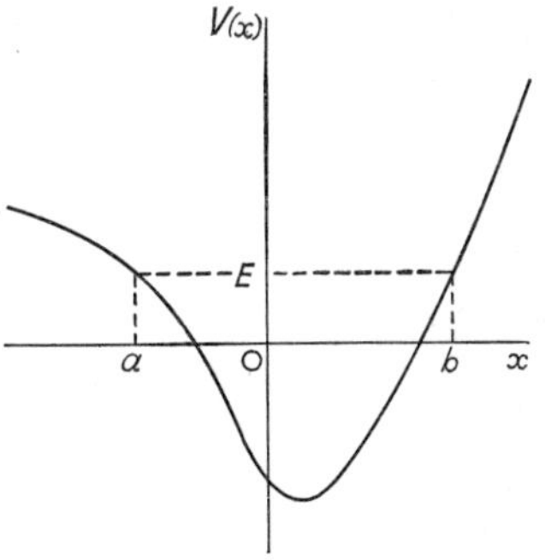

Fig. 1.2.

The conditions we impose upon ψ are simply that it be *single-valued, continuous, smooth* [except at infinities of $V(x)$], *and finite everywhere*. The first three of these, in fact, are conditions we should normally take for granted in solving a differential equation of the type of equation (1.7). If $V(x)$ becomes infinite at any point, $d^2\psi/dx^2$ and hence the curvature of ψ become infinite, so that ψ is not expected to be smooth at that point, but to show a sharp corner there. The last condition, that ψ be finite everywhere, is related to a fifth condition which we shall later discuss in connection with the physical interpretation of the wave function, but which we do not require for the moment. Perhaps it should be remarked in advance that, although $\psi = 0$ is always a solution of equation (1.7), it is not permitted as a wave function.

1.4. Particle in a Rectangular Potential Well

Let us suppose that the potential energy $V(x)$ of a particle of mass m has the constant positive value V_0 when $x < 0$ (region I) and when $x > L$ (region II), and is zero when $0 \leqq x \leqq L$ (region III), as shown in Figure 1.3. We wish to find the energy levels of the *bound* states, that is, states with total energy E less than V_0 — the total energy is necessarily positive, of course, since $V \geqq 0$. We therefore have to find the values of $E < V_0$ for which the Schrödinger equation (1.7) has solutions satisfying the conditions stated above. Let us first consider the three regions separately.

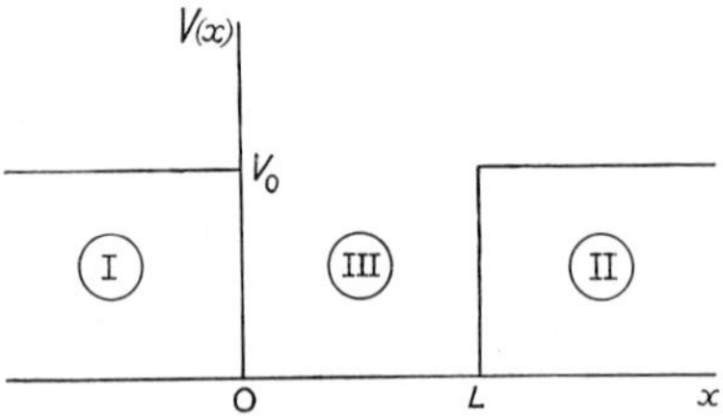

Fig. 1.3.

In region I, $V(x) = V_0$, and equation (1.7) becomes

$$\frac{d^2\psi}{dx^2} + \frac{2m}{\hbar^2}(E - V_0)\psi = 0. \tag{1.13}$$

The general solution of this is

$$\psi = A_1 e^{\alpha x} + B_1 e^{-\alpha x}, \tag{1.14}$$

where A_1 and B_1 are arbitrary constants, and

$$\alpha = \sqrt{\frac{2m}{\hbar^2}(V_0 - E)}. \tag{1.15}$$

α is real, since $E < V_0$, and we will take the positive value of the square root.

In region II the equation is the same, and we have

$$\psi = A_2 e^{\alpha x} + B_2 e^{-\alpha x}, \tag{1.16}$$

with α again given by (1.15).

In region III, however, $V(x) = 0$, and the equation becomes

$$\frac{d^2\psi}{dx^2} + \frac{2mE}{\hbar^2}\psi = 0, \tag{1.17}$$

with the general solution

$$\psi = A_3 \cos \beta x + B_3 \sin \beta x, \tag{1.18}$$

where A_3 and B_3 are arbitrary constants, and

$$\beta = \sqrt{(2mE/\hbar^2)}. \tag{1.19}$$

We note that the second term of the expression (1.14), $B_1 e^{-\alpha x}$, since α is positive, may be made indefinitely large by taking a sufficiently large negative value of x. This violates the last condition on ψ, which demands that ψ be finite everywhere. We must therefore set $B_1 = 0$.

The expression (1.14) is only valid for $x < 0$, so we are not concerned about what happens to the first term when x becomes large and positive. In the case of expression (1.16), however, which is valid for $x > L$, it is the first term which causes difficulty, for $A_2 e^{\alpha x}$ may be made indefinitely large by taking x sufficiently large and positive. We must therefore set $A_2 = 0$.

The three forms of the solution are, thus,

$$\psi = A_1 e^{\alpha x}, \qquad x < 0, \tag{1.20}$$

$$\psi = A_3 \cos \beta x + B_3 \sin \beta x, \qquad 0 \leqq x \leqq L, \tag{1.21}$$

$$\psi = B_2 e^{-\alpha x}, \qquad x > L. \tag{1.22}$$

Now the problem is to determine the values of the constants so that ψ is continuous and smooth everywhere. To do this we simply have to ensure that ψ and $d\psi/dx$ are continuous at $x = 0$ and at $x = L$ — in other words, that the solutions in adjacent regions give the same values of these quantities at the boundaries.

The continuity of ψ at $x = 0$ gives

$$A_1 = A_3, \tag{1.23}$$

and that of $d\psi/dx$ gives

$$\alpha A_1 = \beta B_3. \tag{1.24}$$

Similarly, the continuity of ψ at $x = L$ gives

$$A_3 \cos \beta L + B_3 \sin \beta L = B_2 e^{-\alpha L}, \tag{1.25}$$

and that of $d\psi/dx$ gives

$$-\beta A_3 \sin \beta L + \beta B_3 \cos \beta L = -\alpha B_2 e^{-\alpha L}. \tag{1.26}$$

Dividing (1.26) by (1.25), we obtain

$$\frac{A_3 \sin \beta L - B_3 \cos \beta L}{A_3 \cos \beta L + B_3 \sin \beta L} = \frac{\alpha}{\beta}.$$

After rearrangement, this yields

$$\tan \beta L = \frac{2\alpha\beta}{\beta^2 - \alpha^2}, \tag{1.27}$$

or, from (1.15) and (1.19),

$$\tan\left(L\sqrt{\frac{2mE}{\hbar^2}}\right) = \frac{2\sqrt{E(V_0 - E)}}{2E - V_0}. \tag{1.28}$$

This equation must be solved numerically for E, given the values of V_0 and L. It is immediately apparent that the equation may be satisfied by one or more *discrete* values of E, but not by a continuous range of energies. We thus see that the use of the Schrödinger equation, together with the conditions on ψ, leads to a set of discrete energy levels for bound states.

We shall not proceed further with the solution of (1.28), because it will be sufficient for our future purposes to consider the idealized case in which V_0 tends to infinity — the problem is then generally referred to as that of 'a particle in a one-dimensional box with perfectly reflecting walls'. In this case it is quite easy to obtain an analytical expression for E. Indeed this may be obtained immediately from (1.28), by setting the right-hand side equal to zero, but it is instructive to work from first principles.

1.5. Particle in a One-Dimensional Box

If, in the foregoing problem, we let V_0 tend to infinity, then α tends to infinity also, and the solutions in regions I and II, given by (1.20) and (1.22), both tend to zero. Thus, in the limit, the problem is to determine the constants in the solution (1.21), for the region III, so that this solution is zero at $x = 0$ and at $x = L$.

$\psi(0) = 0$ gives us $A_3 = 0$, and $\psi(L) = 0$ gives us

$$B_3 \sin \beta L = 0,$$

that is,

$$\beta = n\pi/L, \quad n = \pm 1, \pm 2, \pm 3, \ldots,$$

excluding the possibilities $B_3 = 0$ and $\beta = 0$, which would give the disallowed zero solutions.

Since $\beta = \sqrt{(2mE/\hbar^2)}$, the allowed energy levels are given by

$$E_n = \frac{\hbar^2 \pi^2 n^2}{2mL^2}, \qquad n = 1, 2, 3, \ldots. \tag{1.29}$$

The corresponding wave functions, in region III, are given by

$$\psi_n = B_n \sin \frac{n\pi x}{L}, \qquad n = 1, 2, 3, \ldots, \tag{1.30}$$

where B_n is so far an arbitrary non-zero constant. The negative integral values of n merely repeat the same energies and wave functions, and hence may be disregarded.

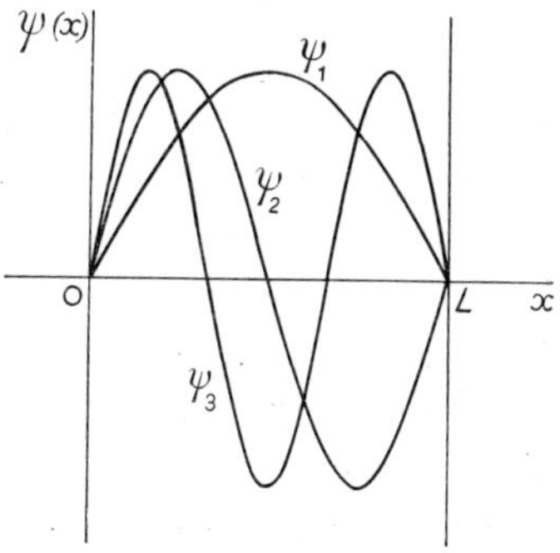

Fig. 1.4. Wave functions for a particle in a one-dimensional box (V_0 infinite).

The wave functions for the first three values of n are shown in Figure 1.4, arbitrarily taking B_n to be the same real constant in each case. It should be noticed that, apart from the zeros at $x = 0$ and at $x = L$, which do not occur when V_0 is finite, ψ_n has $(n-1)$ zeros or *nodes* — the ground state ψ_1 has none, the first excited state ψ_2 has one, and so on. This is generally the case, and provides a rough method of estimating which of two wave functions corresponds to the lower energy, when the energy levels are not immediately available.

The wave functions are all zero outside region III, and it will be seen that there is a discontinuity of slope at $x = 0$ and at $x = L$. This causes no difficulty, however, when it is remembered that it is the result of a limiting process. For any finite value of V_0, however large, there would be no discontinuity of slope, but a smooth exponential decrease in regions I and II — the wave function for the state of lowest energy has the form shown in Figure 1.5 in this case. As V_0 increases, the exponential decrease

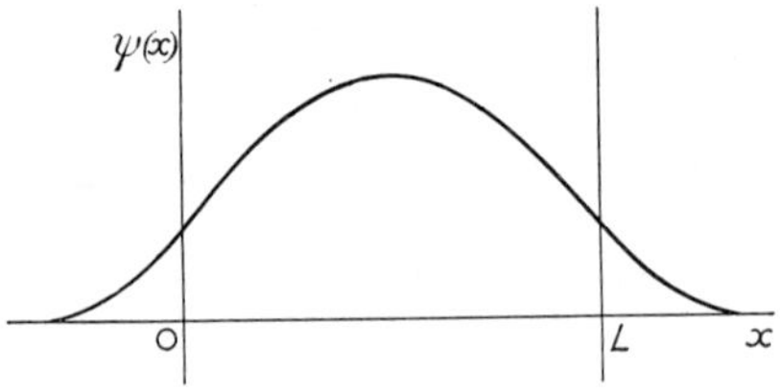

Fig. 1.5. Wave function for the ground state of a particle in a rectangular potential well (V_0 finite).

becomes more and more rapid, until, in the limit of infinite V_0, we get the situation shown in Figure 1.4.

The energy levels E_n and the wave functions ψ_n of the stationary states are frequently referred to as the *eigenvalues* and *eigenfunctions*, respectively, of the Schrödinger equation.

The energy levels of the simple system we have been discussing cannot immediately be compared with experiment, but we shall see in Chapter 7 that a generalization of this model to three dimensions gives results which are in remarkable agreement with experiment. The wave function ψ has so far been merely a tool for obtaining the energy levels. While this is undoubtedly its principal purpose, it has also proved possible to interpret ψ physically in a way which leads to useful results.

1.6. Interpretation of the Wave Function

The wave function ψ is generally a complex function, that is, it may be written in the form

$$\psi(x) = f(x) + ig(x), \tag{1.31}$$

where f and g are real functions of x, and $\mathrm{i} = \sqrt{-1}$. The complex conjugate of ψ, which we denote by ψ^*, is obtained by changing i to $-\mathrm{i}$ wherever it appears in ψ. Thus,

$$\psi^* = f - \mathrm{i}g. \tag{1.32}$$

The product of ψ and ψ^* is real and positive, and its positive square root, denoted by $|\psi|$, is called the *modulus* of ψ. Thus,

$$\psi^*\psi = |\psi|^2 = f^2 + g^2. \tag{1.33}$$

Now, a further condition upon ψ, which we have not yet stated, but whose significance will shortly become apparent, is that the integral of $|\psi|^2$ over all x must be a finite number and not zero, that is

$$\int_{-\infty}^{\infty} |\psi|^2 \mathrm{d}x = \text{finite number}. \tag{1.34}$$

This integral could only be zero, in fact, if ψ were identically zero, which we have already said is not permitted for a wave function.

Schrödinger's equation is linear, so that, if ψ is a solution, so also is $C\psi$, where C is any constant. This may easily be verified by substitution. The wave function is, in fact, always arbitrary to the extent of a multiplying constant, and it follows that we can always choose ψ so that

$$\int_{-\infty}^{\infty} |\psi|^2 \mathrm{d}x = 1. \tag{1.35}$$

The function ψ which satisfies this equation is said to be *normalized*†.

Since ψ is generally complex it is clear that ψ itself cannot have a direct physical meaning. However, it has been suggested, with successful results, that, when ψ is normalized, $|\psi|^2$ may be interpreted as a *probability density*, such that

$|\psi|^2\mathrm{d}x$ *is the probability that the particle be found in the small interval* $\mathrm{d}x$ *at position* x.

More explicitly, if a very large number of observations of the position

---

† It should be mentioned that, although there are no difficulties about the normalization of the wave functions of bound states, difficulties do occur in the case of free particles. The energy levels of the former belong to the discrete spectrum, while those of the latter belong to the continuous spectrum, and in this case equation (1.34) is not satisfied. This difficulty with free particles is simply overcome by doing away with free particles! In other words, every system is considered to be enclosed in a box — clearly, if this box is very large compared with the system under consideration, its presence cannot affect the predicted results of experiments on the system, but the limits it imposes upon the range of any particle gets over the mathematical difficulties of normalization.

of a particle in the state ψ were made at random times, in a fraction $|\psi|^2 \mathrm{d}x$ of them the particle would be found in $\mathrm{d}x$.

It is essential for this interpretation that ψ be normalized, for the particle must be *somewhere*, so that the sum of the probabilities of its being in every interval from $-\infty$ to $+\infty$ must be unity, that is,

$$\int_{-\infty}^{\infty} |\psi|^2 \mathrm{d}x = 1.$$

It also follows from this interpretation that ψ cannot be identically zero.

As an example, let us consider the particle in the one-dimensional box. We have seen that the wave functions are zero outside the box, and inside it are given by

$$\psi_n = B_n \sin \frac{n\pi x}{L}, \qquad n = 1, 2, 3, \ldots.$$

In order to normalize ψ_n we must choose B_n so that

$$B_n^2 \int_0^L \sin^2 \frac{n\pi x}{L} \mathrm{d}x = 1, \tag{1.36}$$

and this gives

$$B_n = \sqrt{2/L}, \tag{1.37}$$

which is independent of n. The normalized wave functions are, therefore, given by

$$\psi_n = \sqrt{\frac{2}{L}} \sin \frac{n\pi x}{L}, \qquad n = 1, 2, 3, \ldots, \tag{1.38}$$

inside the box.

Here we have assumed that B_n is real, but this is not necessary — we could multiply the value of B_n given in (1.37) by e^{ib}, where b is *any* real number, and the wave functions would still be normalized, because $|\mathrm{e}^{ib}| = 1$. In other words, even a normalized wave function is arbitrary to the extent of a multiplying constant with modulus unity. This again emphasizes the fact that the wave function itself has no direct physical meaning — the value of $|\psi|^2$, which we have interpreted physically, is independent of any factor e^{ib} in ψ. It is due to this fact that the time-dependence of stationary states is of no significance, for we shall see in Chapter 11 that the time t only appears in the wave function of a stationary state in a factor of the form e^{ibt}, which has modulus unity.

The graph of $|\psi_1|^2$, the probability distribution for the ground state of the particle in the box, is shown in Figure 1.6. This is quite a different picture from that presented by classical mechanics. According to the latter, a particle in such a box would travel with uniform velocity from wall to wall, and at the walls it would be perfectly reflected — there would consequently be the same probability of finding it anywhere in the box, and its probability distribution would be a straight line at height $1/L$ above the axis, as shown. According to wave mechanics, however, there is a much greater probability of finding the particle in the middle of the box than near the walls.

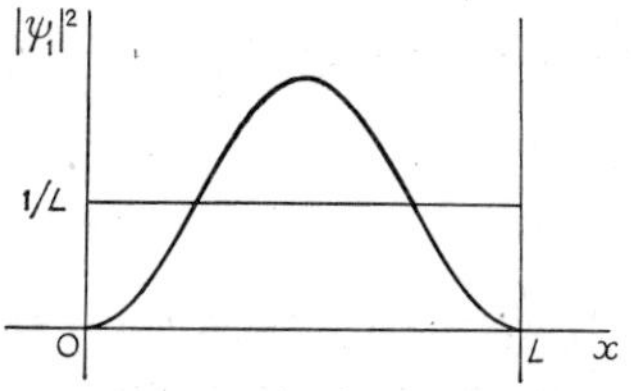

Fig. 1.6. Probability distribution for the ground state of a particle in a box. The horizontal line at height $1/L$ is the probability distribution according to classical mechanics.

The discrepancy between classical and quantum mechanics is even more pronounced in the case of finite potential walls. We have seen that here the wave functions do not become zero at the walls, but fall exponentially to zero in the regions beyond the walls — the wave function for the ground state is shown in Figure 1.5, and the probability distribution has a similar form. This means that, according to wave mechanics, when the potential energy V_0 is finite, there is a non-zero probability of finding the particle outside the box. Such a thing is quite impossible in classical mechanics, according to which a particle whose energy is less than V_0 could never pass beyond the walls — in order to do so its kinetic energy would have to become negative, which is forbidden. The passage of a particle through a potential barrier, which would be impenetrable according to classical mechanics, is known as the 'tunnel effect', and is important, for instance, in the theory of radio-active decay.

1.7. Orthogonality of Wave Functions

If ψ_1 and ψ_2 are wave functions corresponding to the different energy levels E_1 and E_2 respectively, then

$$\int_{-\infty}^{\infty} \psi_1^* \psi_2 \, dx = 0, \tag{1.39}$$

and the two functions are said to be *orthogonal*. Alternatively, taking the complex conjugate of both sides of equation (1.39),

$$\int_{-\infty}^{\infty} \psi_1 \psi_2^* \mathrm{d}x = 0. \tag{1.40}$$

To prove this, let us first note that the Schrödinger equation for ψ^*, the complex conjugate of ψ, is the same as that for ψ itself, so long as the potential energy $V(x)$ is real; thus,

$$\frac{\mathrm{d}^2\psi^*}{\mathrm{d}x^2} + \frac{2m}{\hbar^2}[E - V(x)]\psi^* = 0. \tag{1.41}$$

This can easily be seen by noting that, if $\psi = f + ig$, where f and g are *real* functions of x, then both f and g separately must satisfy equation (1.7), and it follows that any linear combination of the form $Af + Bg$, where A and B are arbitrary constants, must also satisfy it — in particular, the linear combination $\psi^* = f - ig$ must satisfy it.

ψ_1^* and ψ_2 therefore satisfy the equations

$$\frac{\mathrm{d}^2\psi_1^*}{\mathrm{d}x^2} + \frac{2m}{\hbar^2}[E_1 - V(x)]\psi_1^* = 0, \tag{1.42}$$

$$\frac{\mathrm{d}^2\psi_2}{\mathrm{d}x^2} + \frac{2m}{\hbar^2}[E_2 - V(x)]\psi_2 = 0. \tag{1.43}$$

Now, if we multiply the first equation by ψ_2 and subtract from it the second equation multiplied by ψ_1^*, we find

$$\psi_2 \frac{\mathrm{d}^2\psi_1^*}{\mathrm{d}x^2} - \psi_1^* \frac{\mathrm{d}^2\psi_2}{\mathrm{d}x^2} + \frac{2m}{\hbar^2}(E_1 - E_2)\psi_1^*\psi_2 = 0. \tag{1.44}$$

Integrating over all x gives

$$\left[\psi_2 \frac{\mathrm{d}\psi_1^*}{\mathrm{d}x} - \psi_1^* \frac{\mathrm{d}\psi_2}{\mathrm{d}x}\right]_{-\infty}^{\infty} = \frac{2m}{\hbar^2}(E_2 - E_1)\int_{-\infty}^{\infty} \psi_1^*\psi_2 \mathrm{d}x, \tag{1.45}$$

since

$$\psi_2 \frac{\mathrm{d}^2\psi_1^*}{\mathrm{d}x^2} - \psi_1^* \frac{\mathrm{d}^2\psi_2}{\mathrm{d}x^2} = \frac{\mathrm{d}}{\mathrm{d}x}\left(\psi_2 \frac{\mathrm{d}\psi_1^*}{\mathrm{d}x} - \psi_1^* \frac{\mathrm{d}\psi_2}{\mathrm{d}x}\right).$$

In order that equation (1.34) be satisfied, ψ_1^* and ψ_2 must tend to zero as x tends to ∞ or to $-\infty$, and the left-hand side of equation (1.45) therefore vanishes. Also, we have postulated that E_1 and E_2 are *different* energy levels, so that $(E_2 - E_1)$ is not zero, and equation (1.39) follows.

In some problems it may not be necessary to consider the whole range of x from $-\infty$ to $+\infty$. For instance, if ψ_1^* and ψ_2 were both zero at $x = a$ and at $x = b$, then, integrating from $x = a$ to $x = b$ instead of over all x, we would find, in the same way,

$$\int_a^b \psi_1^* \psi_2 \, dx = 0. \tag{1.46}$$

In this case the functions are said to be *orthogonal in the interval* (a, b). Similarly, if

$$\int_a^b |\psi|^2 \, dx = 1, \tag{1.47}$$

the function ψ is said to be *normalized in the interval* (a, b).

A set of functions ψ_n, where $n = 1, 2, 3, \ldots$, which are all normalized and mutually orthogonal in an interval (a, b), are said to form an *orthonormal* set in this interval. As an example, we may take the normalized wave functions of a particle in a potential box:

$$\psi_n = \sqrt{\frac{2}{L}} \sin \frac{n\pi x}{L}, \qquad n = 1, 2, 3, \ldots.$$

We have shown that these functions are normalized in the interval $(0, L)$. Also, if m and n are different integers,

$$\int_0^L \sin \frac{m\pi x}{L} \sin \frac{n\pi x}{L} \, dx$$

$$= \frac{1}{2} \int_0^L \left[\cos \frac{(m-n)\pi x}{L} - \cos \frac{(m+n)\pi x}{L} \right] dx = 0. \tag{1.48}$$

Hence, the functions ψ_n are mutually orthogonal in the interval $(0, L)$, and so form an orthonormal set in this interval. The functions are real in this case, so that ψ_n^* is the same as ψ_n. Since the wave functions are zero outside the interval $(0, L)$, they are also orthonormal in the whole range of x, that is, the interval $(-\infty, \infty)$. Further properties of orthonormal sets are discussed in Appendix 2.

1.8. The Harmonic Oscillator

Before leaving the one-dimensional Schrödinger equation it may be instructive to consider a final example, which has many applications throughout the whole of atomic physics — the linear harmonic oscillator. According to classical mechanics this is defined as a particle moving in a line under the action of a force directed towards a fixed point in the line and of magnitude proportional to the distance of the particle from this point. Let us take the fixed point to be the origin, the line to be the x-axis, and the force to be $-kx$, where k is positive. Then, if m is the mass of the particle, its Newtonian equation of motion is

$$m\frac{\mathrm{d}^2x}{\mathrm{d}t^2} = -kx, \tag{1.49}$$

which has the general solution

$$x = A\sin(\omega t+\delta), \tag{1.50}$$

where $\omega = \sqrt{(k/m)}$, and A and δ are arbitrary constants, which may be fixed by the initial conditions. The particle therefore performs simple harmonic oscillations with frequency $\omega/2\pi$, and ω is called the *angular frequency* of oscillation.

The potential energy $V(x)$ is obtained from the equation

$$\frac{\mathrm{d}V}{\mathrm{d}x} = kx = m\omega^2 x. \tag{1.51}$$

This gives

$$V(x) = \tfrac{1}{2}m\omega^2x^2, \tag{1.52}$$

if the zero of potential energy, which is arbitrary, is taken to be at $x = 0$. This function is shown in Figure 1.7.

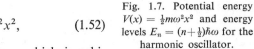

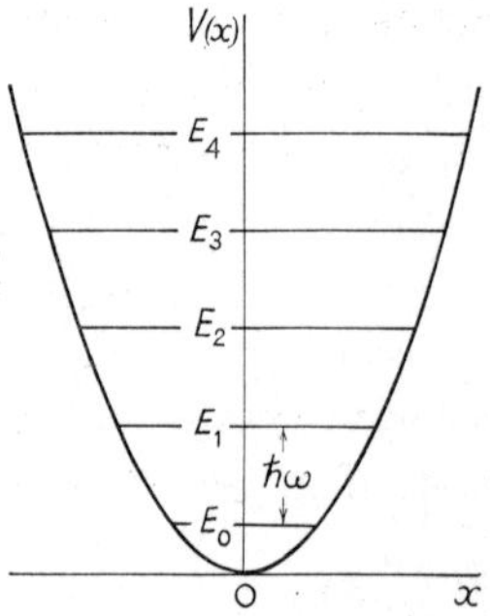

Fig. 1.7. Potential energy $V(x) = \frac{1}{2}m\omega^2x^2$ and energy levels $E_n = (n+\frac{1}{2})\hbar\omega$ for the harmonic oscillator.

Passing now to wave mechanics, the Schrödinger equation, obtained by substituting (1.52) in (1.7), is

$$\frac{\mathrm{d}^2\psi}{\mathrm{d}x^2}+\frac{2m}{\hbar^2}(E-\tfrac{1}{2}m\omega^2x^2)\psi = 0. \tag{1.53}$$

Let us consider the function

$$\psi_0 = \mathrm{e}^{-\alpha x^2}, \tag{1.54}$$

where $\alpha = m\omega/2\hbar$. We have

$$\frac{\mathrm{d}\psi_0}{\mathrm{d}x} = -2\alpha x\mathrm{e}^{-\alpha x^2},$$

and

$$\frac{d^2\psi_0}{dx^2} = -2\alpha e^{-\alpha x^2} + 4\alpha^2 x^2 e^{-\alpha x^2}$$
$$= -\frac{2m}{\hbar^2}(\tfrac{1}{2}\hbar\omega - \tfrac{1}{2}m\omega^2 x^2)\psi_0. \tag{1.55}$$

Equation (1.55) is the same as (1.53), provided $E = \frac{1}{2}\hbar\omega$. Also, the function ψ_0 satisfies all the conditions for a wave function. We have therefore shown that ψ_0 is an eigenfunction of the Schrödinger equation corresponding to the eigenvalue

$$E_0 = \tfrac{1}{2}\hbar\omega. \tag{1.56}$$

What we have not shown, but what is none the less true, is that ψ_0 is the *ground state* of the oscillator, that is, E_0 is the lowest energy level. We might have guessed this, however, for ψ_0 has no nodes, and we have stated previously that this is a characteristic of the ground state wave function.

Following the same argument, we expect the state of next higher energy, or *first excited state*, to have a single node, which, by symmetry, must occur at the origin. Now the function

$$\psi_1 = x e^{-\alpha x^2} \tag{1.57}$$

has a node at the origin, and satisfies all the conditions for a wave function. Also

$$\frac{d^2\psi_1}{dx^2} = -6\alpha x e^{-\alpha x^2} + 4\alpha^2 x^3 e^{-\alpha x^2} \tag{1.58}$$
$$= -\frac{2m}{\hbar^2}(\tfrac{3}{2}\hbar\omega - \tfrac{1}{2}m\omega^2 x^2)\psi_1, \tag{1.59}$$

which is the same as equation (1.53), provided $E = \frac{3}{2}\hbar\omega$. Thus, ψ_1 is an eigenfunction of the Schrödinger equation corresponding to the eigenvalue

$$E_1 = \tfrac{3}{2}\hbar\omega. \tag{1.60}$$

The reader may verify that the second excited state, with two nodes, is

$$\psi_2 = (1 - 4\alpha x^2)e^{-\alpha x^2}, \tag{1.61}$$

corresponding to the eigenvalue

$$E_2 = \tfrac{5}{2}\hbar\omega. \tag{1.62}$$

Of course, the eigenfunctions need not be obtained by guesswork, but may be found by a straightforward process of calculation. This is somewhat lengthy, however, and since it is available in a large number of texts † we shall not reproduce it here.

In general, the eigenvalues or energy levels are given by the formula

$$E_n = (n+\tfrac{1}{2})\hbar\omega, \quad n = 0, 1, 2, \ldots. \tag{1.63}$$

The eigenfunctions given above are not normalized, but may be made so by multiplying each of them by an appropriate constant, so that equation (1.35) is satisfied. We obtain

$$\psi_0 = \left(\frac{2\alpha}{\pi}\right)^{\frac{1}{4}} e^{-\alpha x^2}, \tag{1.64}$$

$$\psi_1 = 2\left(\frac{2\alpha^3}{\pi}\right)^{\frac{1}{4}} x e^{-\alpha x^2}, \tag{1.65}$$

$$\psi_2 = \left(\frac{\alpha}{2\pi}\right)^{\frac{1}{4}} (1-4\alpha x^2) e^{-\alpha x^2}. \tag{1.66}$$

These functions are shown in Figure 1.8.

It should be noticed that in any state, according to our interpretation of $|\psi^2|$, there is a finite probability of finding the particle at large distances from the origin. This again is contrary to classical mechanics — classically permissible ranges of motion of the particle in the various energy levels E_n are shown by the horizontal line segments in Figure 1.7.

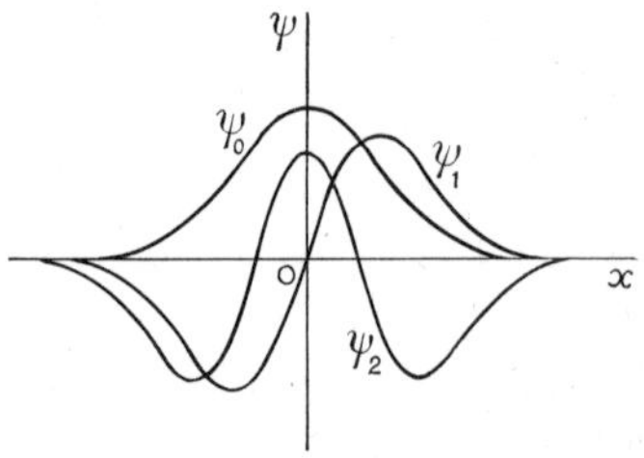

Fig. 1.8. Normalized wave functions for the three states of lowest energy of the harmonic oscillator. The maximum value of ψ_0 is $(2\alpha/\pi)^{\frac{1}{4}}$, and the extrema of ψ_1 occur at $x = \pm\sqrt{(1/2\alpha)}$.

Another point which is worth noticing is the following: according to classical mechanics the oscillator could have zero energy, in which case the particle would be at rest at the origin, but according to wave mechanics this is impossible — the *lowest* energy the oscillator can have is $\frac{1}{2}\hbar\omega$, which is called the *zero-point energy* of the oscillator. This fact has some importance in the theory of metals. For instance, the atomic nuclei in a metal vibrate like harmonic

† See, for instance, Pauling and Wilson, *Introduction to Quantum Mechanics* (McGraw-Hill), p. 67, for a very full treatment.

oscillators. At the absolute zero of temperature, when classical physics would have all the nuclei at rest, they must in fact still vibrate with their zero-point energies, and it is sometimes necessary to take this into account in calculating, for example, the cohesive energy of a metal. Another important application, to the theory of plasma oscillations in metals, will be discussed in Chapter 10.

CHAPTER 2

THE BASIC PRINCIPLES OF WAVE MECHANICS

2.1. Hamiltonian Mechanics and the Schrödinger Equation

The classical Hamiltonian function of a conservative system consisting of a single particle moving in a line is simply the total energy of the particle expressed in terms of its momentum p and positional coordinate x. It is denoted by $H(x, p)$.

The total energy E is given by

$$\begin{aligned} E &= \text{kinetic energy} + \text{potential energy} \\ &= \tfrac{1}{2}mv^2 + V(x), \end{aligned} \tag{2.1}$$

where $v = \dot{x}$, as before. Also, the momentum is $p = mv$, so that the classical energy equation in Hamiltonian form is

$$H(x, p) = E, \tag{2.2}$$

where

$$H(x, p) = \frac{p^2}{2m} + V(x). \tag{2.3}$$

We thus have

$$\frac{\partial H}{\partial p} = \frac{p}{m} \quad \text{and} \quad \frac{\partial H}{\partial x} = \frac{\mathrm{d}V}{\mathrm{d}x}. \tag{2.4}$$

However, $p/m = v = \dot{x}$, and, according to Newton's equations of motion [or, alternatively, by differentiating equation (2.2) with respect to time, remembering that E is constant],

$$-\frac{\mathrm{d}V}{\mathrm{d}x} = m\dot{v} = \dot{p},$$

so that equations (2.4) may be written

$$\frac{\partial H}{\partial p} = \dot{x} \quad \text{and} \quad -\frac{\partial H}{\partial x} = \dot{p}. \tag{2.5}$$

These are called Hamilton's *canonical equations of motion* for the system, and the variables p and x which satisfy them are said to be *canonically conjugate*.

Now, if we tentatively write

$$p = \frac{\hbar}{\mathrm{i}} \frac{\mathrm{d}}{\mathrm{d}x} \tag{2.6}$$

in (2.3), we obtain the *operator*

$$H\left(x, \frac{\hbar}{\mathrm{i}} \frac{\mathrm{d}}{\mathrm{d}x}\right) = -\frac{\hbar^2}{2m} \frac{\mathrm{d}^2}{\mathrm{d}x^2} + V(x), \tag{2.7}$$

and equation (2.2) becomes an operator equation. Operating with both sides upon some function $\psi(x)$, we obtain

$$H\left(x, \frac{\hbar}{\mathrm{i}} \frac{\mathrm{d}}{\mathrm{d}x}\right)\psi = E\psi, \tag{2.8}$$

or

$$-\frac{\hbar^2}{2m} \frac{\mathrm{d}^2\psi}{\mathrm{d}x^2} + V(x)\psi = E\psi, \tag{2.9}$$

which may be re-arranged in the form of equation (1.7), and is just the Schrödinger equation of the system.

It seems, therefore, that there is a close relationship between the classical energy equation in Hamiltonian form and the Schrödinger equation. The essential connection is the representation of the momentum by the differential operator (2.6). It is, in fact, a fundamental principle of quantum mechanics that every dynamical variable may be represented by an operator. For instance, in the operator (2.7), the coordinate x has really become the *operator* 'multiply by x', but since this behaves just like the number x itself it was unnecessary to state this explicitly. It is a fact which must be borne in mind, however, for these operators are not the only possible ones which may be used to represent p and x, and others are sometimes more convenient.

The foregoing treatment of the linear motion of a single particle suggests the way in which we might generalize the Schrödinger equation to account for the three-dimensional motion of a particle or of many particles. We will write down the classical Hamiltonian of the system in terms of the Cartesian coordinates and momentum components of each particle, and then transform it into an operator by substituting for each momentum component a differential operator like (2.6). The Schrödinger equation will then be

$$H\psi = E\psi, \tag{2.10}$$

where H is the Hamiltonian *operator* and ψ is a function of the Cartesian coordinates of all the particles in the system. Once more, it must not be imagined that this is a logically necessary process — it is a *tentative* process, which will be justified by its results.

Let us take the case of a single particle in three dimensions first. The potential energy $V(x, y, z)$ is now a function of x, y, and z, the rectangular Cartesian coordinates of the position of the particle, and the momentum is of magnitude p, given by

$$p^2 = p_x^2 + p_y^2 + p_z^2,$$

where p_x, p_y, and p_z are the Cartesian components of the momentum vector. The classical Hamiltonian, that is, the total energy of the system expressed in terms of the momentum and positional coordinates of the particle, is thus

$$H = \frac{1}{2m}(p_x^2 + p_y^2 + p_z^2) + V(x, y, z). \tag{2.11}$$

As before, we may show that

$$\frac{\partial H}{\partial p_x} = \dot{x} \quad \text{and} \quad -\frac{\partial H}{\partial x} = \dot{p}_x, \tag{2.12}$$

with two similar pairs of equations in y and z. These are Hamilton's canonical equations of motion for the system. The coordinate x and momentum p_x are said to be canonically conjugate, and so also are the pairs of variables (y, p_y) and (z, p_z).

In order to transform (2.11) into the quantum-mechanical Hamiltonian operator we substitute for each momentum component a derivative with respect to its conjugate variable — as in (2.6), except that partial derivatives are now required, since several variables are present. In other words, we write

$$p_x = \frac{\hbar}{\mathrm{i}}\frac{\partial}{\partial x}, \qquad p_y = \frac{\hbar}{\mathrm{i}}\frac{\partial}{\partial y}, \qquad p_z = \frac{\hbar}{\mathrm{i}}\frac{\partial}{\partial z}, \tag{2.13}$$

and the Hamiltonian operator becomes

$$H = -\frac{\hbar^2}{2m}\left(\frac{\partial^2}{\partial x^2}+\frac{\partial^2}{\partial y^2}+\frac{\partial^2}{\partial z^2}\right)+V(x, y, z). \tag{2.14}$$

Substituting this in equation (2.10), we obtain the Schrödinger equation

$$-\frac{\hbar^2}{2m}\left(\frac{\partial^2\psi}{\partial x^2}+\frac{\partial^2\psi}{\partial y^2}+\frac{\partial^2\psi}{\partial z^2}\right)+V(x, y, z)\psi = E\psi, \tag{2.15}$$

where ψ is a function of x, y and z.

The differential operator in (2.14) is generally called the *Laplacian operator*, and may be written ∇^2, thus,

$$\nabla^2 = \frac{\partial^2}{\partial x^2}+\frac{\partial^2}{\partial y^2}+\frac{\partial^2}{\partial z^2}. \tag{2.16}$$

The Schrödinger equation may therefore be re-arranged in the form

$$\nabla^2\psi+\frac{2m}{\hbar^2}[E-V(x, y, z)]\psi = 0, \tag{2.17}$$

which is similar to equation (1.7).

The extension to systems of several particles follows immediately. Let us suppose that there are n particles and that the ith particle has mass m_i, rectangular Cartesian coordinates (x_i, y_i, z_i), and momentum components (p_{xi}, p_{yi}, p_{zi}). Then the classical Hamiltonian is

$$H = \sum_{i=1}^{n}\frac{p_i^2}{2m_i}+V(x_1, y_1, z_1, \ldots x_n, y_n, z_n), \tag{2.18}$$

where $p_i^2 = p_{xi}^2+p_{yi}^2+p_{zi}^2$, since $p_i^2/2m_i$ is the kinetic energy of the ith particle and the sum is over all the particles. The potential energy V is a function of the positional coordinates of all the particles.

In accordance with (2.13) we now make the substitutions

$$p_{xi} = \frac{\hbar}{\mathrm{i}}\frac{\partial}{\partial x_i}, \qquad p_{yi} = \frac{\hbar}{\mathrm{i}}\frac{\partial}{\partial y_i}, \qquad p_{zi} = \frac{\hbar}{\mathrm{i}}\frac{\partial}{\partial z_i}, \tag{2.19}$$

for all i, obtaining the Hamiltonian operator

$$H = -\sum_{i=1}^{n}\frac{\hbar^2}{2m_i}\nabla_i^2+V(x_1, y_1, z_1, \ldots x_n, y_n, z_n), \tag{2.20}$$

where

$$\nabla_i^2 = \frac{\partial^2}{\partial x_i^2} + \frac{\partial^2}{\partial y_i^2} + \frac{\partial^2}{\partial z_i^2}. \tag{2.21}$$

The Schrödinger equation then becomes

$$-\sum_{i=1}^{n} \frac{\hbar^2}{2m_i} \nabla_i^2 \psi + V\psi = E\psi, \tag{2.22}$$

where ψ is a function of all the x_i, y_i, z_i.

2.2. The Wave Function and its Interpretation

Let us first consider a single particle moving in three dimensions, whose Schrödinger equation is (2.17). By direct extension of the one-dimensional case, we assume that its wave function $\psi(x, y, z)$ must be single-valued, continuous, smooth (except at infinities of V), and finite everywhere. *Smooth* here implies that the partial derivatives of ψ with respect to x, y and z are all continuous, or, more concisely, that the gradient of ψ, written grad ψ or $\nabla\psi$, is continuous (see Appendix 1). In addition, we require that the volume integral of $\psi^*\psi$ or $|\psi|^2$ throughout all space be finite and not zero, that is

$$\int_{-\infty}^{\infty}\int_{-\infty}^{\infty}\int_{-\infty}^{\infty} |\psi(x, y, z)|^2 \mathrm{d}x\mathrm{d}y\mathrm{d}z = \text{finite number}. \tag{2.23}$$

The Schrödinger equation is linear, so that any constant multiple of a solution is also a solution, and it therefore follows that we can choose ψ so that the above integral has the value unity. In this case ψ is said to be *normalized*. In the following work we shall find it convenient to write $\psi(\boldsymbol{r})$ instead of $\psi(x, y, z)$, where $\boldsymbol{r}$ is the *position vector* of the point (x, y, z), and also to write $\mathrm{d}\boldsymbol{r}$ for the volume element $\mathrm{d}x\mathrm{d}y\mathrm{d}z$. An integration throughout all space is then represented by a single integral sign. Thus, for a normalized wave function ψ, we have

$$\int |\psi(\boldsymbol{r})|^2 \mathrm{d}\boldsymbol{r} = 1. \tag{2.24}$$

Again, as for the one-dimensional case, when $\psi(\boldsymbol{r})$ is normalized, $|\psi(\boldsymbol{r})|^2$ is interpreted as a probability density, such that $|\psi(\boldsymbol{r})|^2 \mathrm{d}\boldsymbol{r}$ is the probability that the particle be found in the small volume element $\mathrm{d}\boldsymbol{r}$ at $\boldsymbol{r}$.

In the case of a system of several particles, whose Schrödinger equation is (2.22), the conditions upon ψ, and its normalization, are almost exactly the same as above — the only difference being that the integral of $|\psi|^2$ is no longer a triple integral, but a multiple integral with respect to the positional coordinates of all the particles. Thus, for the normalized wave function of a system of n particles, we have

$$\int \ldots \int |\psi(\boldsymbol{r}_1, \boldsymbol{r}_2, \ldots \boldsymbol{r}_n)|^2 \, d\boldsymbol{r}_1 \ldots d\boldsymbol{r}_n = 1, \tag{2.25}$$

each integral being a volume integral throughout all space.

Similarly, if $\psi(\boldsymbol{r}_1, \ldots \boldsymbol{r}_n)$ is normalized, $|\psi(\boldsymbol{r}_1, \ldots \boldsymbol{r}_n)|^2 d\boldsymbol{r}_1 \ldots d\boldsymbol{r}_n$ is interpreted as the probability that particle 1 (that is, the particle with position vector $\boldsymbol{r}_1$) be found in the small volume element $d\boldsymbol{r}_1$ at $\boldsymbol{r}_1$, and simultaneously that particle 2 be found in $d\boldsymbol{r}_2$ at $\boldsymbol{r}_2$, and so on.

The $3n$-dimensional space defined by the coordinates of the n particles is generally known as the *configuration space* of the system. As a further abbreviation we shall sometimes denote a volume element in configuration space by $d\tau$, that is,

$$d\tau = d\boldsymbol{r}_1 \, d\boldsymbol{r}_2 \ldots d\boldsymbol{r}_n. \tag{2.26}$$

An integration throughout the configuration space of a system is then denoted by a single integral sign — for example, (2.25) becomes, simply,

$$\int |\psi|^2 d\tau = 1. \tag{2.27}$$

2.3. The Particle in a Box

As a simple example of the motion of a particle in three dimensions let us consider a particle confined in a cubical potential box of side L. Although highly idealized, this model has an important application in the theory of metals. For simplicity we will take the potential energy of the particle to be zero inside the box and infinite outside, so that the problem is just the three-dimensional extension of that discussed in § 1.5. It follows that the boundary condition upon the wave function $\psi(x, y, z)$ is that it must fall to zero at the surface of the box.

Let us take the origin at one corner and Cartesian axes along three edges of the box, as shown in Figure 2.1. The variation of the potential energy $V(x, y, z)$ along the x-, y- and z-axes is then precisely the same as that in the problem of the one-dimensional box.

Inside the box, $V = 0$, and the Schrödinger equation (2.17) becomes

$$\frac{\partial^2\psi}{\partial x^2} + \frac{\partial^2\psi}{\partial y^2} + \frac{\partial^2\psi}{\partial z^2} + \frac{2m}{\hbar^2} E\psi = 0. \tag{2.28}$$

The procedure now is to look for solutions of the form

$$\psi(x, y, z) = X(x)\, Y(y)\, Z(z), \tag{2.29}$$

where X, Y and Z are functions of one variable only. Such solutions are called *separable solutions*, and, when they exist, all possible solutions of the differential equation may be constructed by taking linear combinations of them. Separable solutions of the Schrödinger equation do not always exist, however — this depends entirely upon the form of the potential energy function — but we shall see that, even when separable solutions do not exist in one system of coordinates, it may be possible to obtain them by transforming to a different coordinate system.

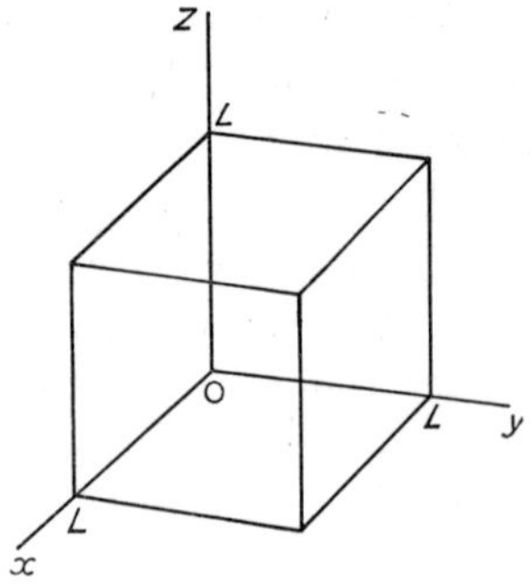

Fig. 2.1.

No difficulty is experienced in our present example. We substitute (2.29) in (2.28), and obtain

$$YZ\frac{\mathrm{d}^2 X}{\mathrm{d}x^2} + XZ\frac{\mathrm{d}^2 Y}{\mathrm{d}y^2} + XY\frac{\mathrm{d}^2 Z}{\mathrm{d}z^2} + \frac{2m}{\hbar^2} EXYZ = 0,$$

or, dividing through by XYZ,

$$\frac{1}{X}\frac{\mathrm{d}^2 X}{\mathrm{d}x^2} + \frac{1}{Y}\frac{\mathrm{d}^2 Y}{\mathrm{d}y^2} + \frac{1}{Z}\frac{\mathrm{d}^2 Z}{\mathrm{d}z^2} + \frac{2mE}{\hbar^2} = 0. \tag{2.30}$$

Now, the first term in this equation is a function of x only, the second a function of y only, and the third a function of z only, while the sum of the three is a constant. This can only be so, in fact, if each term is equal to a constant. We must therefore have

$$\frac{1}{X}\frac{\mathrm{d}^2 X}{\mathrm{d}x^2} = -\frac{2m}{\hbar^2} E_x, \tag{2.31}$$

$$\frac{1}{Y}\frac{\mathrm{d}^2 Y}{\mathrm{d}y^2} = -\frac{2m}{\hbar^2} E_y, \tag{2.32}$$

$$\frac{1}{Z}\frac{d^2Z}{dz^2} = -\frac{2m}{\hbar^2}E_z, \tag{2.33}$$

where E_x, E_y and E_z are constants, such that

$$E_x + E_y + E_z = E. \tag{2.34}$$

The partial differential equation has thus been *separated* into three ordinary equations.

Equation (2.31) is just

$$\frac{d^2X}{dx^2} + \frac{2mE_x}{\hbar^2}X = 0, \tag{2.35}$$

which, apart from the slightly different notation, is the equation for the one-dimensional case, discussed in § 1.5. Also, the same boundary conditions apply, namely, $X(0) = X(L) = 0$, so we may write down the solution immediately. The eigenvalues, or permitted discrete values of E_x, are given by

$$E_x = \frac{\hbar^2\pi^2}{2mL^2}n_x^2, \qquad n_x = 1, 2, 3, \ldots, \tag{2.36}$$

and the corresponding normalized eigenfunctions are given by

$$X(x) = \sqrt{\frac{2}{L}}\sin\frac{n_x\pi x}{L}. \tag{2.37}$$

The solutions for Y and Z are of exactly the same form, so that the wave functions of the stationary states are

$$\psi_{n_xn_yn_z} = \sqrt{\frac{8}{L^3}}\sin\frac{n_x\pi x}{L}\sin\frac{n_y\pi y}{L}\sin\frac{n_z\pi z}{L}, \tag{2.38}$$

and the energy levels, according to (2.34), are

$$E_{n_xn_yn_z} = \frac{\hbar^2\pi^2}{2mL^2}(n_x^2 + n_y^2 + n_z^2), \tag{2.39}$$

where n_x, n_y, n_z are integers. The wave functions are, of course, zero outside the box. It should be noted that changing the sign of n_x, n_y or n_z does not change the energy, nor does it result in a different wave function, but merely multiplies (2.38) by -1. All the stationary states are therefore given by the *positive* integral values of n_x, n_y, n_z. Also, none of these may be zero, for this would make the wave function identically zero, which is not permitted.

It may easily be verified that the wave function (2.38) is normalized: equation (2.24) becomes

$$\frac{8}{L^3}\int_0^L\left(\sin\frac{n_x\pi x}{L}\right)^2 \mathrm{d}x\int_0^L\left(\sin\frac{n_y\pi y}{L}\right)^2 \mathrm{d}y\int_0^L\left(\sin\frac{n_z\pi z}{L}\right)^2 \mathrm{d}z = 1. \qquad (2.40)$$

Three numbers, namely, the integers n_x, n_y and n_z, which are called *quantum numbers*, are required to specify completely each stationary state. It should be noted, however, that the energy E depends only upon the sum of the squares of n_x, n_y and n_z. Consequently, there will in general be several different stationary states, or different wave functions, having the same energy. For example, the four stationary states whose values of (n_x, n_y, n_z) are (5, 1, 1), (1, 5, 1), (1, 1, 5) and (3, 3, 3), respectively, all have the energy $27\hbar^2\pi^2/2mL^2$. Such states and energy levels are said to be *degenerate*. On the other hand, if there is only one wave function corresponding to a certain energy, the state and the energy level are said to be *non-degenerate*. As an example of the latter we may take the ground state, that is, the state with quantum numbers (1, 1, 1) — the energy of this state is $3\hbar^2\pi^2/2mL^2$, and no other state has this energy.

It may easily be seen that any linear combination of several degenerate wave functions is still a wave function belonging to the same energy. Thus, if ψ_1 and ψ_2 are wave functions of states with the same energy E, then

$$H\psi_1 = E\psi_1, \qquad (2.41)$$

and

$$H\psi_2 = E\psi_2. \qquad (2.42)$$

Multiplying (2.41) and (2.42) by the arbitrary constants A and B, respectively, and adding, we obtain

$$H(A\psi_1+B\psi_2) = E(A\psi_1+B\psi_2), \qquad (2.43)$$

showing that the arbitrary linear combination $A\psi_1+B\psi_2$ is a wave function corresponding to the energy E. The number of *independent* wave functions (that is, wave functions which are not merely linear combinations of the others) belonging to an energy level is called the *degree of degeneracy* of the level.

2.4. Particle in a Central Field

As a second important example we will consider a particle moving in a central field of force, that is, under the action of a force which is directed towards a fixed point and whose magnitude is a function only of the distance r of the particle from the point. The potential energy of the particle is then also a function of r only, and may be written $V(r)$: it is said to be *spherically symmetrical.*

The Schrödinger equation is

$$\nabla^2\psi + \frac{2m}{\hbar^2}[E - V(r)]\psi = 0. \tag{2.44}$$

If we take the centre of force to be at the origin, then

$$r^2 = x^2 + y^2 + z^2, \tag{2.45}$$

so that we may write the Schrödinger equation in terms of the Cartesian coordinates of the particle, as in equation (2.15). This is generally inconvenient, however, because equation (2.44) can rarely be separated in Cartesian coordinates. In fact, separable solutions can only be found in Cartesian coordinates when $V(r)$ is constant (free particle) or when $V(r)$ is proportional to r^2 (three-dimensional harmonic oscillator). In other cases, the spherical symmetry of the potential function suggests that we transform to the spherical polar coordinates (r, θ, ϕ). These are shown in Figure 2.2: r is the length of the radius vector, θ is the angle between the radius vector and Oz, and ϕ is the angle between the projection of the radius vector on the xy-plane and Ox. It is easily verified that

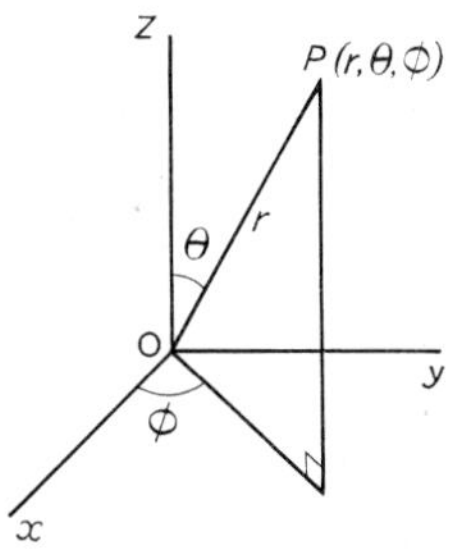

Fig. 2.2. Spherical polar coordinates.

$$\begin{aligned} x &= r \sin\theta \cos\phi, \\ y &= r \sin\theta \sin\phi, \\ z &= r \cos\theta. \end{aligned} \tag{2.46}$$

The transformation of the Laplacian operator (2.16) into spherical polar coordinates is rather lengthy, and we will merely quote the result. The Schrödinger equation (2.44) becomes

$$\frac{1}{r^2}\frac{\partial}{\partial r}\left(r^2\frac{\partial\psi}{\partial r}\right)+\frac{1}{r^2\sin\theta}\frac{\partial}{\partial\theta}\left(\sin\theta\frac{\partial\psi}{\partial\theta}\right)$$
$$+\frac{1}{r^2\sin^2\theta}\frac{\partial^2\psi}{\partial\phi^2}+\frac{2m}{\hbar^2}[E-V(r)]\psi=0, \tag{2.47}$$

where ψ is now a function of r, θ and ϕ. Separable solutions can now be found, of the form

$$\psi(r,\theta,\phi)=R(r)\,\Theta(\theta)\,\Phi(\phi), \tag{2.48}$$

R, Θ and Φ being functions of a single variable only.

Substituting (2.48) into (2.47), multiplying through by $r^2\sin^2\theta/R\Theta\Phi$, and re-arranging, we obtain

$$\frac{\sin^2\theta}{R}\frac{\mathrm{d}}{\mathrm{d}r}\left(r^2\frac{\mathrm{d}R}{\mathrm{d}r}\right)+\frac{\sin\theta}{\Theta}\frac{\mathrm{d}}{\mathrm{d}\theta}\left(\sin\theta\frac{\mathrm{d}\Theta}{\mathrm{d}\theta}\right)$$
$$+\frac{2m}{\hbar^2}[E-V(r)]r^2\sin^2\theta=-\frac{1}{\Phi}\frac{\mathrm{d}^2\Phi}{\mathrm{d}\phi^2}. \tag{2.49}$$

The right-hand side is a function of ϕ only, while the left-hand side is independent of ϕ. Both sides must therefore be equated to the same constant, which we denote by α: thus,

$$\frac{\mathrm{d}^2\Phi}{\mathrm{d}\phi^2}=-\alpha\Phi, \tag{2.50}$$

$$\frac{\sin^2\theta}{R}\frac{\mathrm{d}}{\mathrm{d}r}\left(r^2\frac{\mathrm{d}R}{\mathrm{d}r}\right)+\frac{\sin\theta}{\Theta}\frac{\mathrm{d}}{\mathrm{d}\theta}\left(\sin\theta\frac{\mathrm{d}\Theta}{\mathrm{d}\theta}\right)$$
$$+\frac{2m}{\hbar^2}[E-V(r)]r^2\sin^2\theta=\alpha. \tag{2.51}$$

Dividing equation (2.51) through by $\sin^2\theta$, and re-arranging, gives

$$\frac{1}{R}\frac{\mathrm{d}}{\mathrm{d}r}\left(r^2\frac{\mathrm{d}R}{\mathrm{d}r}\right)+\frac{2m}{\hbar^2}[E-V(r)]r^2$$
$$=\frac{\alpha}{\sin^2\theta}-\frac{1}{\Theta\sin\theta}\frac{\mathrm{d}}{\mathrm{d}\theta}\left(\sin\theta\frac{\mathrm{d}\Theta}{\mathrm{d}\theta}\right). \tag{2.52}$$

The left-hand side of this equation is a function of r only, while the right-hand side is a function of θ only. Hence, both sides must be equated to the same constant, which we denote by β. After slight re-arrangement, the separated equations become

$$\frac{1}{\sin\theta}\frac{\mathrm{d}}{\mathrm{d}\theta}\left(\sin\theta\frac{\mathrm{d}\Theta}{\mathrm{d}\theta}\right)+\left(\beta-\frac{\alpha}{\sin^2\theta}\right)\Theta=0, \tag{2.53}$$

$$\frac{\mathrm{d}^2R}{\mathrm{d}r^2}+\frac{2}{r}\frac{\mathrm{d}R}{\mathrm{d}r}+\left[\frac{2m}{\hbar^2}\{E-V(r)\}-\frac{\beta}{r^2}\right]R=0. \tag{2.54}$$

It should be noted that, of the three separated equations (2.50), (2.53) and (2.54), only equation (2.54) contains the potential function $V(r)$. It follows that the radial function $R(r)$ is the only one which depends upon the *form* of the central field; the angular functions $\Theta(\theta)$ and $\Phi(\phi)$ are *the same for all central fields.*

Two *separation constants,* α and β, have been introduced, about which nothing has been said so far. If ψ is to satisfy the usual conditions, however, we might expect that these constants will not be able to assume arbitrary values. This is most easily seen in the case of α. Two independent solutions of equation (2.50) are

$$\Phi=\mathrm{e}^{\mathrm{i}\sqrt{\alpha}\phi}, \tag{2.55}$$

and

$$\Phi=\mathrm{e}^{-\mathrm{i}\sqrt{\alpha}\phi}. \tag{2.56}$$

An alternative pair of independent solutions (linear combinations of the previous pair), which is sometimes more convenient, is

$$\Phi=\sin\sqrt{\alpha}\phi, \tag{2.57}$$

and

$$\Phi=\cos\sqrt{\alpha}\phi. \tag{2.58}$$

Now, the point (r, θ, ϕ) is the same as the point $(r, \theta, \phi+2\pi)$. Hence, if the wave function is to be single-valued, as required, Φ must not change in value when ϕ is increased by 2π, that is,

$$\Phi(\phi+2\pi)=\Phi(\phi), \tag{2.59}$$

or Φ must have period 2π. In order that this be so, we must have

$$\sqrt{\alpha}=m_l, \tag{2.60}$$

where m_l is a positive or negative integer or zero. We may therefore take the (un-normalized) eigenfunctions of equation (2.50) to be

$$\Phi_{m_l}(\phi) = \mathrm{e}^{\mathrm{i}m_l\phi}, \tag{2.61}$$

where $m_l = 0, \pm 1, \pm 2, \ldots$, and it must be remembered that the positive and negative values correspond to *different* eigenfunctions. Alternatively, we may take them to be

$$\left.\begin{aligned} \Phi_{m_l}(\phi) &= \sin m_l\phi, \quad \text{when } m_l = 1, 2, 3, \ldots, \\ \Phi_{m_l}(\phi) &= \cos m_l\phi, \quad \text{when } m_l = 0, -1, -2, \ldots. \end{aligned}\right\} \tag{2.62}$$

We do not propose to solve equation (2.53) generally, as this is rather tedious. It is found that, for Θ to be finite everywhere, we must have

$$\beta = l(l+1), \tag{2.63}$$

where $l = 0, 1, 2, \ldots$, and, in addition,

$$|m_l| \leqq l, \tag{2.64}$$

The acceptable solutions for Θ are *associated Legendre functions* of $\cos\theta$, generally denoted by $P_l^{m_l}(\cos\theta)$.

Equations (2.53) and (2.54) have now become

$$\frac{1}{\sin\theta}\frac{\mathrm{d}}{\mathrm{d}\theta}\left(\sin\theta\frac{\mathrm{d}\Theta}{\mathrm{d}\theta}\right) + \left[l(l+1) - \frac{m_l^2}{\sin^2\theta}\right]\Theta = 0, \tag{2.65}$$

$$\frac{\mathrm{d}^2R}{\mathrm{d}r^2} + \frac{2}{r}\frac{\mathrm{d}R}{\mathrm{d}r} + \left[\frac{2m}{\hbar^2}\{E - V(r)\} - \frac{l(l+1)}{r^2}\right]R = 0. \tag{2.66}$$

The latter equation cannot be solved in general, since its solution depends upon the form of $V(r)$, and indeed there are only a few forms of $V(r)$ for which analytical solutions can be obtained. However, we expect to obtain eigenfunctions corresponding to a series of discrete values of E, which we may label by means of some quantum number n, say. Since the equation contains l, it is clear that the eigenfunctions, and generally the eigenvalues, will also depend upon l.

Summarizing, then, a wave function corresponding to the energy level E_n, is specified by three quantum numbers n, l, m_l, and may be written

$$\psi_{n,l,m_l}(r, \theta, \phi) = R_{n,l}(r)P_l^{m_l}(\cos\theta)\mathrm{e}^{\mathrm{i}m_l\phi}. \tag{2.67}$$

The states must usually be degenerate, for the energy does not depend upon the quantum number m_l — m_l does not occur in equation (2.66), which determines the energy. Equation (2.64) tells us, in fact, that there are at least $2l+1$ states to each energy level, since m_l may assume the $2l+1$ values

$$-l, -(l-1), \dots -1, 0, 1, \dots (l-1), l. \tag{2.68}$$

We shall see below that in the special case of the hydrogenic atom, the degeneracy is greater than this. The significance of the quantum number n, called the *principal quantum number*, will be brought out more clearly later. l is called the *azimuthal quantum number*, since θ is the azimuthal angle. m_l is called the *magnetic quantum number*, because it is most important in problems involving atoms in magnetic fields.

States for which $l = 0$ are called s states, those for which $l = 1$ are called p states. These are the states which will concern us most later in the book, so it will be as well to consider them in detail.

s *states*. When $l = 0$, equation (2.64) tells us that $m_l = 0$ also, so that the function Φ is a constant. Equations (2.65) and (2.66) then become

$$\frac{\mathrm{d}}{\mathrm{d}\theta}\left(\sin\frac{\mathrm{d}\Theta}{\mathrm{d}\theta}\right) = 0, \tag{2.69}$$

$$\frac{\mathrm{d}^2R}{\mathrm{d}r^2} + \frac{2}{r}\frac{\mathrm{d}R}{\mathrm{d}r} + \frac{2m}{\hbar^2}[E-V(r)]R = 0. \tag{2.70}$$

An obvious solution of equation (2.69) is

$$\Theta = \text{constant}, \tag{2.71}$$

and this is the only solution which is finite everywhere. It follows that the wave function of an s state is *spherically symmetrical* — it is, in fact, just an eigenfunction of equation (2.70). Conversely, if we substitute $\psi = R(r)$ in the Schrödinger equation (2.47), it reduces immediately to equation (2.70), and comparison with equation (2.66) then tells us that $l = 0$. Hence, all spherically symmetrical states are s states.

p *states*. When $l = 1$, equation (2.64) permits m_l to have the values $-1, 0, 1$, so that there are three degenerate wave functions. We say that p states are *triply* or *threefold* degenerate. With $m_l = \pm 1$, equation (2.65) becomes

$$\frac{1}{\sin\theta}\frac{\mathrm{d}}{\mathrm{d}\theta}\left(\sin\theta\frac{\mathrm{d}\Theta}{\mathrm{d}\theta}\right) + \left(2 - \frac{1}{\sin^2\theta}\right)\Theta = 0, \tag{2.72}$$

which has the finite solution

$$\Theta = \sin\theta, \tag{2.73}$$

as may be verified by substitution. With $m_l = 0$, the equation becomes

$$\frac{1}{\sin\theta}\frac{\mathrm{d}}{\mathrm{d}\theta}\left(\sin\theta\frac{\mathrm{d}\Theta}{\mathrm{d}\theta}\right) + 2\Theta = 0, \tag{2.74}$$

which has the finite solution

$$\Theta = \cos\theta. \tag{2.75}$$

If we take the functions Φ given by (2.61), therefore, the three degenerate p states corresponding to a given principal quantum number n, or energy level $E_{n,1}$, are

$$\left.\begin{aligned} \psi_{n,1,-1} &= R_{n,1}(r)\sin\theta\,\mathrm{e}^{-\mathrm{i}\phi}, \\ \psi_{n,1,0} &= R_{n,1}(r)\cos\theta, \\ \psi_{n,1,1} &= R_{n,1}(r)\sin\theta\,\mathrm{e}^{\mathrm{i}\phi}, \end{aligned}\right\} \tag{2.76}$$

where $R_{n,1}(r)$ is the eigenfunction of the equation

$$\frac{\mathrm{d}^2R}{\mathrm{d}r^2} + \frac{2}{r}\frac{\mathrm{d}R}{\mathrm{d}r} + \left[\frac{2m}{\hbar^2}\{E - V(r)\} - \frac{2}{r^2}\right]R = 0, \tag{2.77}$$

with $E = E_{n,1}$.

Alternatively, we could take the functions Φ given by (2.62), and obtain, instead of (2.76),

$$\left.\begin{aligned} \psi_{n,1,-1} &= R_{n,1}(r)\sin\theta\cos\phi, \\ \psi_{n,1,0} &= R_{n,1}(r)\cos\theta, \\ \psi_{n,1,1} &= R_{n,1}(r)\sin\theta\sin\phi. \end{aligned}\right\} \tag{2.78}$$

Recalling equations (2.46), we obtain, in more compact form

$$\left.\begin{aligned} \psi_{n,1,-1} &= xf(r), \\ \psi_{n,1,0} &= zf(r), \\ \psi_{n,1,1} &= yf(r), \end{aligned}\right\} \tag{2.79}$$

where

$$f(r) = R_{n,1}/r. \tag{2.80}$$

Since the Schrödinger equation (2.44) is symmetrical in x, y and z, we should, in fact, expect that, if any one of the above functions is a solution, then the other two must be solutions corresponding to the same energy.

It should be noticed that the function $xf(r)$ is zero over the plane $x = 0$, and the other two functions are zero over the planes $z = 0$, $y = 0$ respectively. Such planes are called *nodal planes*. Thus, a p state, with $l = 1$, has *one* nodal plane passing through the origin. An s state, on the other hand, with $l = 0$, is spherically symmetrical, and has *no* nodal planes. In general, a state with azimuthal quantum number l has l nodal planes passing through the origin. Of course, the radial factor in the wave function will also generally give rise to nodal surfaces, that is, surfaces on which the wave function is zero, but these will be *nodal spheres*, centred at the origin. The principal quantum number n is defined so that $n-1$ *is the total number of nodal surfaces*, both plane and spherical. Since there are l nodal planes, it follows that

$$l \leqq n-1. \tag{2.81}$$

States with higher values of l are also denoted by letters; thus,

$l = 0$	1	2	3	4.
s	p	d	f	g

We shall not discuss f and g states, but it might be worth while to give a brief mention to d states, as they are of some importance in the theory of metals.

d *states*. When $l = 2$, equation (2.64) permits m_l to have the values -2, -1, 0, 1, 2, so that d states are *fivefold* degenerate. The five independent wave functions may be taken to have the forms

$$\begin{gathered} yz\,F(r), \quad zx\,F(r), \quad xy\,F(r), \\ (y^2-z^2)\,F(r), \quad (z^2-x^2)\,F(r), \end{gathered} \tag{2.82}$$

$F(r)$ being an appropriate radial function. It will be noted that each of them has two nodal planes (for example, the first is zero on the planes $y = 0$, $z = 0$) passing through the origin.

Since the energy is not affected by the value of m_l (in the absence of a magnetic field) it is generally suficient to refer to a state by its values of n and l, and this is done by writing the value of n followed by the letter denoting the value of l. Thus, the ground state, with $n = 1$, $l = 0$, is called a 1s state; a state with $n = 3$, $l = 1$, is a 3p state; a state with $n = 3$, $l = 2$, is a 3d state, and so on.

2.5. The Hydrogenic Atom

The foregoing discussion applies quite generally to all central fields. We will now consider a special case of particular importance—the hydrogenic or hydrogen-like atom. This is an atom which consists of a nucleus and a single electron, typical examples being the hydrogen atom itself, the singly-ionized helium atom, the doubly-ionized lithium atom, and so on. Ionization means the removal of an electron or electrons — a neutral atom of helium has two electrons, and when one of these is removed we have a singly-ionized helium atom. Similarly, a neutral atom of lithium has three electrons, and when *two* of these are removed we have a doubly-ionized lithium atom. Hydrogenic atoms of various elements differ from each other only in the charge and mass of the nucleus. We will denote the charge of a proton by e, so that the charge of an electron is $-e$. Then, if the atomic number (the number of electrons in a neutral atom) of an element is Z, the nuclear charge is Ze, so that the attractive force between the nucleus and an electron is of magnitude Ze^2/r^2, where r is the distance between the two. The potential energy of the electron in the field of the nucleus is, therefore,

$$V(r) = -\frac{Ze^2}{r}, \tag{2.83}$$

taking the zero of potential energy to be at infinite separation.

Now, the general motion of a pair of attractive particles can be represented as an orbital motion of the particles about their common centre of mass plus a uniform linear motion of this centre of mass. However, the mass of a proton is 1836 times that of an electron, so that, even in a hydrogen atom, whose nucleus consists of a single proton, the centre of mass lies very close to the nucleus, and in all other atoms, whose nuclei consist of a number of protons and neutrons (the mass of a neutron is the same as that of a proton, but a neutron has no charge) it lies much closer still. It is clear, therefore, that little accuracy will be lost if the orbital motion of the nucleus is ignored and the electron is regarded as revolving about the nucleus as centre of force. Also, in the case of a free atom, the linear motion of the centre of mass is not quantized, that is, it does not give rise to a discrete series of energy levels, and when the atom is bound, as in a solid, so that the motion of the centre of mass *is* quantized, this motion can be treated quite separately from that of the electrons. Hence, for many purposes, the motion of the centre of mass, which we have assumed to be approximately coincident with the nucleus, may be ignored, and we may take the problem of the hydrogenic atom to be that of an electron moving in the central field of a fixed nucleus, with potential energy given by (2.83). All this can be shown quite rigorously, of course, and indeed the difficulty regarding the orbital motion of the nucleus can be completely overcome by replacing the electronic mass m by a *reduced mass* $mM/(m+M)$, where M is the mass of the nucleus. We will not go into this question further, however, and as the reduced mass for hydrogen is 0.9995 m we will ignore the difference between this and m.

The radial equation (2.66) can be solved analytically when $V(r)$ is given by (2.83), but we shall not require the general form of the eigenfunctions, and so will again content ourselves with one or two special cases.

a) $n = 1,\ l = 0.$ This 1s state has no nodal surfaces, either plane or spherical, and, as we might expect, it is the *ground state* of the atom. The un-normalized wave function is

$$\psi_{1,0,0}(r) = R_{1,0}(r) = \mathrm{e}^{-Zr/a_0}, \tag{2.84}$$

where $a_0 = \hbar^2/me^2$, as we will now verify.

R must satisfy the equation

$$\frac{\mathrm{d}^2R}{\mathrm{d}r^2} + \frac{2}{r}\frac{\mathrm{d}R}{\mathrm{d}r} + \frac{2m}{\hbar^2}\left(E + \frac{Ze^2}{r}\right) R = 0. \tag{2.85}$$

Now

$$\frac{\mathrm{d}R}{\mathrm{d}r} = -\frac{Z}{a_0}\,\mathrm{e}^{-Zr/a_0} = -\frac{Zme^2}{\hbar^2}\,\mathrm{e}^{-Zr/a_0}, \tag{2.86}$$

and

$$\frac{\mathrm{d}^2R}{\mathrm{d}r^2} = \left(\frac{Zme^2}{\hbar^2}\right)^2 \mathrm{e}^{-Zr/a_0}. \tag{2.87}$$

Substituting in (2.85), and dividing through by R, gives

$$\left(\frac{Zme^2}{\hbar^2}\right)^2 - \frac{2Zme^2}{\hbar^2 r} + \frac{2m}{\hbar^2}\left(E + \frac{Ze^2}{r}\right) = 0. \tag{2.88}$$

The terms in r cancel, and we are left with

$$E = -\frac{Z^2me^4}{2\hbar^2} = E_{1,0}\,, \tag{2.89}$$

and (2.84) is not a solution unless E has this value, which is thus the lowest energy level of the atom.

b) $n = 2,\ l = 0$. This 2s state has a single nodal sphere, but no nodal planes, and its energy level is the next above the ground state level — it is the *first excited state.* The un-normalized wave function is

$$\psi_{2,0,0}(r) = R_{2,0}(r) = (2a_0 - Zr)\mathrm{e}^{-Zr/2a_0}. \tag{2.90}$$

The equation which R must satisfy is again equation (2.85), but, following the above procedure, this time we find that it will only do so if

$$E = -\frac{Z^2me^4}{2\hbar^2} \cdot \frac{1}{2^2} = E_{2,0}. \tag{2.91}$$

c) $n = 2,\ l = 1$. There are three degenerate 2p states, all with the same radial function

$$R_{2,1}(r) = r\mathrm{e}^{-Zr/2a_0}, \tag{2.92}$$

and angular functions given by (2.76) or (2.78). The only zero of R is at the origin, so that a 2p wave function has no nodal spheres, but one nodal plane.

In this case R must satisfy the equation

$$\frac{\mathrm{d}^2R}{\mathrm{d}r^2} + \frac{2}{r}\frac{\mathrm{d}R}{\mathrm{d}r} + \left[\frac{2m}{\hbar^2}\left(E + \frac{Ze^2}{r}\right) - \frac{2}{r^2}\right] R = 0, \tag{2.93}$$

and it may be verified as before that it will only do so if

$$E = -\frac{Zme^4}{2\hbar^2} \cdot \frac{1}{2^2} = E_{2,1}. \tag{2.94}$$

It will be noticed that $E_{2,1}$ is the same as $E_{2,0}$, so that the energy is independent of l, and the 2s and 2p states are degenerate. This is always true *for a hydrogenic atom* — the energy levels depend only upon the principal quantum number n, and, as suggested by the above expressions, are given by

$$E_n = -\frac{Z^2me^4}{2\hbar^2} \cdot \frac{1}{n^2}. \tag{2.95}$$

The states of the hydrogenic atom thus have a greater degree of degeneracy than do those of an electron in other central fields, for which the energy levels vary with l as well as with n. We have seen in § 2.4 that, for every central field, owing to the degeneracy of the Φ functions, there are $2l+1$ degenerate states with the same values of n and l. In the hydrogenic atom, however, all states with a given value of n and with l having the values $0, 1, 2, \ldots (n-1)$ are degenerate also. Since

$$\sum_{l=0}^{n-1} (2l+1) = n^2, \tag{2.96}$$

the total degeneracy of a state with principal quantum number n is n^2.

Formula (2.95) gives results which can immediately be compared with experiment. For instance, if a hydrogen atom ($Z = 1$) makes a transition from an excited state with principal quantum number n to the ground state, the Bohr frequency rule [equation (1.6)] tells us that radiation of frequency ν will be emitted, where

$$h\nu = E_n - E_1 = \frac{me^4}{2\hbar^2}\left(1 - \frac{1}{n^2}\right). \tag{2.97}$$

Lines corresponding to these frequencies, for different values of n, as well as other series of lines due to transitions to final states other than the ground state, have been observed in the spectrum of hydrogen, in excellent agreement with the theoretical results.

2.6. Electronic Charge Clouds

The radial functions $R_{n,l}$ for states of low energy of the hydrogen atom are shown in Figure 2.3. Excluding the origin, each function has $n-l-1$ zeros.

The usual probability interpretation may be given to $|\psi|^2$, provided ψ is normalized, that is, provided we include in ψ a constant factor such that

$$\int |\psi|^2 \mathrm{d}\boldsymbol{r} = \int_0^\infty \mathrm{d}r \int_0^\pi \mathrm{d}\theta \int_0^{2\pi} |\psi|^2 r^2 \sin\theta \,\mathrm{d}\phi$$

$$= \int_0^\infty r^2 |R|^2 \mathrm{d}r \int_0^\pi |\Theta|^2 \sin\theta \,\mathrm{d}\theta \int_0^{2\pi} |\Phi|^2 \mathrm{d}\phi = 1. \tag{2.98}$$

There is, however, another interpretation, or perhaps another way of looking at the probability interpretation, which is often convenient. This is the *charge cloud* interpretation. Since the electronic charge is $-e$, then, according to the interpretation of $|\psi|^2$ as a probability density, the *average charge density* at any point must be $-e|\psi|^2$. In many problems it is useful, if only as an intuitive aid, to picture the electronic charge as spread out in a cloud having charge density $-e|\psi(\boldsymbol{r})|^2$ at position $\boldsymbol{r}$.

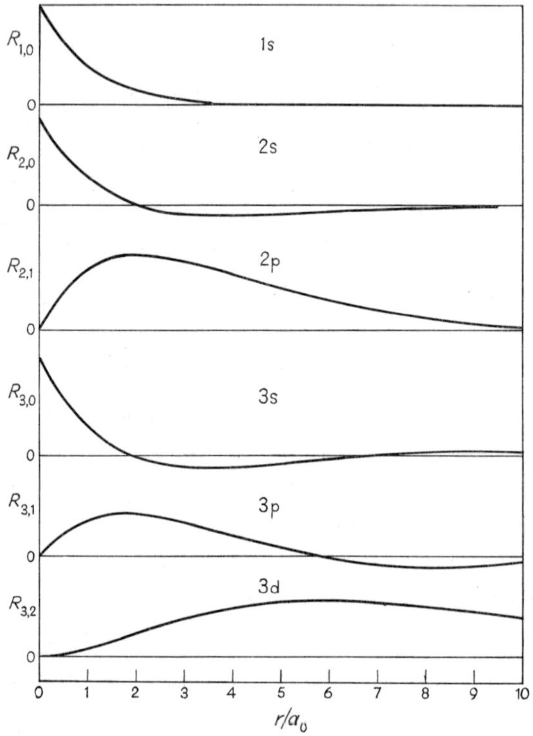

Fig. 2.3. Radial wave functions for states of low energy of the hydrogen atom.

The charge clouds of s states are all spherically symmetrical. Those of p states, however, have a dumb-bell like appearance. Of course, all the charge clouds extend to infinity, but in the case of p states the principal concentration of charge is in two lobes symmetrically placed on either side of the nodal plane. This may be shown as follows: from equations (2.79) and (2.80) we find that a typical p function is

$$\psi = \frac{x}{r} R, \tag{2.99}$$

where R is the radial function, and we will assume that ψ is normalized. The charge density is thus

$$-e|\psi|^2 = -e\left|\frac{x}{r}R\right|^2, \tag{2.100}$$

and this is zero on the plane $x = 0$, is symmetrical with respect to this plane, as well as about the x-axis, and has its greatest values on the x-axis. The angular factor $(x/r)^2$ may be represented by means of a polar diagram, as shown in Figure 2.4 — the length of the radius vector from the origin to the curve gives the value of the function in the direction of the radius vector, and the same curve applies to all planes through the x-axis. The charge clouds of the other two p states have their lobes in the y- and z-directions respectively.

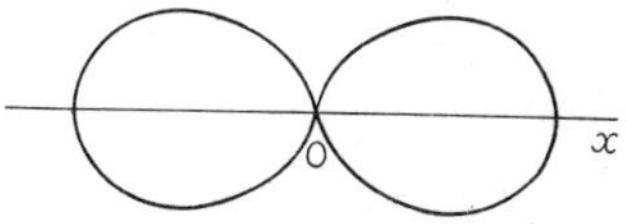

Fig. 2.4. Polar diagram showing the angular variation of charge density for a p state.

Similarly, the charge clouds of states with higher values of l, d states, etc., have a greater number of lobes, corresponding to the greater number of nodal planes.

2.7. Orthogonality of Wave Functions

2.7.1. NON-DEGENERATE STATES

If ψ_1 and ψ_2 are wave functions of a particle moving in three dimensions, corresponding to the *different* energy levels E_1 and E_2 respectively, then

$$\int \psi_1^* \psi_2 \, d\mathbf{r} = 0, \tag{2.101}$$

the integration being throughout all space, and the functions are said to be orthogonal.

This may be proved in the same way as for the one-dimensional case. From equation (2.17) and its complex conjugate, assuming that the potential function $V(\mathbf{r})$ is real, we have

$$\nabla^2\psi_1^* + \frac{2m}{\hbar^2}(E_1 - V)\psi_1^* = 0, \tag{2.102}$$

$$\nabla^2\psi_2 + \frac{2m}{\hbar^2}(E_2 - V)\psi_2 = 0. \tag{2.103}$$

Multiplying the first equation by ψ_2, subtracting from it the second multiplied by ψ_1^*, and integrating throughout all space, gives

$$\int (\psi_2 \nabla^2 \psi_1^* - \psi_1^* \nabla^2 \psi_2) \mathrm{d}\boldsymbol{r} = \frac{2m}{\hbar^2} (E_2 - E_1) \int \psi_1^* \psi_2 \, \mathrm{d}\boldsymbol{r}. \tag{2.104}$$

According to Green's theorem (see Appendix 1) a volume integral such as that on the left-hand side may be transformed into a surface integral over the bounding surface, thus

$$\int (\psi_2 \nabla^2 \psi_1^* - \psi_1^* \nabla^2 \psi_2) \mathrm{d}\boldsymbol{r} = \int \left(\psi_2 \frac{\partial \psi_1^*}{\partial n} - \psi_1^* \frac{\partial \psi_2}{\partial n} \right) \mathrm{d}S, \tag{2.105}$$

where $\partial/\partial n$ denotes differentiation in the direction of the outward normal to the surface. In the present case the volume is the whole of space, so that the surface is infinitely large. Since the wave functions of bound states must vanish at infinity, in order to satisfy equation (2.23), the integrand of the surface integral must be zero, and consequently the integral is zero. The left-hand side of equation (2.104) is therefore zero, and, since $E_2 \neq E_1$, equation (2.101) follows.

To be quite accurate, we must point out that the vanishing of the wave functions at infinity is not in itself sufficient to ensure that the surface integral in (2.105) is zero. The use of the term 'infinity' always implies a limiting process — in this case we are integrating over a large closed surface and finding the limiting value of this integral as the surface swells indefinitely in all directions. Since the surface area itself is increasing, it is clear that the limit will be zero only if the wave functions tend to zero *sufficiently rapidly*. For example, if we take the surface to be a sphere centred at the origin, with radius r and surface area $4\pi r^2$, then, in order that the surface integral vanish in the limit as $r \to \infty$, the integrand must tend to zero more rapidly than $1/r^2$. However, this need not worry us, because it can be shown that *all* bound state wave functions tend to zero with sufficient rapidity.

Of course, it may not be necessary to take the integral (2.101) throughout all space. In the problem of the particle in a box, discussed in § 2.3, we have seen that the wave functions vanish at the surface of the box. The volume integrals may therefore be taken throughout the inside of the box only; the surface integral becomes an integral over the finite surface of the box, and is zero because the wave functions vanish there. The above difficulties then do not arise. When we come to discuss metals we shall reconsider the problem of the particle in a box and impose boundary conditions different from those mentioned above. These new boundary conditions, however, which are called *periodic boundary conditions*, are still of such a nature that the surface integral in (2.105) vanishes over the surface of the box, so that the wave functions remain orthogonal.

2.7.2. DEGENERATE STATES

If ψ_1 and ψ_2 are different wave functions belonging to the same *degenerate* energy level, the foregoing proof, which demands that $E_2 \neq E_1$, breaks down, and the functions *need* not be orthogonal. On the other hand, the functions *may* still be orthogonal, and, if they are not, then linear combinations of them, which *are* orthogonal, can certainly be constructed. This may be done in the following way.

Let us assume that ψ_1 is normalized, so that

$$\int |\psi_1|^2 \mathrm{d}\boldsymbol{r} = 1, \tag{2.106}$$

and also that

$$\int \psi_1^* \psi_2 \, \mathrm{d}\boldsymbol{r} = c, \tag{2.107}$$

where c is some constant. Now let us write

$$\psi_3 = c\psi_1 - \psi_2, \tag{2.108}$$

so that

$$\int \psi_1^* \psi_3 \, \mathrm{d}\boldsymbol{r} = c \int |\psi_1|^2 \mathrm{d}\boldsymbol{r} - \int \psi_1^* \psi_2 \, \mathrm{d}\boldsymbol{r} = 0, \tag{2.109}$$

from (2.106) and (2.107). Thus, ψ_1 and ψ_3 are independent degenerate wave functions which are orthogonal (we proved at the end of § 2.3 that any linear combination of degenerate wave functions is a wave function belonging to the same energy level). This process may be extended to any number of degenerate wave functions, so that a number, equal to the degree of degeneracy, of independent orthogonal wave functions may always be found.

2.8. The Representation of Dynamical Variables by Operators

In this section we will introduce a further abbreviated notation, which will also be used in Chapter 11. We will let q stand for *any* one of the Cartesian coordinates of the particles of a system, and p stand for the conjugate momentum, and simply write $f(q, p)$ for a function of *all* the coordinates and conjugate momenta of the system.

We have seen in § 2.1 that the replacement of p by the operator $(\hbar/\mathrm{i})(\partial/\partial q)$ in the classical Hamiltonian $H(q, p)$ leads to the Schrödinger equation

$$H\left(q, \frac{\hbar}{\mathrm{i}}\frac{\partial}{\partial q}\right)\psi = E\psi. \tag{2.110}$$

We have remarked that q has really become the operator 'multiply by q', although this does not greatly affect the problem. For any stationary state, or eigenfunction ψ, the energy E is constant; it is said to be a *constant of the motion.*

This formal derivation of the Schrödinger equation is not the only use to which the operational form of p may be put. Any dynamical variable which classically may be written as a function $f(q, p)$ of the Cartesian coordinates and conjugate momenta of the particles of a system may be transformed into a quantum-mechanical operator in the same way as the Hamiltonian, and some information about the values of the dynamical variable may so be derived.

For example, it sometimes occurs that the eigenfunction ψ of equation (2.110) also satisfies the equation

$$f\left(q, \frac{\hbar}{\mathrm{i}}\frac{\partial}{\partial q}\right)\psi = \lambda\psi, \tag{2.111}$$

where λ is a constant. In this case it is said that f and H have *simultaneous eigenfunctions*; the obvious interpretation being that the *dynamical variable represented by f is also a constant of the motion*, and that its value is λ in the state ψ. We will not prove this, but will accept it as a fundamental postulate of quantum mechanics.

It should be clear that it is by no means necessary for equation (2.111) to be satisfied by an eigenfunction of the Schrödinger equation. In general, an operator f will act upon ψ to give a function quite different from ψ, and not just a constant multiplied by ψ.

As a simple example, let us consider a particle moving freely along the x-axis. The classical equation of energy in Hamiltonian form, taking the potential energy to be zero, is

$$H(x, p_x) = \frac{1}{2m}p_x^2 = E. \tag{2.112}$$

Setting

$$p_x = \frac{\hbar}{\mathrm{i}} \frac{\partial}{\partial x}, \tag{2.113}$$

and operating upon $\psi(x)$, we obtain the Schrödinger equation

$$-\frac{\hbar^2}{2m} \frac{\partial^2 \psi}{\partial x^2} = E\psi. \tag{2.114}$$

A solution of this is

$$\psi = \mathrm{e}^{ikx}, \tag{2.115}$$

corresponding to the energy

$$E = \frac{\hbar^2 k^2}{2m} \tag{2.116}$$

(we may ignore the normalization difficulty which occurs for free particles, mentioned in a footnote in § 1.6.).

Now, according to classical mechanics, the momentum p_x is certainly a constant of the motion, as is the energy E, so let us see if we can find an equation like (2.111) with f equal to the momentum operator (2.113) and ψ the function (2.115). We have, in fact,

$$\frac{\hbar}{\mathrm{i}} \frac{\partial}{\partial x} \mathrm{e}^{ikx} = \hbar k \mathrm{e}^{ikx}, \tag{2.117}$$

which has the form of (2.111), with $\lambda = \hbar k$. H and p_x thus have simultaneous eigenfunctions, and we deduce that, quantum-mechanically also, p_x is a constant of the motion, with value $\hbar k$. This is not surprising, for the classical value of p_x, obtained from (2.112) and (2.116), is also $\hbar k$.

It is easily seen, however, that

$$x\mathrm{e}^{ikx} \neq \lambda \mathrm{e}^{ikx}, \tag{2.118}$$

for any constant λ. Hence H and x do not have simultaneous eigenfunctions, and x is not a constant of the motion, again in agreement with classical mechanics.

2.8.1. COMMUTATION RELATIONS

By straightforward differentiation, we have

$$\frac{\partial}{\partial x}(x\psi) = \psi + x \frac{\partial \psi}{\partial x}, \tag{2.119}$$

so that

$$\frac{\hbar}{i}\frac{\partial}{\partial x}(x\psi)-x\frac{\hbar}{i}\frac{\partial\psi}{\partial x} = \frac{\hbar}{i}\psi. \tag{2.120}$$

Using equation (2.113), this may be written

$$p_x x\psi - x p_x\psi = \frac{\hbar}{i}\psi, \tag{2.121}$$

where it must be remembered that p_x is the *operator* representing the momentum. From (2.121) we obtain the *operator equation*

$$p_x x - x p_x = \frac{\hbar}{i}. \tag{2.122}$$

The left-hand side of this equation is called the *commutator* of p_x and x, and is generally denoted by $[p_x, x]$, so that we have the *commutation relation*

$$[p_x, x] = \frac{\hbar}{i}. \tag{2.123}$$

In general, for any two operators A and B, the commutator is defined by

$$[A, B] = AB-BA. \tag{2.124}$$

On the other hand, we see that

$$\frac{\partial}{\partial x}(y\psi) = y\frac{\partial\psi}{\partial x}, \tag{2.125}$$

since x and y are independent variables, and consequently

$$\frac{\hbar}{i}\frac{\partial}{\partial x}(y\psi)-y\frac{\hbar}{i}\frac{\partial\psi}{\partial x} = 0, \tag{2.126}$$

or

$$p_x y - y p_x = [p_x, y] = 0. \tag{2.127}$$

Two variables, such as these, whose commutator is zero, are said to *commute*. We have shown that canonically conjugate variables, such as x and p_x, do not commute. In quantum mechanics the commutation relation (2.123) is, in fact, taken to be the *definition* of canonically conjugate coordinates and momenta, rather than Hamilton's equations (2.12).

Equation (2.122) represents the fundamental difference between quantum mechanics and classical mechanics. According to the latter, the right-hand side would be zero. This equation may be taken, instead of the Schrödinger equation, as the basis of quantum mechanics. It was used, in fact, before the discovery of wave mechanics, and it is still the fundamental equation of the other branch of quantum mechanics, namely, matrix mechanics — in this case, however, p_x is not a differential operator, but both p_x and x are *matrices*.

We may also obtain the condition that an operator f will represent a constant of the motion, that is, have simultaneous eigenfunctions with H, in the form of a commutation relation. The equations

$$H\psi = E\psi, \tag{2.128}$$

$$f\psi = \lambda\psi, \tag{2.129}$$

must be satisfied by the same ψ. Operating on both sides of equation (2.128) with f, we have

$$fH\psi = fE\psi = Ef\psi = E\lambda\psi. \tag{2.130}$$

Similarly, operating on both sides of equation (2.129) with H, we have

$$Hf\psi = H\lambda\psi = \lambda H\psi = \lambda E\psi. \tag{2.131}$$

Hence,

$$fH\psi = Hf\psi,$$

or

$$(fH - Hf)\psi = 0, \tag{2.132}$$

from which we obtain the commutation relation

$$[f, H] = 0. \tag{2.133}$$

In other words, *any operator which represents a constant of the motion commutes with* H. The converse is also true.

2.8.2. ANGULAR MOMENTUM

As a useful example of the representation of dynamical variables by operators, let us consider the angular momentum of a particle in a central field of force. According to classical mechanics, the angular momentum, or moment of momentum, $\boldsymbol{L}$ about the origin is defined by the vector equation

$$\boldsymbol{L} = \boldsymbol{r} \wedge \boldsymbol{p}, \tag{2.134}$$

where $\boldsymbol{r}$ is the position vector of the particle and $\boldsymbol{p}$ its linear momentum. In some system of rectangular Cartesian coordinates (see Appendix 1) $\boldsymbol{L}$ therefore has the components

$$\left.\begin{aligned} L_x &= yp_z - zp_y, \\ L_y &= zp_x - xp_z, \\ L_z &= xp_y - yp_x. \end{aligned}\right\} \tag{2.135}$$

We have seen [equation (2.67)] that the eigenfunctions of H, that is, the solutions of the Schrödinger equation, may be taken to have the form

$$\psi = R_{n,l}(r) P_l^{m_l}(\cos\theta) \mathrm{e}^{\mathrm{i}m_l\phi}. \tag{2.136}$$

We will now show that these are also eigenfunctions of L_z.

Writing

$$p_x = \frac{\hbar}{\mathrm{i}} \frac{\partial}{\partial x}, \qquad p_y = \frac{\hbar}{\mathrm{i}} \frac{\partial}{\partial y},$$

in the usual way, we obtain the operator

$$L_z = \frac{\hbar}{\mathrm{i}} \left(x \frac{\partial}{\partial y} - y \frac{\partial}{\partial x} \right). \tag{2.137}$$

We must transform this to spherical polar coordinates. We have

$$\begin{aligned} \frac{\partial}{\partial \phi} &= \frac{\partial x}{\partial \phi} \frac{\partial}{\partial x} + \frac{\partial y}{\partial \phi} \frac{\partial}{\partial y} + \frac{\partial z}{\partial \phi} \frac{\partial}{\partial z} \\ &= -r \sin\theta \sin\phi \frac{\partial}{\partial x} + r \sin\theta \cos\phi \frac{\partial}{\partial y} \\ &= -y \frac{\partial}{\partial x} + x \frac{\partial}{\partial y}, \end{aligned} \tag{2.138}$$

from equations (2.46). Hence,

$$L_z = \frac{\hbar}{\mathrm{i}} \frac{\partial}{\partial \phi}. \tag{2.139}$$

Operating with this upon the ψ in (2.136), we obtain

$$\frac{\hbar}{\mathrm{i}}\frac{\partial\psi}{\partial\phi} = \hbar m_l\psi, \tag{2.140}$$

since ϕ only occurs in the factor $\exp(\mathrm{i}m_l\phi)$. This equation is of the same form as (2.111), with λ equal to $\hbar m_l$. Thus, the z-component of the angular momentum is a constant of the motion, and has the value $\hbar m_l$, in the given state ψ. Corresponding to any value of l, therefore, there are $(2l+1)$ possible values of L_z, since there are $(2l+1)$ possible values of the magnetic quantum number m_l.

In the same way, by transforming to spherical polar coordinates, it may be shown that the operator representing the square of the total angular momentum,

$$L^2 = L_x^2+L_y^2+L_z^2, \tag{2.141}$$

satisfies the equation

$$L^2\psi = \hbar^2 l(l+1)\psi, \tag{2.142}$$

again with ψ given by (2.136). Thus, the angular momentum $\boldsymbol{L}$ has the constant magnitude $\hbar\sqrt{l(l+1)}$ in the state ψ. For this reason l is often referred to as the *angular momentum quantum number.*

2.9. The Average or Expectation Value of a Dynamical Variable

If a large number of measurements of a dynamical variable f is made on a system in a state ψ, the *average* or *expectation value* of f, which we will denote by $\langle f\rangle$, for this state, may be defined as the mean of the measured values. Alternatively, the measurements may be made on a large number of identical systems all in the state ψ.

From the interpretation of $|\psi|^2$ as a probability density, when ψ is a normalized wave function, it follows, for example, that the expectation value of x for a state ψ of a single particle is given by

$$\langle x\rangle = \int x|\psi|^2\,\mathrm{d}\boldsymbol{r} = \int \psi^* x\psi\,\mathrm{d}\boldsymbol{r}. \tag{2.143}$$

Both forms of the integrand are equally correct, but we prefer the latter for a reason which will appear below. The same applies to any function g *of the coordinates only* of any system: we have

$$\langle g \rangle = \int \psi^* g \psi \, d\tau, \tag{2.144}$$

the integration being throughout the configuration space of the system.

As a simple example, let us consider the radial distance r of the electron in the ground state of the hydrogen atom. It may be verified that the normalized wave function is

$$\psi = \frac{1}{\sqrt{(\pi a_0^3)}} e^{-r/a_0}, \tag{2.145}$$

that is, the function (2.48) with $Z = 1$ and normalized according to (2.98). Thus,

$$\langle r \rangle = \int \psi^* r \psi \, d\boldsymbol{r} = \frac{1}{\pi a_0^3} \int r e^{-2r/a_0} \, d\boldsymbol{r}$$

$$= \frac{4}{a_0^3} \int_0^\infty r^3 e^{-2r/a_0} dr = \tfrac{3}{2} a_0. \tag{2.146}$$

According to the early Bohr theory of the hydrogen atom, the electron in the ground state was supposed to describe a circular orbit of radius a_0, so that r was equal to a_0 (see also Problem 2.3, p. 355).

Now let us consider what happens when the dynamical variable is a function of the momenta as well as the positional coordinates of the particles of a system. In this case the variable is represented by a differential operator. An obvious example is provided by the Hamiltonian or energy function. If the energy of a system in the state ψ is E, then

$$H\psi = E\psi, \tag{2.147}$$

and we know that the expectation value of H is E, since the energy is constant. This result follows, however, from an equation of the same form as (2.144); thus,

$$\langle H \rangle = \int \psi^* H \psi \, d\tau, \tag{2.148}$$

which is equal to E because of equation (2.147) and the normalization of ψ. The H in the integrand is, of course, a differential operator. It is not difficult to see that a similar result must hold for any quantity which is a constant of the motion.

The foregoing suggests that the expectation value of any dynamical variable should be given by an equation like (2.144), whether the *operator* which appears in the integrand is a function of position only or a differential operator. We will not attempt to prove this, but will take it as a further fundamental postulate of quantum mechanics, to be justified by results. The formal statement of this postulate is as follows:

the expectation value of a dynamical variable f, represented by the operator f_{op}, for a state whose normalized wave function is ψ, is given by

$$\langle f \rangle = \int \psi^* f_{\text{op}} \psi \, \mathrm{d}\tau, \tag{2.149}$$

the integration being throughout the configuration space of the system. Here, to remove all ambiguity, we have denoted the operator by f_{op}, but it is customary to use precisely the same symbol to denote both the dynamical variable and the operator which represents it — as, indeed, we have already done in several places.

For example, let us take the x-component of the momentum of a particle in the state ψ. We have, in general,

$$\langle p_x \rangle = \int \psi^* \frac{\hbar}{\mathrm{i}} \frac{\partial \psi}{\partial x} \, \mathrm{d}\mathbf{r}. \tag{2.150}$$

Now, more specifically, in the case of the ground state of a particle in a one-dimensional box, whose normalized wave function, obtained from equation (1.38), is

$$\psi = \sqrt{\frac{2}{L}} \sin \frac{\pi x}{L},$$

within the box, we find

$$\langle p_x \rangle = \frac{2\pi\hbar}{L^2 \mathrm{i}} \int_0^L \sin \frac{\pi x}{L} \cos \frac{\pi x}{L} \, \mathrm{d}x = 0. \tag{2.151}$$

Thus, the expectation value of the momentum is zero for this state, in agreement with classical mechanics, according to which the particle would move to and fro between the walls with constant speed. The same is true for all states of this system.

2.10. The Uncertainty Principle

Another principle which emphasizes the distinction between classical and quantum mechanics is the uncertainty principle of Heisenberg. This states essentially that it is impossible to specify simultaneously, with unlimited accuracy, both the position and the momentum of a particle. More expressly, if Δx is the *uncertainty* in our knowledge of the x-coordinate of a particle, and if Δp_x is the uncertainty in our simultaneous knowledge of the conjugate momentum p_x, then

$$\Delta x \cdot \Delta p_x \gtrsim \hbar \tag{2.152}$$

— in other words, the product of the uncertainties in x and p_x must be greater than a quantity of the order of magnitude of $\hbar$. There are two further *uncertainty relations*, like (2.152), for the other coordinates and conjugate momenta of the particle — also, in § 11.5, we shall consider yet another such relation, involving energy and time.

The uncertainty relation (2.152) can be derived from the principles adopted in the foregoing sections, and incidentally it can be made more precise, if we define Δx and Δp_x more exactly. Several definitions are possible, but generally the uncertainty in a variable is taken to be the *root-mean-square deviation from the mean*, the latter being the expectation value defined in the previous section. Thus,

$$\begin{aligned}(\Delta x)^2 &= \langle (x-\langle x\rangle)^2\rangle \\ &= \langle (x^2-2x\langle x\rangle+\langle x\rangle^2\rangle = \langle x^2\rangle-\langle x\rangle^2,\end{aligned} \tag{2.153}$$

since $\langle x\langle x\rangle\rangle = \langle x\rangle^2$.

Similarly,

$$(\Delta p_x)^2 = \langle (p_x-\langle p_x\rangle)^2\rangle = \langle p_x^2\rangle-\langle p_x\rangle^2. \tag{2.154}$$

For simplicity, we will restrict ourselves to a one-dimensional system, but the generalization is immediate. For a state whose normalized wave function is ψ we have

$$\left.\begin{aligned}\langle x\rangle &= \int \psi^* x\psi\,\mathrm{d}x, & \langle x^2\rangle &= \int \psi^* x^2\psi\,\mathrm{d}x,\\ \langle p_x\rangle &= \frac{\hbar}{\mathrm{i}}\int \psi^* \frac{\mathrm{d}\psi}{\mathrm{d}x}\,\mathrm{d}x, & \langle p_x^2\rangle &= -\hbar^2\int \psi^* \frac{\mathrm{d}^2\psi}{\mathrm{d}x^2}\,\mathrm{d}x,\end{aligned}\right\} \tag{2.155}$$

the integrals being over all values of x.

Now, the inequality

$$\left|\frac{\mathrm{d}\psi}{\mathrm{d}x}+(Ax+B+\mathrm{i}C)\psi\right|^2 \geqq 0 \tag{2.156}$$

is obviously true, since the squared modulus of a complex number cannot be negative. We will take A, B and C to be *real* constants, to which we will ascribe values later. We may then write (2.156) in the form

$$\left[\frac{\mathrm{d}\psi^*}{\mathrm{d}x}+(Ax+B-\mathrm{i}C)\psi^*\right]\left[\frac{\mathrm{d}\psi}{\mathrm{d}x}+(Ax+B+\mathrm{i}C)\psi\right]$$

$$=\frac{\mathrm{d}\psi^*}{\mathrm{d}x}\frac{\mathrm{d}\psi}{\mathrm{d}x}+(Ax+B)\left(\psi\frac{\mathrm{d}\psi^*}{\mathrm{d}x}+\psi^*\frac{\mathrm{d}\psi}{\mathrm{d}x}\right)+\mathrm{i}C\left(\psi\frac{\mathrm{d}\psi^*}{\mathrm{d}x}-\psi^*\frac{\mathrm{d}\psi}{\mathrm{d}x}\right)$$

$$+A^2x^2\psi^*\psi+(B^2+C^2)\psi^*\psi+2ABx\psi^*\psi \geqq 0. \tag{2.157}$$

Integrating over all values of x, we obtain

$$\int\frac{\mathrm{d}\psi^*}{\mathrm{d}x}\frac{\mathrm{d}\psi}{\mathrm{d}x}\,\mathrm{d}x+A\int x\left(\psi\frac{\mathrm{d}\psi^*}{\mathrm{d}x}+\psi^*\frac{\mathrm{d}\psi}{\mathrm{d}x}\right)\mathrm{d}x$$

$$+B\int\left(\psi\frac{\mathrm{d}\psi^*}{\mathrm{d}x}+\psi^*\frac{\mathrm{d}\psi}{\mathrm{d}x}\right)\mathrm{d}x+\mathrm{i}C\int\left(\psi\frac{\mathrm{d}\psi^*}{\mathrm{d}x}-\psi^*\frac{\mathrm{d}\psi}{\mathrm{d}x}\right)\mathrm{d}x$$

$$+A^2\int\psi^*x^2\psi\,\mathrm{d}x+(B^2+C^2)\int\psi^*\psi\,\mathrm{d}x$$

$$+2AB\int\psi^*x\psi\,\mathrm{d}x \geqq 0. \tag{2.158}$$

Elementary integration by parts, using the fact that ψ vanishes at both limits of integration, yields the following expressions:

$$\int\frac{\mathrm{d}\psi^*}{\mathrm{d}x}\frac{\mathrm{d}\psi}{\mathrm{d}x}\,\mathrm{d}x = -\int\psi^*\frac{\mathrm{d}^2\psi}{\mathrm{d}x^2}\,\mathrm{d}x, \tag{2.159}$$

$$\int\psi\frac{\mathrm{d}\psi^*}{\mathrm{d}x}\,\mathrm{d}x = -\int\psi^*\frac{\mathrm{d}\psi}{\mathrm{d}x}\,\mathrm{d}x, \tag{2.160}$$

$$\int x\left(\psi\frac{\mathrm{d}\psi^*}{\mathrm{d}x}+\psi^*\frac{\mathrm{d}\psi}{\mathrm{d}x}\right)\mathrm{d}x=\int x\frac{\mathrm{d}}{\mathrm{d}x}(\psi^*\psi)\mathrm{d}x = -\int\psi^*\psi\,\mathrm{d}x = -1. \tag{2.161}$$

Substituting in (2.158), and using equations (2.155), we find

$$\hbar^{-2}\langle p_x^2\rangle-A+2C\hbar^{-1}\langle p_x\rangle+A^2\langle x^2\rangle+B^2+C^2+2AB\langle x\rangle \geqq 0. \tag{2.162}$$

This is true for any real values of A, B and C. Let us therefore set

$$A = \frac{1}{2(\Delta x)^2}, \qquad B = -\frac{\langle x \rangle}{2(\Delta x)^2}, \qquad C = -\frac{\langle p_x \rangle}{\hbar}.$$

Then (2.162) becomes

$$\frac{1}{\hbar^2}(\langle p_x^2 \rangle - \langle p_x \rangle^2) - \frac{1}{2(\Delta x)^2} + \frac{1}{4(\Delta x)^4}(\langle x^2 \rangle - \langle x \rangle^2) \geqq 0,$$

or

$$\frac{1}{\hbar^2}(\Delta p_x)^2 - \frac{1}{4(\Delta x)^2} \geqq 0,$$

from which it follows that

$$\Delta x \cdot \Delta p_x \geqq \hbar/2. \qquad (2.163)$$

Thus, the more accurately we measure x, the less accurately can we simultaneously measure p_x. In particular, if we measure x precisely, we can obtain no information about the simultaneous value of p_x, and *vice versa.* It must be realized that this is not due merely to the crudity of our present experimental apparatus and techniques. It is now generally accepted that the uncertainty principle is a fundamental law of quantum mechanics, and is due to the necessary and unavoidable interaction between observer and observed whenever an observation is made. Indeed, we have derived (2.163) from the interpretive postulates of quantum mechanics, without reference to experimental techniques, so that a denial of the necessity of the uncertainty principle would entail a rejection of these postulates. None the less, there are those — and Einstein was foremost among them — who are not convinced that the uncertainty relations impose an essential limitation upon our detailed knowledge of a single system.

Although the uncertainty relations apply to macroscopic bodies as well as to elementary particles, it is clear that they are only of importance in atomic problems, owing to the small size of h. The degree of uncertainty involved in the simultaneous measurement of the position and momentum of a cannon ball, as a result of the uncertainty principle, is quite irrelevant to even the most sensitive experiment in ballistics.

2.11. The Helium Atom

We will end this chapter with an illustration of some of the difficulties which arise when a system contains several interacting particles. The simplest atomic system of this kind is the helium atom, which has two electrons. Admittedly, the hydrogen atom consists of two interacting particles — a proton and an electron — but we saw earlier that in this case the problem can be reduced to that of a single particle moving in a central field of force — in fact, it was a sufficiently good approximation to take the proton as fixed. In the present case it is an even better approximation to assume that the nucleus is fixed, for the nucleus of a helium atom consists of two protons and two neutrons, and so has a mass four times that of the hydrogen nucleus. We will therefore consider the problem of two electrons, each of charge $-e$ and mass m, moving in the field of a fixed nucleus of charge $2e$.

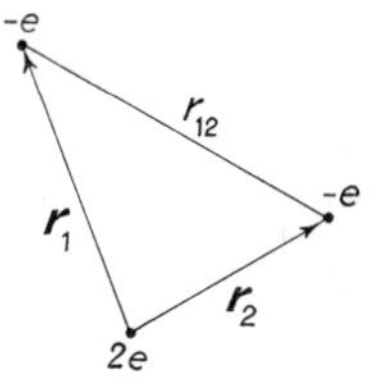

Fig. 2.5. The helium atom: a nucleus, of charge $2e$, and two electrons.

As shown in Figure 2.5, we denote by $\boldsymbol{r}_1$ and $\boldsymbol{r}_2$ the position vectors of the two electrons with respect to the nucleus, and by r_{12} the distance between them. The total potential energy of the system is then

$$V(\boldsymbol{r}_1, \boldsymbol{r}_2) = -\frac{2e^2}{r_1} - \frac{2e^2}{r_2} + \frac{e^2}{r_{12}}, \tag{2.163}$$

the first two terms being the potential energies of the electrons in the field of the nucleus, and the last term the potential energy of the electrons due to the repulsive force between them — the zero of potential energy is thus taken to be when the electrons are infinitely separated from each other and from the nucleus. From equation (2.22) we then obtain the Schrödinger equation

$$\left[-\frac{\hbar^2}{2m}(\nabla_1^2+\nabla_2^2) - \frac{2e^2}{r_1} - \frac{2e^2}{r_2} + \frac{e^2}{r_{12}}\right]\psi = E\psi, \tag{2.164}$$

where E is the total energy. The wave function $\psi(\boldsymbol{r}_1, \boldsymbol{r}_2)$ is, of course, a function of the positional coordinates of both electrons.

Equation (2.164) is difficult to solve, and indeed cannot be solved analytically, owing to the presence of the term e^2/r_{12} in the potential energy function. Let us, as an approximation, drop this term — in other words, let us assume that the electrons do not interact. Equation (2.164) can then be separated into two equations of hydrogenic form. We may write

$$\psi(\boldsymbol{r}_1, \boldsymbol{r}_2) = \psi_a(\boldsymbol{r}_1)\psi_b(\boldsymbol{r}_2), \tag{2.165}$$

and

$$E = \varepsilon_a + \varepsilon_b\,, \tag{2.166}$$

where

$$-\frac{\hbar^2}{2m}\nabla_1^2\psi_a - \frac{2e^2}{r_1}\psi_a = \varepsilon_a\psi_a, \tag{2.167}$$

and

$$-\frac{\hbar^2}{2m}\nabla_2^2\psi_b - \frac{2e^2}{r_2}\psi_b = \varepsilon_b\psi_b. \tag{2.168}$$

This is easily verified, because equation (2.167) multiplied by ψ_b, added to equation (2.168) multiplied by ψ_a, gives equation (2.164) with the term e^2/r_{12} omitted. Both equations (2.167) and (2.168) are of the form of the Schrödinger equation for a hydrogenic atom, with $Z = 2$, so that the energy levels ε_a and ε_b for each electron separately are given by equation (2.95). The energy levels for the atom are obtained by summing these *one-electron* levels, as shown in equation (2.166). In particular, the lowest energy level of the atom is just twice the ground state energy of a single electron, that is,

$$E = -4me^4/\hbar^2. \tag{2.169}$$

This amounts to -108.8 eV, whereas the experimental value is -79.0 eV. The error, of about 40 per cent, is due to the neglect of the Coulomb interaction between the electrons, and it is therefore clear that this is not permissible. Unfortunately, if this interaction is included, equation (2.164) cannot be separated. This difficulty persists in all problems involving systems of more than one electron. Approximate methods of solution must be employed, but better than that discussed above. We shall consider some of these in the following chapters.

CHAPTER 3

THE VARIATIONAL METHOD AND PERTURBATION THEORY

3.1. The Variational Method

Let us suppose that a system, which may consist of one or more particles, and whose Hamiltonian operator is H, has an infinite set of discrete energy levels, denoted by E_i, and normalized wave functions ψ_i. Then

$$H\psi_i = E_i\psi_i. \tag{3.1}$$

If we multiply each side of this equation by ψ_i^* and integrate throughout the configuration space of the system, we obtain

$$E_i = \int \psi_i^* H\psi_i \mathrm{d}\tau, \tag{3.2}$$

since, owing to the normalization of ψ_i,

$$\int \psi_i^* \psi_i \mathrm{d}\tau = 1. \tag{3.3}$$

In particular, the lowest energy E_1, which is the energy of the ground state ψ_1, is given by

$$E_1 = \int \psi_1^* H\psi_1 \mathrm{d}\tau. \tag{3.4}$$

Now let us consider *any* function ϕ of the positional coordinates of the system, which is not necessarily a wave function, but is single-valued and continuous, and is normalized, so that

$$\int \phi^*\phi \mathrm{d}\tau = 1. \tag{3.5}$$

Then, the *variation principle*, which is the basis of the variational method, states that the integral

$$E = \int \phi^* H\phi \mathrm{d}\tau \tag{3.6}$$

is greater than or equal to the ground state energy E_1 of the system. Equality is only obtained if, in fact, ϕ is the function ψ_1, so we may also say that the function ϕ which minimizes the integral E is the ground state wave function of the system.

The variation principle may be proved quite easily by expanding the function ϕ in terms of the orthonormal set of functions ψ_i, assumed to be complete, as discussed in Appendix 2. No generality is lost by supposing that the functions ψ_i are orthogonal since, if any of these functions are degenerate, orthogonal linear combinations of them can always be constructed by the method described in § 2.7.2. We thus have

$$\phi = \sum_i a_i \psi_i. \tag{3.7}$$

The a_i are fixed constants, and, owing to the normalization of ϕ and the orthonormality of the ψ_i, we find

$$\int \phi^* \phi \, \mathrm{d}\tau = \sum_i \sum_j a_j^* a_i \int \psi_j^* \psi_i \, \mathrm{d}\tau = 1,$$

or

$$\sum_i a_i^* a_i = 1. \tag{3.8}$$

Substitution of (3.7) in (3.6) gives

$$\begin{aligned} E &= \sum_i \sum_j a_j^* a_i \int \psi_j^* H \psi_i \, \mathrm{d}\tau \\ &= \sum_i \sum_j a_j^* a_i E_i \int \psi_j^* \psi_i \, \mathrm{d}\tau \\ &= \sum_i a_i^* a_i E_i, \end{aligned} \tag{3.9}$$

owing to equation (3.1) and the orthonormality of the ψ_i.

Now, if we subtract the ground state energy E_1 from both sides of equation (3.9), using equation (3.8), we obtain

$$E - E_1 = \sum_i a_i^* a_i (E_i - E_1). \tag{3.10}$$

Since E_1 is the lowest energy of the system, E_i is greater than or equal to it for all i, and $a_i^* a_i$, or $|a_i|^2$, cannot be negative. The right-hand side of equation (3.10) is therefore positive or zero, so that

$$E \geqq E_1. \tag{3.11}$$

Furthermore, E is equal to E_1 only if all the a_i are zero except a_1 — in other words, only if ϕ is the function ψ_1.

If the function ϕ is not normalized, then the variation principle applies to the integral

$$E = \frac{\int \phi^* H \phi \, \mathrm{d}\tau}{\int \phi^* \phi \, \mathrm{d}\tau}, \tag{3.12}$$

instead of (3.6), since the denominator normalizes the functions ϕ and ϕ^* in the numerator. Clearly, if ϕ is normalized, (3.12) reduces to (3.6).

The variational method, based upon a general method devised by Ritz in 1909, makes use of the variation principle to find approximations to the ground state energy and wave function of an atomic system. The function ϕ, generally called the *trial function*, is chosen to be of an analytical form which is likely to be close to that of the true ground state wave function ψ_1, but containing several undetermined parameters. The integral E, in equation (3.12), is evaluated in terms of these parameters, and their values are then chosen so as to minimize E. This minimum value will be the best approximation to the ground state energy E_1 for the analytical form of ϕ which has been used.

For example, if the chosen form of ϕ is

$$\phi = \mathrm{e}^{-\alpha r}(1+\beta r+\gamma r^2), \tag{3.13}$$

for a one-particle system, and this is substituted in equation (3.12), E is obtained as a function of the parameters α, β and γ. E is now minimized with respect to these parameters — in other words, those values of α, β and γ are chosen which satisfy the equations

$$\frac{\partial E}{\partial \alpha} = \frac{\partial E}{\partial \beta} = \frac{\partial E}{\partial \gamma} = 0. \tag{3.14}$$

How this works in practice will be seen in the following sections.

Of course, the analytical form of ϕ may be chosen arbitrarily, without reference to the likely form of ψ_1, but then E will probably be a poor approximation to E_1. To obtain the best results from the variational method it is desirable that the form of ϕ be as close as possible to that of ψ_1. Where this is difficult to assess with sufficient accuracy, several different forms of ϕ may be tried — the one which gives the lowest value of E may be taken to be the best as far as the evaluation of the energy is concerned.

3.2. The Ground State of the Harmonic Oscillator

We have already determined the ground state of the harmonic oscillator in § 1.8. However, in order to illustrate the use of the variational method, let us pretend to be ignorant of this fact.

The Hamiltonian operator for this system [see equation (1.53)] is

$$H = -\frac{\hbar^2}{2m}\frac{\mathrm{d}^2}{\mathrm{d}x^2} + \tfrac{1}{2}m\omega^2 x^2. \tag{3.15}$$

Now, the potential function is symmetrical about the origin, so we expect the ground state wave function to be symmetrical about the origin. Also we expect this wave function to have no nodes and to tend to zero as x tends to $\pm\infty$. The simplest function with these properties, which easily comes to mind, is

$$\phi(x) = \mathrm{e}^{-\alpha x^2}, \tag{3.16}$$

where α is a *positive* constant, which we leave as our adjustable parameter.

We have, then,

$$\int \phi^*\phi\,\mathrm{d}x = \int_{-\infty}^{\infty} \mathrm{e}^{-2\alpha x^2}\mathrm{d}x = \sqrt{\frac{\pi}{2\alpha}} \tag{3.17}$$

(see Appendix 4 for some useful integrals).

Also,

$$H\phi = -\frac{\hbar^2}{2m}\left[\left(4\alpha^2 - \frac{m^2\omega^2}{\hbar^2}\right)x^2 - 2\alpha\right]\mathrm{e}^{-\alpha x^2},$$

so that

$$\int \phi^* H\phi\,\mathrm{d}x = -\frac{\hbar^2}{2m}\int_{-\infty}^{\infty}\left[\left(4\alpha^2 - \frac{m^2\omega^2}{\hbar^2}\right)x^2 - 2\alpha\right]\mathrm{e}^{-2\alpha x^2}\mathrm{d}x$$

$$= -\frac{\hbar^2}{2m}\left[\left(4\alpha^2 - \frac{m^2\omega^2}{\hbar^2}\right)\frac{1}{4\alpha} - 2\alpha\right]\sqrt{\frac{\pi}{2\alpha}}, \tag{3.18}$$

since integration by parts gives

$$\int_{-\infty}^{\infty} x^2\mathrm{e}^{-2\alpha x^2}\mathrm{d}x = \frac{1}{4\alpha}\sqrt{\frac{\pi}{2\alpha}}. \tag{3.19}$$

Thus, from equations (3.17) and (3.18),

$$E(\alpha) = \frac{\int \phi^* H \phi \, \mathrm{d}x}{\int \phi^* \phi \, \mathrm{d}x} = \frac{m\omega^2}{8\alpha} + \frac{\hbar^2 \alpha}{2m} . \tag{3.20}$$

To minimize this we choose α such that

$$\frac{\mathrm{d}E}{\mathrm{d}\alpha} = -\frac{m\omega^2}{8\alpha^2} + \frac{\hbar^2}{2m} = 0. \tag{3.21}$$

This gives $\alpha = m\omega/2\hbar$, and the minimum value of E is $\hbar\omega/2$. We have seen in § 1.8 that, with this value of α, the function ϕ in equation (3.16) is, in fact, the true ground state wave function, and $\hbar\omega/2$ is the ground state energy.

In this case, then, owing to our fortunate choice of ϕ, the variational method has provided the correct solution of the Schrödinger equation. This very rarely happens, because only a few systems have ground state wave functions of such simple analytical form that they can be guessed immediately. It should be noted also that the variational method itself does not tell us how *close* the value of E is to the lowest energy level. In the present instance, only by previous knowledge, or by substitution in the Schrödinger equation, can we deduce that we have obtained the true ground state wave function — as far as the variational method goes there might well have been other forms of ϕ which would give lower values of E.

3.3. The Ground State of the Helium Atom

As a more useful example let us consider the ground state, or normal state, of the helium atom, which has already been discussed in § 2.11. The Hamiltonian operator for this system is

$$H = -\frac{\hbar^2}{2m}(\nabla_1^2 + \nabla_2^2) - \frac{2e^2}{r_1} - \frac{2e^2}{r_2} + \frac{e^2}{r_{12}}, \tag{3.22}$$

which gives rise to the Schrödinger equation (2.164).

Before proceeding with the problem it will prove convenient to introduce a new system of units, which will be used frequently throughout the book. In this system the unit of energy is the *rydberg* (ryd) and the unit of length is the *Bohr unit* (B.u.), defined as follows:

$$1 \text{ rydberg} = me^4/2\hbar^2 = 13.60 \text{ eV},$$
$$1 \text{ Bohr unit} = \hbar^2/me^2 = 0.5292 \text{ Å}.$$

For brevity we shall refer to these as *atomic units*, although this name is generally applied to another system, introduced by Hartree, in which the unit of energy is *two* rydbergs. It may be seen that one rydberg is the energy of the ground state of a hydrogen atom, calculated on the assumption that the nucleus is fixed. One Bohr unit is the length we have previously denoted by a_0, and is sometimes called the 'Bohr radius'.

If H, r_1, r_2 and r_{12} are now expressed in terms of these units, we have, from equation (3.22),

$$\left(\frac{me^4}{2\hbar^2}\right) H = -\frac{\hbar^2}{2m}\left(\frac{me^2}{\hbar^2}\right)^2 (\nabla_1^2+\nabla_2^2)+\left(\frac{me^2}{\hbar^2}\right)\left(-\frac{2e^2}{r_1}-\frac{2e^2}{r_2}+\frac{e^2}{r_{12}}\right),$$

or

$$H = -\nabla_1^2-\nabla_2^2-\frac{4}{r_1}-\frac{4}{r_2}+\frac{2}{r_{12}}. \tag{3.23}$$

We have seen previously that, if the Coulomb interaction between the electrons, that is, the term $2/r_{12}$ in equation (3.23), is ignored, the Schrödinger equation is separable into two hydrogenic equations. The ground state wave function is then, in atomic units,

$$\psi = e^{-2(r_1+r_2)}, \tag{3.24}$$

which is the product of two hydrogenic ground state functions. It has been remarked that the ground state energy, -8 ryd or -108.8 eV, given by this approximation is in error by some 40 per cent. However, let us see if we can improve on this by including the Coulomb interaction and using the variational method, with trial function ϕ of the form, suggested by (3.24),

$$\phi = e^{-\alpha(r_1+r_2)}. \tag{3.25}$$

Here α is a parameter, assumed real and positive, whose value we shall choose by minimizing the integral

$$E(\alpha) = \frac{\iint \phi^* H\phi \, d\mathbf{r}_1 \, d\mathbf{r}_2}{\iint \phi^*\phi \, d\mathbf{r}_1 \, d\mathbf{r}_2}. \tag{3.26}$$

Since ϕ is a real function, of course, ϕ^* is the same as ϕ.

Now, we have

$$\iint \phi^2 \,\mathrm{d}\boldsymbol{r}_1 \,\mathrm{d}\boldsymbol{r}_2 = \iint \mathrm{e}^{-2\alpha(r_1+r_2)} \,\mathrm{d}\boldsymbol{r}_1 \,\mathrm{d}\boldsymbol{r}_2$$

$$= \int_0^\infty \mathrm{e}^{-2\alpha r_1} 4\pi r_1^2 \,\mathrm{d}r_1 \int_0^\infty \mathrm{e}^{-2\alpha r_2} 4\pi r_2^2 \,\mathrm{d}r_2$$

$$= 16\pi^2 \frac{2}{(2\alpha)^3} \frac{2}{(2\alpha)^3} = \frac{\pi^2}{\alpha^6}. \tag{3.27}$$

For a spherically symmetrical function $f(r)$ we may write

$$\nabla^2 f = \frac{1}{r^2} \frac{\mathrm{d}}{\mathrm{d}r} \left(r^2 \frac{\mathrm{d}f}{\mathrm{d}r} \right),$$

from which it follows that

$$\nabla_1^2 \mathrm{e}^{-\alpha r_1} = \left(\alpha^2 - \frac{2\alpha}{r_1} \right) \mathrm{e}^{-\alpha r_1}, \tag{3.28}$$

with a similar expression for $\nabla_2^2 \mathrm{e}^{-\alpha r_2}$. Hence,

$$H\phi = -\left(\alpha^2 - \frac{2\alpha}{r_1} \right) \mathrm{e}^{-\alpha(r_1+r_2)} - \left(\alpha^2 - \frac{2\alpha}{r_2} \right) \mathrm{e}^{-\alpha(r_1+r_2)}$$

$$+ \left(-\frac{4}{r_1} - \frac{4}{r_2} + \frac{2}{r_{12}} \right) \mathrm{e}^{-\alpha(r_1+r_2)}$$

$$= \left[-2\alpha^2 + \frac{(2\alpha-4)}{r_1} + \frac{(2\alpha-4)}{r_2} + \frac{2}{r_{12}} \right] \mathrm{e}^{-\alpha(r_1+r_2)}, \tag{3.29}$$

and

$$\iint \phi^* H \phi \,\mathrm{d}\boldsymbol{r}_1 \,\mathrm{d}\boldsymbol{r}_2$$

$$= \iint \left[-2\alpha^2 + \frac{(2\alpha-4)}{r_1} + \frac{(2\alpha-4)}{r_2} + \frac{2}{r_{12}} \right] \mathrm{e}^{-2\alpha(r_1+r_2)} \,\mathrm{d}\boldsymbol{r}_1 \,\mathrm{d}\boldsymbol{r}_2 . \tag{3.30}$$

We have

$$\iint \frac{1}{r_1} \mathrm{e}^{-2\alpha(r_1+r_2)} \,\mathrm{d}\boldsymbol{r}_1 \,\mathrm{d}\boldsymbol{r}_2 = \int_0^\infty \frac{1}{r_1} \mathrm{e}^{-2\alpha r_1} 4\pi r_1^2 \,\mathrm{d}r_1 \int_0^\infty \mathrm{e}^{-2\alpha r_2} 4\pi r_2^2 \,\mathrm{d}r_2$$

$$= 16\pi^2 \frac{1}{(2\alpha)^2} \frac{2}{(2\alpha)^3} = \frac{\pi^2}{\alpha^5}, \tag{3.31}$$

and it is shown in Appendix 4 that

$$\iint \frac{1}{r_{12}} e^{-2\alpha(r_1+r_2)} \mathrm{d}\boldsymbol{r}_1 \mathrm{d}\boldsymbol{r}_2 = \frac{5\pi^2}{8\alpha^5}. \tag{3.32}$$

Using these two integrals in (3.30), we obtain

$$\iint \phi^* H \phi \, \mathrm{d}\boldsymbol{r}_1 \mathrm{d}\boldsymbol{r}_2 = -2\alpha^2 \frac{\pi^2}{\alpha^6} + 2(2\alpha - 4)\frac{\pi^2}{\alpha^5} + 2\frac{5\pi^2}{8\alpha^5}, \tag{3.33}$$

and substituting (3.33) and (3.27) in (3.26) gives

$$E(\alpha) = 2\alpha^2 - \frac{27}{4}\alpha. \tag{3.34}$$

To minimize this we set

$$\frac{\mathrm{d}E}{\mathrm{d}\alpha} = 4\alpha - \frac{27}{4} = 0, \tag{3.35}$$

giving

$$\alpha = \frac{27}{16}, \tag{3.36}$$

and the minimum value of E for the chosen form of ϕ is

$$E\left(\frac{27}{16}\right) = 2\left(\frac{27}{16}\right)^2 - \frac{27}{4}\left(\frac{27}{16}\right) = -\frac{729}{128} = -5.69 \text{ ryd}. \tag{3.37}$$

The observed value of the ground state energy is -5.81 ryd, so that the calculated value is in error by only 0.12 ryd, or about 2 per cent. Even with quite a crude trial function, therefore, the method gives an excellent value for the energy. With more complicated forms of ϕ, involving several parameters, the value of the ground state energy of helium calculated by the variational method has, in fact, been brought into almost perfect agreement with the experimental value.

3.4. Linear Variation Functions

A frequently useful form of trial function ϕ is one which consists of a linear combination of definite functions, with coefficients which are treated as variational parameters. Let us consider just two such functions, ϕ_1

and ϕ_2, so that

$$\phi = a_1\phi_1 + a_2\phi_2 . \tag{3.38}$$

Also, for simplicity, let us assume that ϕ_1, ϕ_2 and the parameters a_1, a_2 are all real, although the final result is the same if this is not so. It should be noted that ϕ_1 and ϕ_2 need not be orthogonal or normalized.

According to the variational method, then, we wish to choose a_1 and a_2 so as to minimize the function

$$E(a_1, a_2) = \frac{\int \phi H \phi \, \mathrm{d}\tau}{\int \phi^2 \mathrm{d}\tau}$$
$$= \frac{a_1^2 \int \phi_1 H \phi_1 \mathrm{d}\tau + a_1 a_2 \int \phi_1 H \phi_2 \mathrm{d}\tau + a_2 a_1 \int \phi_2 H \phi_1 \mathrm{d}\tau + a_2^2 \int \phi_2 H \phi_2 \mathrm{d}\tau}{a_1^2 \int \phi_1^2 \mathrm{d}\tau + 2a_1 a_2 \int \phi_1 \phi_2 \mathrm{d}\tau + a_2^2 \int \phi_2^2 \mathrm{d}\tau} . \tag{3.39}$$

In order to simplify this equation we define the following symbols:

$$H_{ij} = \int \phi_i H \phi_j \mathrm{d}\tau, \qquad S_{ij} = \int \phi_i \phi_j \mathrm{d}\tau, \tag{3.40}$$

where i and j can have the values 1 and 2. It is obvious that

$$S_{12} = S_{21}, \tag{3.41}$$

and it is easily shown that

$$H_{12} = H_{21} . \tag{3.42}$$

Thus, consider a single-particle system, whose Hamiltonian is

$$H = -\frac{\hbar^2}{2m} \nabla^2 + V(\boldsymbol{r}). \tag{3.43}$$

Then,

$$H_{12} = -\frac{\hbar^2}{2m} \int \phi_1 \nabla^2 \phi_2 \mathrm{d}\boldsymbol{r} + \int \phi_1 V \phi_2 \mathrm{d}\boldsymbol{r}. \tag{3.44}$$

If the subscripts 1 and 2 are interchanged in the last term, its value is clearly unaltered, since V is a function of the coordinates only. Also, it follows from the work of § 2.7.1, involving the use of Green's theorem, that, provided ϕ_1 and ϕ_2 satisfy the same boundary conditions as a wave function,

$$\int (\phi_1 \nabla^2 \phi_2 - \phi_2 \nabla^2 \phi_1) \mathrm{d}\boldsymbol{r} = 0. \tag{3.45}$$

This proves equation (3.42) for a single-particle system, and the same is true for any number of particles.

Equation (3.39) may now be written in the form

$$(a_1^2 S_{11}+2a_1a_2S_{12}+a_2^2S_{22})E = a_1^2H_{11}+2a_1a_2H_{12}+a_2^2H_{22}. \tag{3.46}$$

In order to minimize E we must choose a_1 and a_2 so that

$$\frac{\partial E}{\partial a_1} = 0, \qquad \frac{\partial E}{\partial a_2} = 0. \tag{3.47}$$

Differentiating equation (3.46) partially with respect to a_1, and using the first of equations (3.47), we obtain

$$(a_1S_{11}+a_2S_{12})E = a_1H_{11}+a_2H_{12}. \tag{3.48}$$

Similarly, differentiating (3.46) partially with respect to a_2, and using the second of equations (3.47), we obtain

$$(a_1S_{12}+a_2S_{22})E = a_1H_{12}+a_2H_{22},$$

or, from equations (3.41) and (3.42),

$$(a_1S_{21}+a_2S_{22})E = a_1H_{21}+a_2H_{22}. \tag{3.49}$$

We prefer the latter form because it leads to a result which agrees with that of the more general theory, which we will discuss later.

Equations (3.48) and (3.49) may be re-arranged as follows:

$$a_1(H_{11}-ES_{11})+a_2(H_{12}-ES_{12}) = 0, \tag{3.50}$$

$$a_1(H_{21}-ES_{21})+a_2(H_{22}-ES_{22}) = 0. \tag{3.51}$$

Now, a_1 and a_2 cannot both be zero, for this would make ϕ zero, which is not allowed. Therefore, a_1 and a_2 may be eliminated from equations (3.50) and (3.51), by elementary algebra, to give

$$(H_{11}-ES_{11})(H_{22}-ES_{22})-(H_{12}-ES_{12})(H_{21}-ES_{21}) = 0, \tag{3.52}$$

which is equivalent to the determinantal equation (see Appendix 3)

$$\begin{vmatrix} H_{11}-ES_{11} & H_{12}-ES_{12} \\ H_{21}-ES_{21} & H_{22}-ES_{22} \end{vmatrix} = 0. \tag{3.53}$$

ϕ_1 and ϕ_2 are definite functions, containing no undetermined parameters, so that H_{ij} and S_{ij} are numbers which can be calculated. Equation (3.52) is therefore a simple quadratic in E, and, according to the variation principle, its lower root is an approximation to the lowest energy level E_1 of the system, being greater than or equal to it. It can also be shown that its higher root is an approximation, although generally not so good a one, to the next higher energy level E_2 of the system.

In general, if a linear combination of N functions is used, so that

$$\phi = \sum_{i=1}^{N} a_i \phi_i , \tag{3.54}$$

a set of N linear equations, each with N terms like those in (3.50) and (3.51), is obtained. Since the a_i may not all be zero, the determinant of their coefficients in these equations must vanish, as in equation (3.53). The equation for E is, therefore,

$$\begin{vmatrix} H_{11}-ES_{11} & H_{12}-ES_{12} & \ldots & H_{1N}-ES_{1N} \\ H_{21}-ES_{21} & H_{22}-ES_{22} & \ldots & H_{2N}-ES_{2N} \\ \vdots & \vdots & & \vdots \\ H_{N1}-ES_{N1} & H_{N2}-ES_{N2} & \ldots & H_{NN}-ES_{NN} \end{vmatrix} = 0. \tag{3.55}$$

This determinant is a polynomial of degree N in E, and the lowest root of the equation is an approximation to the lowest energy level of the system. The other roots again are, generally less good, approximations to the next $N-1$ energy levels.

The proof of this general case, when the a_i and ϕ_i may be complex, is only slightly different from that given in the particular case considered above, and we will omit it. One point should be mentioned, however. In general, we define

$$H_{ij} = \int \phi_i^* H \phi_j \mathrm{d}\tau, \qquad S_{ij} = \int \phi_i^* \phi_j \mathrm{d}\tau. \tag{3.56}$$

It can be seen immediately that here S_{ij} is not necessarily equal to S_{ji}, but

$$S_{ij} = S_{ji}^* . \tag{3.57}$$

Furthermore, it can be shown by the method used to prove equation (3.42) that

$$H_{ij} = H_{ji}^* . \tag{3.58}$$

Owing to this property H is said to be a *Hermitian operator*.

In this general case the element $H_{21}-ES_{21}$, for example, in the determinant of equation (3.55), may not be written $H_{12}-ES_{12}$, which is permissible in equation (3.53).

3.5. Perturbation Theory

Another important approximational method is known as *perturbation theory*, because it is used mainly to calculate the change in energy of an atomic system when the system is *perturbed*, that is, when it is acted upon by some small external force, called a *perturbation*. For example, perturbation theory may be used to calculate the change in energy of a hydrogen atom when a small electric or magnetic field is switched on. The original state of the atom is called the *unperturbed state*, and the final state, in the presence of the field, is called the *perturbed state*.

On the other hand, the unperturbed state may be purely fictitious. We may require to calculate the energy of a system whose Hamiltonian contains a small term which makes this very difficult. If we can calculate the energy levels and wave functions which the system would have without this awkward term, then perturbation theory can be used to calculate the additional energy due to the presence of this term, which is regarded as a perturbation. For example, we saw in § 2.11 that the solution of the Schrödinger equation for the helium atom would be a very simple matter were it not for the presence of the term e^2/r_{12} in the Hamiltonian, for without this term the equation separates into two hydrogenic equations. We may therefore calculate the energy levels and wave functions without this term, the Schrödinger equation corresponding to no real system, and then use perturbation theory to obtain the corrections. The ground state of the helium atom will be considered in detail from this point of view below.

Perturbation theory is mathematically rather complicated, and we will first of all consider only its most elementary form, called first-order perturbation theory, which will be sufficient for most of the purposes of the present book. A more general treatment will then be given, for the sake of its intrinsic interest and importance, but this may be omitted at a first reading, if desired.

3.6. First-Order Perturbation Theory for a Non-Degenerate State

Suppose that the Schrödinger equation for the state Ψ of some system is

$$H\Psi = E\Psi, \tag{3.59}$$

and that the Hamiltonian H can be expressed as the sum of two parts,

$$H = H^0 + H', \tag{3.60}$$

the effect of H' on the energy levels and wave functions being small. Also, assume that the equation

$$H^0 \psi = E^0 \psi \tag{3.61}$$

has been solved, subject to the same boundary conditions as equation (3.59), and that the wave function ψ is non-degenerate. H^0 is the Hamiltonian of the unperturbed system, H that of the perturbed system, and H' is the perturbation term.

In order to avoid a complexity of subscripts and superscripts, which sometimes occurs in the more general theory, we have denoted the unperturbed state by a small ψ and the perturbed state by a capital Ψ — instead of considering all the states of the system, we focus our attention upon one of them, and assume that the state Ψ is that into which ψ is changed by the perturbation.

If the perturbation is truly small, then Ψ will not differ very much from ψ. According to first-order perturbation theory an approximation to the change in energy is obtained by substituting ψ for Ψ in the integral expression for E; thus, *approximately*,

$$\begin{aligned} E &= \frac{\int \psi^* H \psi \, \mathrm{d}\tau}{\int \psi^* \psi \, \mathrm{d}\tau} = \frac{\int \psi^* (H_0 + H') \psi \, \mathrm{d}\tau}{\int \psi^* \psi \, \mathrm{d}\tau} \\ &= E^0 + \frac{\int \psi^* H' \psi \, \mathrm{d}\tau}{\int \psi^* \psi \, \mathrm{d}\tau} \end{aligned} \tag{3.62}$$

from equations (3.60) and (3.61). In other words, the first-order perturbation energy, the second term on the right of equation (3.62), is obtained by averaging the perturbation term over the unperturbed state of the system. If ψ is normalized, of course, the denominators in equation (3.62) reduce to unity.

In some cases, owing to the symmetries of ψ and H', the first-order energy correction vanishes. In this case it is necessary to go to second-order perturbation theory, which we shall discuss in § 3.8, in order to obtain a non-zero correction.

3.6.1. THE GROUND STATE OF THE HELIUM ATOM

The Hamiltonian of the helium atom, in atomic units, is given in equation (3.23). We will regard the Coulomb interaction term, $2/r_{12}$, as a perturbation, so that, in the above notation,

$$H^0 = -\nabla_1^2 - \nabla_2^2 - \frac{4}{r_1} - \frac{4}{r_2}, \tag{3.63}$$

$$H' = \frac{2}{r_{12}}. \tag{3.64}$$

As shown in § 2.11, the Schrödinger equation for the unperturbed state,

$$H^0\psi = E^0\psi, \tag{3.65}$$

separates into two hydrogenic equations, and the unperturbed ground state wave function, as given in equation (3.24) in our present units, is

$$\psi = e^{-2(r_1+r_2)}. \tag{3.66}$$

The unperturbed ground state energy, obtained from equation (2.169), is

$$E^0 = -8 \text{ ryd}. \tag{3.67}$$

The ground state energy of the perturbed system, according to first-order perturbation theory, is

$$\begin{aligned} E &= \frac{\iint \psi^* H \psi \, \mathrm{d}\boldsymbol{r}_1 \mathrm{d}\boldsymbol{r}_2}{\iint \psi^* \psi \, \mathrm{d}\boldsymbol{r}_1 \mathrm{d}\boldsymbol{r}_2} \\ &= E^0 + \frac{\iint \psi^2 (2/r_{12}) \mathrm{d}\boldsymbol{r}_1 \mathrm{d}\boldsymbol{r}_2}{\iint \psi^2 \mathrm{d}\boldsymbol{r}_1 \mathrm{d}\boldsymbol{r}_2}, \end{aligned} \tag{3.68}$$

since ψ is real. There is no need for us to calculate this, however, for the work has already been done in the application of the variational method to this system. The unperturbed wave function (3.66) has the same form as the trial function ϕ in equation (3.25), with $\alpha = 2$ — indeed, this is what suggested the form of the trial function. Thus, comparing equations (3.26) and (3.68), we see that all we have to do to obtain E in our present problem is to put $\alpha = 2$ in the final expression for $E(\alpha)$, equation (3.34). This gives

$$E = 2(2)^2 - \tfrac{27}{4}(2) = -5.5 \text{ ryd}. \tag{3.69}$$

This is quite a good approximation to the observed value, -5.81 ryd; the error being about 5 per cent. It is not so good as the result of the variational method, however; which was to be expected, for ψ has the same form as ϕ but not the optimum value of α, namely, 27/16.

The first-order energy correction is

$$E-E^0 = -5.5+8 = 2.5 \text{ ryd}. \tag{3.70}$$

This is by no means small — in other words, the Coulomb interaction is hardly a small perturbation — so it is not surprising that first-order perturbation theory does not give a more accurate result.

3.7. First-Order Perturbation Theory for a Degenerate State

Using the same notation as in § 3.6, let us now assume that the unperturbed state ψ is *doubly degenerate*; that is to say, there are two independent wave functions ψ_1, ψ_2 corresponding to the same unperturbed energy E^0, so that

$$H^0\psi_1 = E^0\psi_1, \tag{3.71}$$

and

$$H^0\psi_2 = E^0\psi_2. \tag{3.72}$$

In order to simplify the algebra slightly we will assume that ψ_1 and ψ_2 are orthogonal and normalized. No generality is lost in this way, because we have seen in § 2.7.2 that, if the degenerate wave functions are not at first orthogonal, linear combinations of them which are orthogonal can always be constructed.

Now, *any* function of the form

$$\psi = a_1\psi_1+a_2\psi_2, \tag{3.73}$$

where a_1 and a_2 are constants, is also a wave function of the unperturbed system corresponding to the energy E^0 — clearly, by multiplying equations (3.71) and (3.72) by a_1 and a_2 respectively, and adding, we obtain

$$H^0(a_1\psi_1+a_2\psi_2) = E^0(a_1\psi_1+a_2\psi_2). \tag{3.74}$$

In the non-degenerate case we obtained an approximation to the energy E of the perturbed system by assuming that its wave function Ψ was the same as that of the unperturbed system. Let us do the same in the present case — in other words, let us assume that the perturbed wave function is given as a first approximation by (3.73), the values of a_1 and a_2 remaining undetermined for the present.

We will denote the perturbation energy by E', so that

$$E = E^0 + E'. \tag{3.75}$$

Then, as a first approximation, we assume that ψ satisfies the equation

$$H\psi = E\psi,$$

or

$$(H^0 + H')(a_1\psi_1 + a_2\psi_2) = (E^0 + E')(a_1\psi_1 + a_2\psi_2). \tag{3.76}$$

Using equation (3.74), this reduces to

$$(H' - E')(a_1\psi_1 + a_2\psi_2) = 0. \tag{3.77}$$

We now multiply this equation by ψ_1^* and integrate over the configuration space of the system, and then do the same thing with ψ_2^*, obtaining the two equations

$$\int \psi_1^*(H' - E')(a_1\psi_1 + a_2\psi_2)\mathrm{d}\tau = 0, \tag{3.78}$$

$$\int \psi_2^*(H' - E')(a_1\psi_1 + a_2\psi_2)\mathrm{d}\tau = 0. \tag{3.79}$$

Notice that ψ_1^* and ψ_2^* are kept to the left of H', which might be a differential operator.

As in § 3.4, we define the following symbols:

$$H'_{ij} = \int \psi_i^* H' \psi_j \mathrm{d}\tau, \tag{3.80}$$

in terms of which equations (3.78) and (3.79) become

$$a_1 H'_{11} + a_2 H'_{12} - E'a_1 \int \psi_1^*\psi_1 \mathrm{d}\tau - E'a_2 \int \psi_1^*\psi_2 \mathrm{d}\tau = 0, \tag{3.81}$$

$$a_1 H'_{21} + a_2 H'_{22} - E'a_1 \int \psi_2^*\psi_1 \mathrm{d}\tau - E'a_2 \int \psi_2^*\psi_2 \mathrm{d}\tau = 0. \tag{3.82}$$

Owing to the orthonormality of ψ_1 and ψ_2 these equations reduce to

$$a_1(H'_{11} - E') + a_2 H'_{12} = 0, \tag{3.83}$$

$$a_1 H'_{21} + a_2(H'_{22} - E') = 0. \tag{3.84}$$

One solution would be $a_1 = a_2 = 0$, but this is not permitted as it would make ψ identically zero. In order that the same non-zero values of a_1 and a_2 may satisfy both equations, the determinant of their coefficients must vanish; that is,

$$\begin{vmatrix} H'_{11}-E' & H'_{12} \\ H'_{21} & H'_{22}-E' \end{vmatrix} = 0. \tag{3.85}$$

The expansion of the determinant gives

$$(H'_{11}-E')(H'_{22}-E')-H'_{12}H'_{21} = 0, \tag{3.86}$$

which may be verified by eliminating a_1 and a_2 from (3.83) and (3.84) by elementary algebra.

The determinant in equation (3.85) is generally called the *secular determinant* for the perturbation, and the equation is called the *secular equation.* The latter is a quadratic in E' and will usually have two distinct roots. In this case the perturbation has *split* the doubly degenerate unperturbed level into two different levels, and we say that it has *removed the degeneracy.* On the other hand, the secular equation might have equal roots, in which case the perturbation has merely displaced the unperturbed level, and we say that the *degeneracy is not removed to the first order* by the perturbation.

It is generally not required to find the values of a_1 and a_2, but if necessary the two values of a_1/a_2 corresponding to the two values of E' can be obtained directly from either of equations (3.83) and (3.84). The values of a_1 and a_2 are not fixed separately by these equations, so that ψ still remains arbitrary to the extent of a multiplying constant — which, of course, may be fixed by normalization.

It is useful to notice that

$$\begin{aligned} H'_{11}-E' &= \int \psi_1^*(H-H^0)\psi_1 \mathrm{d}\tau - E' \\ &= H_{11}-E^0-E' = H_{11}-E, \end{aligned} \tag{3.87}$$

and

$$\begin{aligned} H'_{12} &= \int \psi_1^*(H-H^0)\psi_2 \mathrm{d}\tau \\ &= H_{12}-E^0\int \psi_1^*\psi_2 \mathrm{d}\tau = H_{12}, \end{aligned} \tag{3.88}$$

owing to the orthonormality of ψ_1 and ψ_2, with similar equations for the other elements of the secular determinant. Thus, the secular equation may equally well be written

$$\begin{vmatrix} H_{11}-E & H_{12} \\ H_{21} & H_{22}-E \end{vmatrix} = 0. \tag{3.89}$$

This is true in general: the secular determinant has the same form whether it is written in terms of the Hamiltonian H and energy E of the perturbed system, or in terms of the perturbation H' and energy correction E'.

So far we have considered only a doubly degenerate unperturbed level, but the method is the same for an N-fold degenerate level. In this case we take the wave function to be

$$\psi = \sum_{i=1}^{N} a_i \psi_i \,, \tag{3.90}$$

where the ψ_i constitute an orthonormal set of degenerate functions corresponding to the unperturbed energy E^0, and the secular equation turns out to be

$$\begin{vmatrix} H'_{11}-E' & H'_{12} & \dots & H'_{1N} \\ H'_{21} & H'_{22}-E' & \dots & H'_{2N} \\ \vdots & \vdots & & \vdots \\ H'_{N1} & H'_{N2} & \dots & H'_{NN}-E' \end{vmatrix} = 0. \tag{3.91}$$

We will leave the proof of this until § 3.8. This equation is of the Nth degree in E' and has N roots which may not all be distinct, so that the degeneracy may not be completely removed to the first order.

As in the doubly degenerate case, the secular equation has the same form if written in terms of H and E; thus,

$$\begin{vmatrix} H_{11}-E & H_{12} & \dots & H_{1N} \\ H_{21} & H_{22}-E & \dots & H_{2N} \\ \vdots & \vdots & & \vdots \\ H_{N1} & H_{N2} & \dots & H_{NN}-E \end{vmatrix} = 0. \tag{3.92}$$

The similarity of this equation to equation (3.55), which arose out of the method of linear variation functions, should be noted. If the *variation functions* ϕ_i had been chosen to be an orthonormal set, then (3.55) would reduce exactly to (3.92). Similarly, if the degenerate functions ψ_i of our present method had not been orthonormal, the secular equation would have had the form of equation (3.55).

It should be remembered, however, that the functions ψ_i of the perturbation method are not arbitrarily chosen variation functions, but are wave functions of the unperturbed system. Furthermore, the method of linear variation functions, as we have given it, applies only to the lower energy levels, whereas perturbation theory applies to all states of the system. None the less, there is a close connection between the variational method and perturbation theory, which will be brought out more clearly in our general treatment of the latter subject.

3.7.1. PARTICLE IN A BOX, SUBJECT TO A PERTURBING FIELD

As an example of the application of first-order perturbation theory to a degenerate level, let us consider the particle in a box, discussed in § 2.3, when the system is subjected to a perturbing field in which the potential energy of the particle is λx^2, where λ is a small constant. The particle might be an electron, for instance, and the perturbing field an electrostatic one, proportional to x and in the x-direction (we will not consider how such a field might be produced — the problem is a purely artificial one).

We will discuss specifically the first triply degenerate state, with unperturbed energy

$$E^0 = \frac{6\hbar^2\pi^2}{2mL^2}, \tag{3.93}$$

obtained from equation (2.39), and quantum numbers (n_x, n_y, n_z) which can have the values (2, 1, 1), (1, 2, 1) and (1, 1, 2). The three unperturbed wave functions, from equation (2.38), are

$$\psi_1 = \sqrt{\frac{8}{L^3}} \sin\frac{2\pi x}{L} \sin\frac{\pi y}{L} \sin\frac{\pi z}{L},$$

$$\psi_2 = \sqrt{\frac{8}{L^3}} \sin\frac{\pi x}{L} \sin\frac{2\pi y}{L} \sin\frac{\pi z}{L},$$

$$\psi_3 = \sqrt{\frac{8}{L^3}} \sin\frac{\pi x}{L} \sin\frac{\pi y}{L} \sin\frac{2\pi z}{L}.$$

These functions are normalized, and it can easily be verified that they are orthogonal; thus,

$$\int \psi_1^* \psi_2 \mathrm{d}\boldsymbol{r} = \int_0^L \int_0^L \int_0^L \psi_1 \psi_2 \mathrm{d}x \mathrm{d}y \mathrm{d}z$$

$$= \frac{8}{L^3} \int_0^L \sin \frac{2\pi x}{L} \sin \frac{\pi x}{L} \mathrm{d}x \int_0^L \sin \frac{\pi y}{L} \sin \frac{2\pi y}{L} \mathrm{d}y \int_0^L \sin^2 \frac{\pi z}{L} \mathrm{d}z$$

$$= 0, \tag{3.94}$$

and similarly for the other pairs of functions.

In the notation used above, the Hamiltonian of the unperturbed state, within the box, is

$$H^0 = -\frac{\hbar^2}{2m} \nabla^2, \tag{3.95}$$

and the perturbation term is

$$H' = \lambda x^2. \tag{3.96}$$

We are not concerned with what happens outside the box, since the potential energy is infinite there and the wave functions are zero.

The secular equation is, then,

$$\begin{vmatrix} H'_{11} - E' & H'_{12} & H'_{13} \\ H'_{21} & H'_{22} - E' & H'_{23} \\ H'_{31} & H'_{32} & H'_{33} - E' \end{vmatrix} = 0, \tag{3.97}$$

where E' is, as usual, the first-order energy correction. We must now evaluate the quantities H'_{ij}, where

$$H'_{ij} = \int \psi_i^* H' \psi_j \mathrm{d}\boldsymbol{r} = \lambda \int x^2 \psi_i \psi_j \mathrm{d}\boldsymbol{r}. \tag{3.98}$$

We have

$$H'_{12} = H'_{21}$$

$$= \frac{8\lambda}{L^3} \int_0^L x^2 \sin \frac{2\pi x}{L} \sin \frac{\pi x}{L} \mathrm{d}x \int_0^L \sin \frac{\pi y}{L} \sin \frac{2\pi y}{L} \mathrm{d}y \int_0^L \sin^2 \frac{\pi z}{L} \mathrm{d}z$$

$$= 0 \tag{3.99}$$

because

$$\int_0^L \sin \frac{\pi y}{L} \sin \frac{2\pi y}{L} \mathrm{d}y = 0,$$

and, similarly,

$$H'_{13} = H'_{31} = H'_{23} = H'_{32} = 0. \tag{3.100}$$

Thus, all the off-diagonal elements of the secular determinant — those which do not contain E' — are zero, so that the secular equation reduces to

$$(H'_{11}-E')(H'_{22}-E')(H'_{33}-E') = 0, \tag{3.101}$$

and its roots are H'_{11}, H'_{22}, H'_{33}.

Now,

$$\begin{aligned} H'_{11} &= \frac{8\lambda}{L^3}\int_0^L x^2 \sin^2\frac{2\pi x}{L}\,\mathrm{d}x \int_0^L \sin^2\frac{\pi y}{L}\,\mathrm{d}y \int_0^L \sin^2\frac{\pi z}{L}\,\mathrm{d}z \\ &= \lambda L^2\left(\frac{1}{3}-\frac{1}{8\pi^2}\right), \end{aligned} \tag{3.102}$$

and

$$\begin{aligned} H'_{22} &= H'_{33} \\ &= \frac{8\lambda}{L^3}\int_0^L x^2 \sin^2\frac{\pi x}{L}\,\mathrm{d}x \int_0^L \sin^2\frac{2\pi y}{L}\,\mathrm{d}y \int_0^L \sin^2\frac{\pi z}{L}\,\mathrm{d}z \\ &= \lambda L^2\left(\frac{1}{3}-\frac{1}{2\pi^2}\right), \end{aligned} \tag{3.103}$$

since interchanging the y and z in the latter integral does not change its value. The integrations involved are elementary — integration by parts gives

$$\int_0^L x^2 \sin^2\frac{2\pi x}{L}\,\mathrm{d}x = \frac{L^3}{6} - \frac{L^3}{16\pi^2},$$

$$\int_0^L x^2 \sin^2\frac{\pi x}{L}\,\mathrm{d}x = \frac{L^3}{6} - \frac{L^3}{4\pi^2},$$

and, in addition, we have

$$\int_0^L \sin^2\frac{2\pi y}{L}\,\mathrm{d}y = \int_0^L \sin^2\frac{\pi y}{L}\,\mathrm{d}y = \frac{L}{2}.$$

We see, then, that two of the roots of the secular equation are equal, which means that the degeneracy is not completely removed to the first order. The triply degenerate unperturbed level E^0 is split by the perturbation into two distinct levels

$$E_1 = \frac{6\hbar^2\pi^2}{2mL^2} + \lambda L^2\left(\frac{1}{3} - \frac{1}{8\pi^2}\right), \tag{3.104}$$

$$E_2 = \frac{6\hbar^2\pi^2}{2mL^2} + \lambda L^2\left(\frac{1}{3} - \frac{1}{2\pi^2}\right), \tag{3.105}$$

the second of these remaining *doubly* degenerate.

Although, as remarked above, this example is rather an artificial one, it brings out quite simply the main points of the preceding section.

3.8. Generalized Perturbation Theory

We will now show how second-order and higher-order perturbation corrections to the energy of a system may be obtained. Let us assume that we know *all* the wave functions ψ_i and energy levels E_i^0 of the unperturbed system, whose Hamiltonian, as before, is H^0 — that is to say, we know the eigenfunctions and eigenvalues of the equation

$$H^0\psi = E^0\psi. \tag{3.106}$$

The problem is to find the eigenfunctions Ψ_i and eigenvalues E_i of the equation

$$H\Psi = E\Psi, \tag{3.107}$$

where

$$H = H^0 + H'. \tag{3.108}$$

Again, to avoid unnecessary superscripts, we have used a small ψ for an unperturbed state and a capital Ψ for a perturbed state — here, however, it will be necessary to use subscripts to distinguish between different states of the same system.

If we assume that all the energy levels E_i^0 of the unperturbed system are discrete, and that the wave functions ψ_i form a complete orthonormal set, then we may express a wave function Ψ of the perturbed system *exactly* in the form

$$\Psi = \sum_{i=1}^{\infty} a_i\psi_i, \tag{3.109}$$

by suitable choice of the coefficients a_i. Substituting this expression in equation (3.107), we obtain

$$\sum_i a_i H\psi_i = E \sum_i a_i \psi_i. \tag{3.110}$$

Multiplication by ψ_j^*, and integration over the configuration space of the system, now gives

$$\sum_i a_i \int \psi_j^* H\psi_i \mathrm{d}\tau = E \sum_i a_i \int \psi_j^* \psi_i \mathrm{d}\tau. \tag{3.111}$$

As before, we use the notation

$$H_{ij} = \int \psi_i^* H\psi_j \mathrm{d}\tau, \tag{3.112}$$

and we may express the orthonormality of the functions ψ_i by the equation

$$\int \psi_i^* \psi_j \mathrm{d}\tau = \delta_{ij}, \tag{3.113}$$

where δ_{ij} is a standard mathematical symbol, called the *Kronecker delta*, which has the value unity when $i = j$, and the value zero when $i \neq j$. Equation (3.111) may then be written

$$\sum_i a_i(H_{ji} - E\delta_{ji}) = 0. \tag{3.114}$$

There is an infinite number of such equations, corresponding to the infinity of integers j, and each equation has an infinite number of terms. We may write them out, incompletely, but a little more explicitly, thus

$$\left.\begin{array}{l} a_1(H_{11}-E)+a_2H_{12}+a_3H_{13}+\ldots = 0, \\ a_1H_{21}+a_2(H_{22}-E)+a_3H_{23}+\ldots = 0, \\ a_1H_{31}+a_2H_{32}+a_3(H_{33}-E)+\ldots = 0, \\ \cdot\ \cdot\ \cdot\ \cdot\ \cdot\ \cdot\ \cdot\ \cdot\ \cdot\ \cdot\ \cdot\ \cdot\ \cdot\ \cdot \\ \cdot\ \cdot\ \cdot\ \cdot\ \cdot\ \cdot\ \cdot\ \cdot\ \cdot\ \cdot\ \cdot\ \cdot\ \cdot\ \cdot \end{array}\right\} \tag{3.115}$$

Just as for a finite set of linear equations (see Appendix 3), in order that the a_i may not all be zero, the determinant of their coefficients, this time of infinite order, must vanish. Hence

$$\begin{vmatrix} H_{11}-E & H_{12} & H_{13} & \ldots \\ H_{21} & H_{22}-E & H_{23} & \ldots \\ H_{31} & H_{32} & H_{33}-E & \ldots \\ \cdot\ \cdot\ \cdot & \cdot\ \cdot\ \cdot & \cdot\ \cdot\ \cdot & \cdot\ \cdot\ \cdot \end{vmatrix} = 0. \tag{3.116}$$

We wish to emphasize that everything we have done up till now has been *exact* — no approximations have been introduced. Of course, there are mathematical difficulties connected with the convergence, and the evaluation, of infinite determinants, but we will ignore these. Equation (3.116), then, is an equation of infinite degree in E, and its infinite number of roots, if they could be found, would be the exact energy levels of the perturbed system.

It should also be remarked that equation (3.116) is just what one would obtain by means of the method of linear variation functions, discussed in § 3.4, with a trial function of the form given in equation (3.109). We see therefore that, *ultimately*, perturbation theory and the variational method are equivalent, and both may provide exact solutions of the problem — but with infinite labour! Of course, in both the variational method and in the method we have used, *any* complete orthonormal set of functions ψ_i, not necessarily wave functions of the unperturbed system, would have led to equation (3.116). However, our derivation of the first-order and second-order perturbation energies, which we shall give below, depends upon our using the set of unperturbed wave functions.

As in § 3.7, if

$$E = E^0 + E', \tag{3.117}$$

we have

$$\begin{aligned} H_{ij} - E\delta_{ij} &= H^0_{ij} + H'_{ij} - E^0\delta_{ij} - E'\delta_{ij} \\ &= H'_{ij} - E'\delta_{ij}, \end{aligned} \tag{3.118}$$

since

$$H^0_{ij} = \int \psi_i^* H^0 \psi_j \mathrm{d}\tau = E^0 \int \psi_i^* \psi_j \mathrm{d}\tau = E^0 \delta_{ij}. \tag{3.119}$$

It follows that, as before, equation (3.116) has the same form whether it is written in terms of H' and E' or in terms of H and E — this, of course, would not be so if the ψ_i were not eigenfunctions of equation (3.106). None the less, we shall continue to work in terms of H and E.

Another point which should be noticed is that, in deriving equation (3.116), no mention was made of the *size* of H' — the equation is correct, in fact, whether the effect of H' on Ψ is large or small. However, for the practical purpose of evaluating the energies, with reasonable accuracy and without excessive labour, it is important that H' should be a *small* perturbation, which means that the perturbed wave functions and energies do not differ very much from the unperturbed ones — we shall assume this in the following work.

Now, if the perturbation term were zero, so that the functions ψ_i were exact eigenfunctions of H, the off-diagonal elements of the determinant in equation (3.116) would vanish, for we should have, for $i \neq j$,

$$H_{ij} = \int \psi_i^* H \psi_j \mathrm{d}\tau = E_j \int \psi_i^* \psi_j \mathrm{d}\tau = 0. \tag{3.120}$$

The equation would then reduce to

$$\begin{vmatrix} H_{11}-E & 0 & 0 & \dots \\ 0 & H_{22}-E & 0 & \dots \\ 0 & 0 & H_{33}-E & \dots \\ \cdot & \cdot & \cdot & \cdot \end{vmatrix} = 0, \tag{3.121}$$

or

$$(H_{11}-E)(H_{22}-E)(H_{33}-E)\dots = 0, \tag{3.122}$$

with the roots $H_{11}, H_{22}, H_{33}, \dots$

Although the perturbation term is not *exactly* zero, we are assuming that it is small, so that it is reasonable as a first approximation to neglect the off-diagonal elements and take the perturbed energy levels to be

$$E_1 = H_{11}, \; E_2 = H_{22}, \text{ etc.} \tag{3.123}$$

This agrees with what was said before about the first-order perturbation theory for a non-degenerate level. If any of the unperturbed levels are degenerate, however, equations (3.123) may not provide very useful corrections to these levels. The reason for this is that we have an infinite choice of orthonormal sets of wave functions for a degenerate level, and any such set may be used in deriving equation (3.116). However, not all of them will give equally small values of the off-diagonal elements of the determinant. Thus, although equations (3.123) will give the rough positions of the perturbed levels, even though the unperturbed levels are degenerate, any *splitting* of the levels, and this is generally of most interest, is likely to be very badly represented. To overcome this difficulty we leave in the off-diagonal elements which are derived from the degenerate functions only, so that there is no question of arbitrarily neglecting terms which might be important.

For example, if the unperturbed wave functions ψ_1 and ψ_2 are degenerate, and all the rest are non-degenerate, so that $E_1^0 = E_2^0$, but all the other E_i^0 are different, we set all the off-diagonal elements equal to zero except H_{12} and H_{21}. Equation (3.116) then becomes

$$\begin{vmatrix} H_{11}-E & H_{12} & 0 & \dots \\ H_{21} & H_{22}-E & 0 & \dots \\ 0 & 0 & H_{33}-E & \dots \\ \cdot & \cdot & \cdot & \cdot \end{vmatrix} = 0, \tag{3.124}$$

which factorizes into

$$\begin{vmatrix} H_{11}-E & H_{12} \\ H_{21} & H_{22}-E \end{vmatrix} (H_{33}-E)(H_{44}-E)\dots = 0. \tag{3.125}$$

Thus, the perturbed levels corresponding to the non-degenerate ψ_i are

$$E_3 = H_{33}, \; E_4 = H_{44}, \text{ etc.,}$$

whereas the perturbed levels corresponding to the degenerate ψ_1 and ψ_2 are the roots of the equation

$$\begin{vmatrix} H_{11}-E & H_{12} \\ H_{21} & H_{22}-E \end{vmatrix} = 0. \tag{3.126}$$

This is just the secular equation we obtained before, equation (3.89), for a doubly degenerate level. If the level is N-fold degenerate — for example, if $E_1^0 = E_2^0 = \dots = E_N^0$, so that the functions $\psi_1, \psi_2, \dots \psi_N$ are degenerate — it is clear that the secular equation (3.92) will be obtained instead. This result is quite general and applies to every degenerate level — we have chosen the ψ_i with the smallest subscripts as our degenerate wave functions, but this is merely for convenience in writing the equations; we have nowhere implied in this section that they must correspond to the lowest energy level.

The same method will obviously be advantageous if a set of ψ_i, although not degenerate, are almost so — in other words, their corresponding E_i^0 are very nearly equal. Again, a much better approximation to the perturbed levels will be obtained by 'leaving in' the off-diagonal elements derived from the almost-degenerate functions.

It is rarely necessary to go beyond first-order perturbation theory for a degenerate level, so let us return to non-degenerate levels and consider how to find a second-order perturbation correction to the energy. Suppose, for example, that E_1^0 is non-degenerate, and we wish to find the perturbed level E_1 corresponding to it. We have seen above that a first approximation to E_1 is H_{11}, so let us substitute H_{11} for E in every diagonal element of the determinant in equation (3.116) except the first, which we now write $H_{11}-E_1$. Also, let us retain all the non-diagonal elements which involve ψ_1, and put all the others equal to zero, since they affect E_1 only indirectly. The equation for E_1 is then

$$\begin{vmatrix} H_{11}-E_1 & H_{12} & H_{13} & H_{14} & \dots \\ H_{21} & H_{22}-H_{11} & 0 & 0 & \dots \\ H_{31} & 0 & H_{33}-H_{11} & 0 & \dots \\ H_{41} & 0 & 0 & H_{44}-H_{11} & \dots \\ \cdot & \cdot & \cdot & \cdot & \cdot \end{vmatrix} = 0. \qquad (3.127)$$

To solve this equation we make use of the fact that the value of a determinant is unchanged if to any row is added a constant multiple of any other row. We first multiply the second row by $H_{12}/(H_{22}-H_{11})$, and then subtract it from the first. The result is that the element H_{12} disappears from the first row, and the first element becomes

$$H_{11}-E_1-\frac{H_{12}H_{21}}{H_{22}-H_{11}},$$

all the other elements remaining unchanged. This process is now repeated with the third row — this is multiplied by $H_{13}/(H_{33}-H_{11})$, and subtracted from the first row. The result is now the disappearance of H_{13} and the further addition of

$$-\frac{H_{13}H_{31}}{H_{33}-H_{11}}$$

to the first element. Each repetition removes an element from the first row and adds a term of the form $-H_{1j}H_{j1}/(H_{jj}-H_{11})$ to the first element. Eventually, then, all the non-diagonal elements of the first row are removed, and the first element becomes

$$H_{11}-E_1-\sum_{j=2}^{\infty}\frac{H_{1j}H_{j1}}{H_{jj}-H_{11}}.$$

Expanding the determinant in terms of the first row then gives

$$\left(H_{11}-E_1-\sum_{j\neq 2}^{\infty}\frac{H_{1j}H_{j1}}{H_{jj}-H_{11}}\right)(H_{22}-H_{11})(H_{33}-H_{11})\dots = 0. \qquad (3.128)$$

Since ψ_1 is non-degenerate, none of the factors can be zero except the first.

We therefore find

$$E_1 = H_{11} - \sum_{j=2}^{\infty} \frac{H_{1j}H_{j1}}{H_{jj}-H_{11}}. \tag{3.129}$$

H_{11} is the first-order approximation, and the second term on the right is the second-order correction. Now, we have

$$H_{jj}-H_{11} = E_j^0 - E_1^0 + H'_{jj} - H'_{11},$$

and $H'_{jj}-H'_{11}$, the difference between two first-order corrections, should be very small compared with $E_j^0 - E_1^0$, the difference between two energy levels, so that it is a sufficiently good approximation to write

$$E_1 = H_{11} - \sum_{j=2}^{\infty} \frac{H_{1j}H_{j1}}{E_j^0 - E_1^0}. \tag{3.130}$$

The same formula holds, of course, for any non-degenerate level. In general, the second-order approximation to the perturbed level E_i, corresponding to the non-degenerate unperturbed level E_i^0, is

$$E_i = H_{ii} - \sum_{j\neq i} \frac{H_{ij}H_{ji}}{E_j^0 - E_i^0}. \tag{3.131}$$

Owing to the Hermitian property of H, equation (3.58), this equation may be written

$$E_i = H_{ii} - \sum_{j\neq i} \frac{|H_{ij}|^2}{E_j^0 - E_i^0}. \tag{3.132}$$

Also, since

$$\begin{aligned} H_{ij} &= \int \psi_i^*(H^0 + H')\psi_j \mathrm{d}\tau \\ &= E_j^0 \int \psi_i^*\psi_j \mathrm{d}\tau + \int \psi_i^* H' \psi_j \mathrm{d}\tau \\ &= E_j^0 \delta_{ij} + H'_{ij}, \end{aligned} \tag{3.133}$$

equation (3.132) could equally well be written

$$E_i = E_i^0 + H'_{ii} - \sum_{j\neq i} \frac{|H'_{ij}|^2}{E_j^0 - E_i^0}, \tag{3.134}$$

which gives the first- and second-order corrections to E_i^0 directly in terms of the perturbation H'.

Although it is possible to proceed in this way, and, by retaining further off-diagonal elements in equation (3.116), obtain better and better approximations to the perturbed levels, this is rarely done. If the effects of the perturbing term are so great that even second-order perturbation theory fails to give a reasonable result, then a different approach to the problem is generally attempted. We shall have an example of this later, when we discuss the effects of the interaction of electrons in metals. Perhaps it should be pointed out, however, that new and powerful techniques of perturbation theory have recently been developed, which offer the possibility of solving the perturbation problem exactly, or sufficiently so for all practical purposes, by virtually summing the whole perturbation series, to infinite order. These techniques are much too complicated for inclusion in the present book — and, indeed, there is little reason for including them, since their impact upon the electron theory of metals has so far been slight.

3.9. Matrix Elements

Although we do not intend to give any account of matrix mechanics in this work, some of the terminology of this branch of quantum mechanics is regularly used even in work of an entirely wave-mechanical nature, so it is advisable that the reader be acquainted with it.

The quantities H_{ij}, defined by

$$H_{ij} = \int \psi_i^* H \psi_j \mathrm{d}\tau, \qquad (3.135)$$

as before, are referred to as the *matrix elements* of the operator H with respect to the set of functions ψ_i, and the *matrix* of H is the following array of these quantities:

$$\begin{pmatrix} H_{11} & H_{12} & H_{13} \ldots \\ H_{21} & H_{22} & H_{23} \ldots \\ H_{31} & H_{32} & H_{33} \ldots \\ . & . & . \quad . \quad . \quad . \quad . \end{pmatrix}. \qquad (3.136)$$

It must be understood that this is *not* a determinant, which is why curved brackets, or sometimes square brackets, are used, instead of lines, to enclose the array. There are mathematical rules for the addition and multiplication of such matrices, just as there are for vectors — indeed, a vector can be represented by a particularly simple kind of matrix. Similar matrices may be set up for other operators, and matrix mechanics deals directly with these rather than with the operators and wave functions of wave mechanics.

The matrix elements H_{11}, H_{22}, H_{33}, etc., are called *diagonal elements.* If the ψ_i are eigenfunctions of H, so that

$$H\psi_i = E_i\psi_i, \tag{3.137}$$

then

$$H_{ij} = E_j\delta_{ij}, \tag{3.138}$$

and the Hamiltonian, or energy, matrix (3.136) reduces to

$$\begin{pmatrix} E_1 & 0 & 0 & \dots \\ 0 & E_2 & 0 & \dots \\ 0 & 0 & E_3 & \dots \\ . & . & . & . & . & . \end{pmatrix}, \tag{3.139}$$

which is called a *diagonal matrix*, and the diagonal elements are the energy levels of the system. For this reason the problem of finding the energy levels and wave functions is often referred to as the *diagonalization* of the energy matrix.

CHAPTER 4

THE MANY-ELECTRON PROBLEM AND THE ONE-ELECTRON APPROXIMATION

4.1. The Many-Electron Atom

Let us now consider the general case of an atom with nuclear charge Ze, or atomic number Z, and N electrons. If $N = Z$, the atom is *neutral*, since its total charge is zero; but N may not equal Z, in which case the atom is *ionized.* We shall again treat the nucleus as a fixed centre of force, this being an even better approximation for the heavier atoms than it is for hydrogen and helium.

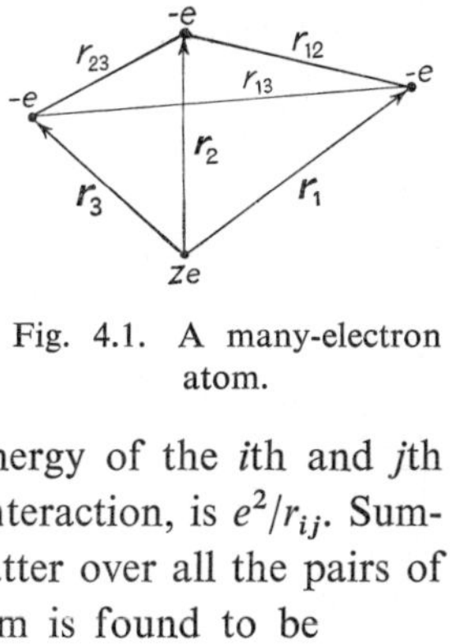

Fig. 4.1. A many-electron atom.

Extending the notation used in the case of the helium atom, we denote by $\boldsymbol{r}_i$ the position vector of the ith electron, and by r_{ij} the distance between the ith and jth electrons. The potential energy of the ith electron in the field of the nucleus is $-Ze^2/r_i$, and the mutual potential energy of the ith and jth electrons, due to their electrostatic or Coulomb interaction, is e^2/r_{ij}. Summing the former over all the electrons, and the latter over all the pairs of electrons, the total potential energy of the system is found to be

$$V(\boldsymbol{r}_1, \boldsymbol{r}_2, \ldots \boldsymbol{r}_n) = -\sum_{i=1}^{N} \frac{Ze^2}{r_i} + \frac{1}{2}\sum_{i \neq j}^{N}\sum^{N} \frac{e^2}{r_{ij}}. \tag{4.1}$$

The second term is a double sum over all values of i and j, those terms in which i and j have the same value being excluded, since an electron does not repel itself. The factor $\frac{1}{2}$ arises because the double sum as it stands contains the interaction between any pair of electrons twice — e^2/r_{ij} and e^2/r_{ji} both equal the potential energy of interaction between the ith and jth electrons. It is easily verified that this term may equally well be written

$$\sum_{i>j}^{N}\sum^{N} \frac{e^2}{r_{ij}},$$

the double sum now being over all values of j and over those values of i which are *greater* than j, so that no factor $\frac{1}{2}$ is required. It should be noted that often a single summation sign is used to represent double, or multiple, sums.

The zero of potential energy is here obtained when all the particles of the system are infinitely separated. Any *magnetic* interaction among the electrons, due to their motion, is neglected, as it is of very much smaller order of magnitude than the electrostatic interaction.

The quantum-mechanical Hamiltonian operator, from equation (2.20), is

$$H = -\sum_{i=1}^{N} \frac{\hbar^2}{2m} \nabla_i^2 - \sum_{i=1}^{N} \frac{Ze^2}{r_i} + \frac{1}{2} \sum_{i \neq j}^{N} \sum^{N} \frac{e^2}{r_{ij}}$$

$$= -\sum_{i=1}^{N} \left(\frac{\hbar^2}{2m} \nabla_i^2 + \frac{Ze^2}{r_i} \right) + \frac{1}{2} \sum_{i \neq j}^{N} \sum^{N} \frac{e^2}{r_{ij}}, \tag{4.2}$$

and the Schrödinger equation is

$$H\Psi = E\Psi. \tag{4.3}$$

Here, and in future, we shall use a capital Ψ for the wave function, $\Psi(\boldsymbol{r}_1, \boldsymbol{r}_2 \ldots)$, of a system of several electrons, reserving the small ψ for a function of the coordinates of a single particle.

The main difficulty with the solution of equation (4.3) is the presence of the last term in H, the electronic interaction term. If this term were absent, we could write

$$\Psi = \psi_1(\boldsymbol{r}_1)\psi_2(\boldsymbol{r}_2) \ldots \psi_N(\boldsymbol{r}_N), \tag{4.4}$$

and equation (4.3) would become

$$-\sum_{i=1}^{N} \left(\frac{\hbar^2}{2m} \nabla_i^2 + \frac{Ze^2}{r_i} \right) \psi_1\psi_2 \ldots \psi_N = E\psi_1\psi_2 \ldots \psi_N. \tag{4.5}$$

Dividing through by Ψ gives

$$-\sum_{i=1}^{N} \frac{1}{\psi_i} \left(\frac{\hbar^2}{2m} \nabla_i^2 + \frac{Ze^2}{r_i} \right) \psi_i = E, \tag{4.6}$$

and, as each term of the sum depends upon the coordinates of one particle only, this equation can be separated into the N equations

$$-\left(\frac{\hbar^2}{2m} \nabla_i^2 + \frac{Ze^2}{r_i} \right) \psi_i = \varepsilon_i \psi_i, \qquad i = 1, 2, \ldots N, \tag{4.7}$$

where

$$\sum_{i=1}^{N} \varepsilon_i = E. \tag{4.8}$$

Each of these equations is of hydrogenic form and can therefore be solved analytically. Unfortunately, the electronic interaction term cannot be neglected in this way and it is impossible to obtain an analytical solution of equation (4.3), as we have already seen in the simplest case of helium.

Of course, the interaction term could be treated by perturbation theory, using unperturbed functions of the form given in equation (4.4). However, the Coulomb interaction is by no means a small perturbation, so that first-order perturbation theory is not expected to give accurate results — it will be remembered that it gave an error of 5 per cent in the ground state energy of helium, and the error increases with the number of electrons. Also, convergence difficulties occur in the case of second-order perturbation theory, which involves the summing of an infinite series. Treating the whole of the Coulomb interaction as a perturbation, therefore, is not very helpful in general.

An approximation to the energy of the ground state may be found by means of the variational method, but reasonable accuracy, without excessive labour, is only attainable in this way for the lighter atoms, such as helium and lithium. Even for helium, trial functions which give close agreement with experiment are by no means simple, and, as the number of electrons increases, the complexity of the trial function required makes the method impracticable.

Any analytical solution of the problem, even an approximate one of reasonable accuracy, would therefore seem to be out of the question for the heavier atoms. Consequently, equation (4.3) must be solved by numerical methods, with the aid of calculating machines if possible. In other words, the attempt to approximate to Ψ by a closed analytical formula is abandoned, and by direct numerical computation we attempt to obtain the function in tabulated form, that is, as a table of values corresponding to closely spaced points covering the whole of configuration space. A difficulty arises here, however, for, in the case of a heavy atom, Ψ is a function of a large number of variables — the coordinates of all the electrons. It has been aptly said that a function of one variable might be adequately tabulated on a single page, a function of two variables would take a book, and a function of three variables would need a library. Now, a neutral atom of sodium, for example, which is not particularly heavy, has 11 electrons, so that Ψ

is a function of 33 variables, and therefore quite impossible to tabulate adequately.

When dealing with systems of many electrons, then, we are virtually compelled to adopt what is known as the *one-electron approximation*, which we shall discuss in the following section. This, by ascribing to each electron a separate wave function, reduces the problem to that of tabulating functions of three variables, or, with a slight further approximation, functions of a single variable — one table for each electron in the atom.

4.2. The One-Electron Approximation

We now assume, as would be the case if the Schrödinger equation were separable, that each electron can be represented by its own wave function, which is a function of the coordinates of that electron only. This *one-electron* wave function is calculated just as if the problem were that of a single electron moving in the field of the nucleus and some additional field which represents the average effect of all the other electrons. Thus, the equation which the one-electron function $\psi_i(\boldsymbol{r}_i)$ of the ith electron satisfies is taken to be of the form

$$\left[-\frac{\hbar^2}{2m}\nabla_i^2 - \frac{Ze^2}{r_i} + V_i(r_i)\right]\psi_i = \varepsilon_i\psi_i, \tag{4.9}$$

where the potential function $V_i(r_i)$ approximately represents the interaction of the ith electron with all the other electrons. The initial problem is to choose a suitable form for the function V_i, but let us defer this for the moment, except to remark that we take V_i to be spherically symmetrical, which is very reasonable for an atom and simplifies the solution of equation (4.9) enormously. There are N equations like (4.9), one for each electron, and the function V_i could be taken to be the same for all of them, in which case we could dispense with the subscript i; but this is not necessary, and, for a reason which will become apparent, it may be rather a poor approximation. If V_i were zero, of course, equation (4.9) would reduce to equation (4.7), but we have seen that this does not lead to results of great accuracy. Notice that in equation (4.9) we have used a Greek letter ε to denote the eigenvalue — we shall retain this notation for the eigenvalues of one-electron equations throughout the remainder of the book.

Although equation (4.9) is not hydrogenic, since $V_i(r_i)$ will not in general be proportional to $1/r_i$, the potential energy function still has spherical symmetry, so that the problem is one of a particle in a central field, as discussed in § 2.4. Any eigenfunction of equation (4.9) may be expressed, in spherical polar coordinates, as a product of three functions

$$\psi(r, \theta, \phi) = R(r)\,\Theta(\theta)\,\Phi(\phi),$$

and the equation separated into three ordinary differential equations for R, Θ, and Φ. The angular functions Θ and Φ will be exactly the same as in the hydrogenic case, but the radial function will not, although it will have a similar form. The solutions will depend upon three quantum numbers n, l, and m_l, where $n-l-1$ is equal to the number of nodal spheres, l is equal to the number of nodal planes, and m_l can have any integral value, including zero, from $-l$ to $+l$. The states are specified as 1s, 2s, 2p, 3d, and so on, according to the values of n and l. It should be noted that the eigenvalue ε will in this case depend upon both n and l, not only upon n, which is peculiar to the hydrogenic atom.

Now, having solved the N equations, we may take one eigenfunction of each and write an approximate *total* wave function Ψ as their product

$$\Psi = \psi_1(\boldsymbol{r}_1)\psi_2(\boldsymbol{r}_2)\dots\psi_N(\boldsymbol{r}_N), \tag{4.10}$$

just as in equation (4.4), and an approximation to the total energy E of this particular state is given by

$$E = \frac{\int \Psi^* H \Psi \,\mathrm{d}\tau}{\int \Psi^* \Psi \,\mathrm{d}\tau}. \tag{4.11}$$

It is easy to verify that E is *not*, in general, equal to the sum of the eigenvalues ε_i. These eigenvalues do not really correspond to any energies which are experimentally measurable. However, we shall see that, with the best choice of the function V_i, the magnitude of ε_i is very roughly equal to the *ionization energy* of the electron in the state ψ_i, that is, the energy required to remove this electron completely from the atom.

4.3. The Pauli Exclusion Principle

Equation (4.9) has, of course, an infinite number of eigenfunctions, as also have the other $N-1$ equations. It might at first be thought possible to choose *any* of these eigenfunctions, one from each equation, for insertion in (4.10), and so obtain an approximation to some energy level of the system. For atoms with more than two electrons this is found not to be the case — many of the resulting values of E approximate to no energy level which can be deduced from spectroscopic data.

We have previously remarked that the one-electron states may be 1s, 2s, 2p, 3s, 3p, and so on, and the *configuration* of a state of the atom as a whole is just the number of electrons in each type of one-electron state. Now, it is generally found that the energy rises along the given series — in other words, a 2s state has a higher energy than a 1s state, and so on. This might lead us to expect that, in the ground state of an atom, *all* the electrons will be in 1s states, the states of lowest energy. This is perfectly true for hydrogen and helium, with one and two electrons respectively. The ground state of hydrogen is certainly a 1s state, and the configuration is written, simply, (1s). The ground state of helium corresponds, in the one-electron approximation, to both electrons being in 1s states, and the configuration is written $(1s)^2$, the superscript denoting two electrons. However, when we come to a neutral atom of lithium, which has three electrons, the lowest energy level is found to correspond *not* to all three electrons being in 1s states, which would be the configuration $(1s)^3$, but to two electrons being in 1s states and one electron in a 2s state, and the configuration is written $(1s)^2(2s)$. In the same way the ground state, or *normal*, configuration of beryllium, with four electrons, is found to be $(1s)^2(2s)^2$, and that of boron, with five electrons, is found to be, not $(1s)^2(2s)^3$, but $(1s)^2(2s)^2(2p)$. Proceeding in this way, comparing the observed ground state energies with the energies given by the one-electron approximation, a general rule has been deduced, which is as follows:

not more than two electrons may occupy any orbital state.

This is known as the *Pauli exclusion principle* and must be added to our list of the fundamental principles of quantum mechanics — it cannot be deduced from any of the principles we have introduced previously. It should be emphasized, however, that the above form of the principle is an approximation, albeit a very good one, because the one-electron states to which it is applied exist only as approximations. In the following chapter, after introducing a further property of electrons, known as *electron spin*, we shall give a more fundamental statement of the Pauli principle, which is independent of the one-electron approximation, but which reduces to the above whenever the one-electron approximation is used. We have used the name *orbital state* to distinguish the one-electron states we are discussing in this chapter, and which are functions only of the positional coordinates of an electron, from one-electron states in which electron spin is included.

The normal configuration of an atom is thus obtained by filling the orbital states of lowest energy in a manner consistent with the Pauli principle. It is important to notice that the degeneracies of the one-electron functions must be taken into account. Thus, every p state is triply degenerate, corresponding to three possible values -1, 0, 1 of the magnetic quantum number m_l, and the Pauli principle permits two electrons to each value of m_l, so that we may have *six* electrons in p states with a given value of the principal quantum number n. For example, the normal configuration of sodium, which has eleven electrons, is $(1s)^2(2s)^2(2p)^6(3s)$. Similarly, as d states are fivefold degenerate, we may have as many as *ten* electrons in d states with the same value of n.

We do not wish to give the normal configurations of all the atoms, but we summarize those already quoted and add one or two others in the following list, the total number of electrons being given in brackets after the symbol of the element:

H (1) : $(1s)$
He (2) : $(1s)^2$
Li (3) : $(1s)^2 (2s)$
Be (4) : $(1s)^2 (2s)^2$
B (5) : $(1s)^2 (2s)^2 (2p)$
Na (11) : $(1s)^2 (2s)^2 (2p)^6 (3s)$
Mg (12) : $(1s)^2 (2s)^2 (2p)^6 (3s)^2$
K (19) : $(1s)^2 (2s)^2 (2p)^6 (3s)^2 (3p)^6 (4s)$
Ca (20) : $(1s)^2 (2s)^2 (2p)^6 (3s)^2 (3p)^6 (4s)^2$
Ni (28) : $(1s)^2 (2s)^2 (2p)^6 (3s)^2 (3p)^6 (3d)^8 (4s)^2$
Cu (29) : $(1s)^2 (2s)^2 (2p)^6 (3s)^2 (3p)^6 (3d)^{10} (4s)$
Ag (47) : $(1s)^2 (2s)^2 (2p)^6 (3s)^2 (3p)^6 (3d)^{10} (4s)^2 (4p)^6 (4d)^{10} (5s)$.

It should be noted that the states of higher energy are not always filled in the order suggested by the energy levels of hydrogen. In hydrogen, where the energy is $-1/n^2$ ryd, a 3d state has lower energy than a 4s state, but we see that in potassium and calcium, for example, 4s states are filled before any 3d state has been filled. Similarly, in nickel, with 28 electrons, two electrons are in 4s states, whereas in copper, with 29 electrons, only one electron is in a 4s state, the other having gone into a vacant 3d state. These anomalies are due to the fact that any electron is 'screened' from the full effect of the field of the nucleus by the presence of the other electrons, and this screening varies according to the state of the electron, in such a way as to cause some electrons in different shells to have very similar energies. The order of filling the one-electron states would appear to be roughly as follows:

1s, 2s, 2p, 3s, 3p, 4s, 3d, 4p, 5s, 4d, 5p, 6s, 4f, 5d, 6p, 7s, 5f, 6d.

Electrons in states with the same value of the principal quantum number n are said to occupy the same *shell*. If a shell contains its maximum number of electrons consistent with the Pauli principle it is said to be *closed*. Shells corresponding to $n = 1, 2, 3, 4, 5$ are denoted by the letters K, L, M, N, O respectively, and the number of electrons in a closed shell is $2n^2$. We thus have

$n = 1$: K shell (2 electrons)
$n = 2$: L shell (8 electrons)
$n = 3$: M shell (18 electrons)
$n = 4$: N shell (32 electrons)
$n = 5$: O shell (50 electrons).

Frequently the electrons in states with the same values of n *and* l are referred to as 'shells' — for example, the ten 3d electrons in copper are often called the '3d shell'. This can be misleading, however, so we shall refer to such groups of electrons as *sub-shells*. The chemical behaviour of an atom depends upon those electrons which lie outside closed shells and sub-shells, and this can easily be shown to provide an explanation of the Periodic System of the elements, but we will omit details.

The whole of the foregoing discussion has been based upon the solutions of equations like (4.9), but we have not so far considered any specific method for constructing the functions V_i. Several methods have been used, but we will at present confine our discussion to the most popular and most successful of these, which was first suggested by D. R. Hartree in 1928. This method, known as the method of the *self-consistent field*, not only makes a direct appeal to physical intuition, but, as we shall see, can be justified by means of the variation principle.

4.4. The Hartree Method Applied to the Ground State of Helium

Before describing the Hartree method in general it might be useful to consider its application to the normal helium atom, which was the first atom to be treated by this method. According to the general procedure described in § 4.2, we write the total wave function in the approximate form

$$\Psi(\boldsymbol{r}_1, \boldsymbol{r}_2) = \psi_1(\boldsymbol{r}_1)\psi_2(\boldsymbol{r}_2), \tag{4.12}$$

where the one-electron function ψ_1 satisfies the equation

$$\left[-\frac{\hbar^2}{2m}\nabla_1^2 - \frac{2e^2}{r_1} + V_1(r_1)\right]\psi_1 = \varepsilon_1\psi_1, \tag{4.13}$$

and there is a similar equation for ψ_2. In fact, for the ground state, we know that the functions ψ_1 and ψ_2 will both be the same 1s function, so that there is really only one equation to solve, but let us disregard this for the moment.

Hartree chose the potential function $V_1(r_1)$ to be the potential energy of the first electron, or electron 1, in the field of the *average* charge distribution or *charge cloud* of electron 2. As described in § 2.6, we may regard the average charge distribution of electron 2 as a charge cloud whose density, at any point $\boldsymbol{r}_2$, is $-e|\psi_2(\boldsymbol{r}_2)|^2$, and the potential energy of electron 1 due to a charged volume element $d\boldsymbol{r}_2$ is $e^2|\psi_2(\boldsymbol{r}_2)|^2 d\boldsymbol{r}_2/r_{12}$. The potential energy of electron 1 due to the whole charge cloud is, thus,

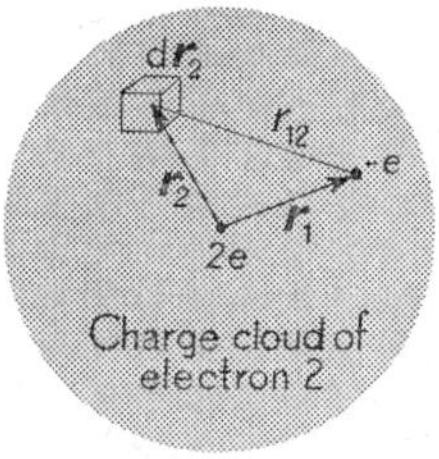

Fig. 4.2. According to the Hartree theory of the helium atom, the potential energy of electron 1 is due to the nucleus and the charge cloud of electron 2.

$$V_1(r_1) = e^2 \int \frac{|\psi_2(\boldsymbol{r}_2)|^2}{r_{12}} d\boldsymbol{r}_2, \tag{4.14}$$

the integration being throughout all space.

It may remove a source of confusion if we point out that this definite integral is *not* a function of $\boldsymbol{r}_2$, so that any symbol, except $\boldsymbol{r}_1$, could be substituted for $\boldsymbol{r}_2$. The distance r_{12} is defined as $|\boldsymbol{r}_1 - \boldsymbol{r}_2|$, so that we could equally well write, for example,

$$V_1(r_1) = e^2 \int \frac{|\psi_2(\boldsymbol{r})|^2}{|\boldsymbol{r}_1 - \boldsymbol{r}|} d\boldsymbol{r}. \tag{4.15}$$

The Hartree equation for ψ_1 is, therefore,

$$\left[-\frac{\hbar^2}{2m}\nabla_1^2 - \frac{2e^2}{r_1} + e^2 \int \frac{|\psi_2(\boldsymbol{r}_2)|^2}{r_{12}} d\boldsymbol{r}_2\right]\psi_1 = \varepsilon_1\psi_1, \tag{4.16}$$

with a similar equation for ψ_2, having the subscripts 1 and 2 interchanged.

If we now concentrate on the ground state, a simplification is introduced, as previously remarked, because ψ_1 and ψ_2 are then the same function [and are also spherically symmetrical, which justifies our implied assumption that $V_1(r_1)$ is spherically symmetrical]. We have, in fact,

$$\Psi(\boldsymbol{r}_1, \boldsymbol{r}_2) = \psi(r_1)\psi(r_2), \tag{4.17}$$

and the equation for $\psi(r)$ is

$$\left[-\frac{\hbar^2}{2m}\nabla^2 - \frac{2e^2}{r} + e^2 \int \frac{|\psi(r')|^2}{|\boldsymbol{r}-\boldsymbol{r}'|}\,\mathrm{d}\boldsymbol{r}'\right]\psi = \varepsilon\psi. \tag{4.18}$$

We have dropped all subscripts here, to emphasize that the equation is the same for both electrons, and this necessitates the use of $\boldsymbol{r}'$, or some symbol other than $\boldsymbol{r}$, as the variable of integration. This equation is true, of course, only if ψ is normalized.

The problem is simply to find the eigenfunction of equation (4.18) which has the lowest eigenvalue. Clearly, this cannot be done analytically, and cannot even be done directly by numerical integration, because the potential energy depends upon the function ψ. An equation of this sort is called an integro-differential equation, and it is necessary to employ a method of successive approximations in order to solve it. We first choose an approximation to ψ — for example, we might choose the function $\exp(-27r/16a_0)$, which gave reasonably good results in the variational method — and, after normalizing this chosen function, we use it to evaluate the integral in equation (4.18). This equation then becomes an ordinary Schrödinger equation, which we can solve by numerical methods, and its solution should be a better approximation to ψ. This process is repeated again and again until two successive repetitions yield results which do not differ significantly — this means that, in the final repetition, practically the same ψ is used in calculating the potential function as is found by solving the equation. The solution is then said to be self-consistent, and the associated field is called the *self-consistent field.*

The rapidity of convergence of the process depends, of course, upon the closeness of our original approximation to ψ. Also, it must be remembered that equation (4.18) has an infinite number of eigenfunctions, so that at each stage we must be careful to choose the solution which interests us — in this case, for the ground state, we require a 1s type of solution, that is, a spherically symmetrical function without nodes.

Since ψ is normalized, the total wave function must also be, for

$$\iint \Psi^* \Psi \, \mathrm{d}\boldsymbol{r}_1 \, \mathrm{d}\boldsymbol{r}_2 = \int |\psi(r_1)|^2 \mathrm{d}\boldsymbol{r}_1 \int |\psi(r_2)|^2 \mathrm{d}\boldsymbol{r}_2 = 1. \tag{4.19}$$

Equation (4.11) therefore gives, for the approximate energy of the ground state,

$$E = \int \Psi^* H \Psi \, \mathrm{d}\tau$$

$$= \iint \psi^*(r_1)\psi^*(r_2) \left[-\frac{\hbar^2}{2m} (\nabla_1^2 + \nabla_2^2) - \frac{2e^2}{r_1} - \frac{2e^2}{r_2} + \frac{e^2}{r_{12}} \right] \psi(r_1)\psi(r_2) \mathrm{d}\boldsymbol{r}_1 \, \mathrm{d}\boldsymbol{r}_2$$

$$= 2\varepsilon - \iint \frac{e^2}{r_{12}} |\psi(r_1)|^2 |\psi(r_2)|^2 \mathrm{d}\boldsymbol{r}_1 \, \mathrm{d}\boldsymbol{r}_2, \tag{4.20}$$

using equation (4.18).

The eigenvalue ε has already been found during the calculation of ψ, and the integral, which represents the mean interaction energy of the electrons, can be evaluated by the method given in Appendix 4 — numerical integrations are necessary, of course, since ψ is obtained as a tabulated function. In this way E is found to be -5.73 ryd, compared with the experimental value of -5.81 ryd. The error of 1.4 per cent is only two thirds of that obtained by the variational method given in § 3.3. The latter, however, employed a trial function which was the product of two simple exponential functions — by the use of more complicated trial functions the variational method can, as remarked before, give results of much greater accuracy. We shall show below that the Hartree wave function is, from the point of view of the variation principle, the *best* wave function of the simple product form (4.12).

The error is due essentially to the fact that the electrons do not move independently, which is neglected in the Hartree method. Owing to their mutual repulsion, the electrons tend to avoid each other, and their motions are said to be *correlated.* The Hartree method, although it does not completely ignore the interaction between the electrons, does not account for this correlated motion. The energy given by the Hartree method is therefore too high, for it assumes that the electrons spend more time in the immediate vicinity of each other than is actually the case. We shall see later in the book that this question is of great importance in the theory of metals. Of course, in the variational method, the correlation between the motions of the electrons can be taken into account by the inclusion of terms involving

r_{12}, the distance between the electrons, in the trial function, but the variational method is not a practical proposition for systems of large numbers of electrons.

4.5. The Hartree Method in General

The generalization of the foregoing procedure to the case of N electrons is so obvious that we need do little more than write down the results. Each electron is supposed to move in the field of the nucleus and that due to the charge cloud of all the other electrons. The potential energy of electron i, due to the latter, is just the sum of expressions like (4.14), one for each electron except electron i itself — in other words, it is

$$V_i(r_i) = e^2 \sum_{j \neq i}^{N} \int \frac{|\psi_j(\boldsymbol{r}_j)|^2}{r_{ij}} \, \mathrm{d}\boldsymbol{r}_j. \tag{4.21}$$

Since we are at the moment dealing with atoms, we have again written this as a spherically symmetrical function — a function of r_i rather than of $\boldsymbol{r}_i$. This is always so if the ψ_j are s states, and it can be shown that the total charge cloud of the electrons in closed shells and sub-shells is spherically symmetrical, so that their contribution to V_i must also be. An incomplete p or d sub-shell might, however, have a charge cloud which is not spherically symmetrical — in this case, for purposes of computation, an average is taken over the angular coordinates so as to obtain a spherically symmetrical contribution to V_i. This is an additional approximation, but gives rise to an error which is negligible compared with those already involved. We wish to make it quite clear, however, that this spherical symmetrization is only justifiable for atoms. The Hartree method can, of course, in principle be applied to molecules and to solids — we shall, in fact, consider it in relation to metals later in the book — and in these cases, although the Hartree potential function is still that given in equation (4.21), it is no longer even approximately spherically symmetrical, since there are several centres of force present.

The Hartree equations for the system are obtained by substituting (4.21) in equation (4.9):

$$\left[-\frac{\hbar^2}{2m}\nabla_i^2 - \frac{Ze^2}{r_i} + e^2 \sum_{j \neq i}^{N} \int \frac{|\psi_j(\boldsymbol{r}_j)|^2}{r_{ij}} \, \mathrm{d}\boldsymbol{r}_j\right] \psi_i(\boldsymbol{r}_i) = \varepsilon_i \psi_i(\boldsymbol{r}_i), \quad i = 1, 2, \ldots N. \tag{4.22}$$

We are thus faced with the problem of solving N integro-differential equations simultaneously, since the potential function in each depends upon the solutions of all the others. This would appear to be, and indeed is, a formidable task, but it is by no means an impossible one for atoms, and the method has been applied successfully to a large number of them. The procedure is similar to that given for helium. Bearing in mind the configuration of the state whose energy we are seeking, we choose a set of approximate ψ_i and with them calculate the N potential functions. The Hartree equations then become ordinary Schrödinger equations and we may solve them all by numerical methods, choosing in every case the particular eigenfunction we require, that is, 1s, 2s, 2p, and so on. With these solutions we re-calculate the potential functions and repeat the whole cycle of operations. We go on repeating until self-consistency is attained, that is, until the last set of solutions differs negligibly from the previous set.

The approximate total wave function is now taken to be

$$\Psi = \psi_1(\boldsymbol{r}_1)\psi_2(\boldsymbol{r}_2)\ldots\psi_N(\boldsymbol{r}_N), \tag{4.23}$$

and this is normalized, since the one-electron functions are — it must be remembered that the solutions have to be normalized at every stage of the above calculation. The approximate total energy is, thus,

$$\begin{aligned} E = \int \Psi^* H \Psi \,\mathrm{d}\tau &= \int\ldots\int \psi_1^*(\boldsymbol{r}_1)\ldots\psi_N^*(\boldsymbol{r}_N)\left[-\sum_{i=1}^{N}\left(\frac{\hbar^2}{2m}\nabla_i^2 + \frac{Ze^2}{r_i}\right)\right. \\ &\quad \left. + \frac{1}{2}\sum_{i\neq j}^{N}\sum^{N}\frac{e^2}{r_{ij}}\right]\psi_1(\boldsymbol{r}_1)\ldots\psi_N(\boldsymbol{r}_N)\mathrm{d}\boldsymbol{r}_1\ldots\mathrm{d}\boldsymbol{r}_N \\ &= -\sum_{i=1}^{N}\int\psi_i^*(\boldsymbol{r}_i)\left(\frac{\hbar^2}{2m}\nabla_i^2 + \frac{Ze^2}{r_i}\right)\psi_i(\boldsymbol{r}_i)\mathrm{d}\boldsymbol{r}_i \\ &\quad + \frac{1}{2}\sum_{i\neq j}^{N}\sum^{N}\iint\psi_i^*(\boldsymbol{r}_i)\psi_j^*(\boldsymbol{r}_j)\frac{e^2}{r_{ij}}\psi_i(\boldsymbol{r}_i)\psi_j(\boldsymbol{r}_j)\mathrm{d}\boldsymbol{r}_i\mathrm{d}\boldsymbol{r}_j, \end{aligned} \tag{4.24}$$

all the other factors being unity owing to the normalization of the ψ_i. Now, using equations (4.22), we find

$$E = \sum_{i=1}^{N}\varepsilon_i - \frac{1}{2}\sum_{i\neq j}^{N}\sum^{N}\iint\frac{e^2}{r_{ij}}|\psi_i(\boldsymbol{r}_i)|^2|\psi_j(\boldsymbol{r}_j)|^2\mathrm{d}\boldsymbol{r}_i\mathrm{d}\boldsymbol{r}_j. \tag{4.25}$$

The total energy is not just the sum of the one-electron eigenvalues, therefore, but this minus the average interaction energy of the electrons.

4.6. The Hartree Method and the Variation Principle

Suppose we wish to apply the variational method to our N-electron atom, using a trial function of the product form (4.23). We now make no assumption about the ψ_i, except that they are normalized, the problem being to choose these one-electron functions so as to obtain the best approximation to the ground state energy of the system. In other words, the problem is to choose the ψ_i so as to minimize the quantity E given by equation (4.24).

Now the only terms on the right-hand side of equation (4.24) which contain the particular function ψ_i are

$$-\int \psi_i^*(\boldsymbol{r}_i)\left(\frac{\hbar^2}{2m}\nabla_i^2+\frac{Ze^2}{r_i}\right)\psi_i(\boldsymbol{r}_i)\mathrm{d}\boldsymbol{r}_i + \sum_{j\neq i}^{N}\iint \psi_i^*(\boldsymbol{r}_i)\psi_j^*(\boldsymbol{r}_j)\frac{e^2}{r_{ij}}\psi_i(\boldsymbol{r}_i)\psi_j(\boldsymbol{r}_j)\mathrm{d}\boldsymbol{r}_i\mathrm{d}\boldsymbol{r}_j, \tag{4.26}$$

and this expression may be written

$$\int \psi_i^*(\boldsymbol{r}_i)H_i\psi_i(\boldsymbol{r}_i)\mathrm{d}\boldsymbol{r}_i, \tag{4.27}$$

where

$$H_i = -\frac{\hbar^2}{2m}\nabla_i^2-\frac{Ze^2}{r_i}+e^2\sum_{j\neq i}^{N}\int\frac{|\psi_j(\boldsymbol{r}_j)|^2}{r_{ij}}\mathrm{d}\boldsymbol{r}_j. \tag{4.28}$$

If the one-electron functions are to be chosen to minimize E, then ψ_i must be chosen so as to minimize (4.27), for no other terms contain ψ_i. The variation principle tells us, however, that the function ψ_i which minimizes expression (4.27) is the eigenfunction, corresponding to the lowest eigenvalue ε_i, of the equation

$$H_i\psi_i = \varepsilon_i\psi_i,$$

or

$$\left[-\frac{\hbar^2}{2m}\nabla_i^2-\frac{Ze^2}{r_i}+e^2\sum_{j\neq i}^{N}\int\frac{|\psi_j(\boldsymbol{r}_j)|^2}{r_{ij}}\mathrm{d}\boldsymbol{r}_j\right]\psi_i = \varepsilon_i\psi_i. \tag{4.29}$$

Comparing this equation with (4.22) we see that it is, in fact, the Hartree equation for electron i.

The variational method with a trial function in the form of a single product therefore gives the same one-electron functions as are obtained by the method of the self-consistent field. We may conclude that the Hartree functions are the *best* one-electron functions to be used in a single product form of wave function for the ground state. Admittedly, the application of the Pauli principle causes a slight complication, for it does not, except in the case of helium, permit all the one-electron functions to be the eigenfunctions of *lowest* energy of the corresponding Hartree equations, but a full discussion of this lies outside the scope of the present work.

Now, if we remove electron i from the atom, that is, if we remove ψ_i from Ψ, then the terms (4.26) are removed from E. Consequently, if we assume that all the other one-electron functions are unaltered by this operation, we have merely reduced E by the amount ε_i, this being the value of (4.26) or (4.27), as shown by (4.29). In other words, $-\varepsilon_i$ is approximately the energy required to remove electron i from the atom. This is not quite accurate, in fact, because the removal of any electron alters the self-consistent fields and wave functions of the others. None the less, it is reasonably accurate, particularly for the inner shell electrons — those electrons whose charge clouds are concentrated close to the nucleus.

Although the Hartree method gives the best ground state wave function of the form (4.23), it is not the most accurate method of computing the energy, simply because this single product of one-electron functions is not the best approximation to the total wave function. We shall consider improvements to the Hartree method in later chapters.

CHAPTER 5

ELECTRON SPIN AND THE PAULI PRINCIPLE

5.1. Orbital Angular Momentum and Magnetic Moment

Let us first consider the classical picture of an electron moving in a small circular orbit of radius r, with speed v. For convenience we will assume that the orbit is in the plane $z = 0$ and is centred at the origin O, and also that the motion is clockwise when sighting along the positive z-axis.

The components of the *angular momentum* of the electron about O are thus

$$L_x = L_y = 0, \quad L_z = mrv. \tag{5.1}$$

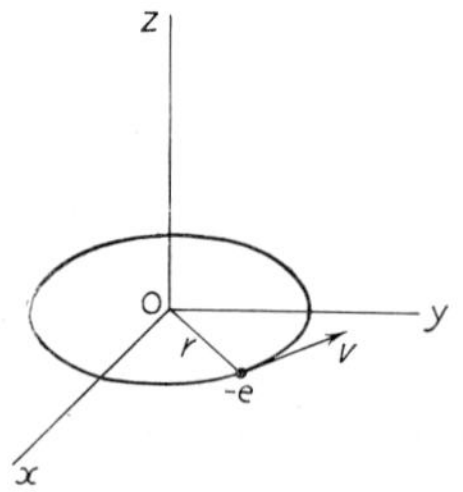

Fig. 5.1. Electron moving in a circle of radius r, centred at O, in the plane $z = 0$.

Now the motion of the electron is equivalent to an electric current I flowing around the orbit, and I is equal to the charge $-e$ divided by the time taken to make one revolution, or

$$I = -\frac{ev}{2\pi r}, \tag{5.2}$$

in the same direction as that of the electron.

Also, it is known that a current I in a small loop of area A is equivalent to a magnetic dipole of magnetic moment IA/c, in Gaussian units, perpendicular to the plane of the loop, in a sense given by the right-handed screw rule with respect to the sense of the current. In our present case, then, the motion of the electron gives rise to an *orbital magnetic moment* whose z-component is

$$\mu_z = -\frac{evr}{2c} = -\frac{e}{2mc} L_z, \tag{5.3}$$

the other two components being zero.

A magnetic dipole of moment $\boldsymbol{\mu}$ has a potential energy $-\boldsymbol{\mu} \cdot \boldsymbol{H}$ in a magnetic field $\boldsymbol{H}$. If we assume, in our example, that there is a field $\boldsymbol{H}$ in the positive z-direction, the electron will have a potential energy

$$-\mu_z H = \frac{e}{2mc} L_z H \tag{5.4}$$

due to the interaction of its orbital magnetic moment with the field. This result remains true whatever the shape and orientation of the orbit. In fact, if the electron is moving in a central electrostatic field, its orbit will not in general remain in the same plane when a magnetic field is switched on, but will *precess* around the direction of the magnetic field, and the energy of this precessional motion is given by (5.4).

What is more important for our purposes is that the result (5.4) remains true in wave mechanics, except that now L_z is quantized, that is, it may only assume a discrete set of values. We have seen in § 2.8.2 that, for a particle in a central field of force, $L_z = m_l\hbar$ and can have $2l+1$ values corresponding to the possible values $-l, -l+1, \ldots l$ of m_l, the magnetic quantum number. Consequently, the z-component of the magnetic moment can have any one of the $2l+1$ values given by

$$\mu_z = -\frac{e\hbar m_l}{2mc}, \tag{5.5}$$

and in the presence of a magnetic field H in the positive z-direction the $(2l+1)$-fold degenerate level with azimuthal quantum number l will split into $2l+1$ separate levels spaced at intervals of $e\hbar H/2mc$. This gives rise to what is known as the *normal Zeeman effect* in atomic spectra, whereby some spectral lines are split into three by a magnetic field. The reason why only three lines appear, rather than in general $2l+1$, is due to the operation of certain *selection rules*, which we shall not prove, but which state that in transitions from one state to another, due to the absorption or emission of light, m_l may change only by 0 or ± 1.

We do not wish to go into full details of the wave-mechanical treatment of atoms in magnetic fields, but the foregoing discussion can be made more plausible in a very simple way. The Schrödinger equation for an electron in a central field is

$$\left[-\frac{\hbar^2}{2m}\nabla^2 + V(r)\right]\psi = \varepsilon^0\psi, \tag{5.6}$$

say, and we have seen in § 2.4, equation (2.67), that the eigenfunctions may be written

$$\psi_{n,l,m_l}(r, \theta, \phi) = R_{n,l}(r)P_l^{m_l}(\cos\theta)\mathrm{e}^{\mathrm{i}m_l\phi}, \tag{5.7}$$

those with $m_l = -l, \ -l+1, \ldots l$ being degenerate. Now, if a magnetic field H is switched on, in the positive z-direction, we expect the potential energy to be increased by the amount given in (5.4). Representing L_z by the quantum-mechanical operator

$$L_z = \frac{\hbar}{\mathrm{i}} \frac{\partial}{\partial \phi}, \tag{5.8}$$

as given in equation (2.139), the Schrödinger equation for the system in the presence of the magnetic field becomes

$$\left[-\frac{\hbar^2}{2m}\nabla^2 + V(r) + \frac{e\hbar H}{2mc\mathrm{i}}\frac{\partial}{\partial\phi}\right]\psi = \varepsilon\psi. \tag{5.9}$$

Although the derivation has not been rigorous, this equation is correct, in fact, provided the field H is not too large. Since ϕ only occurs in the factor $\mathrm{e}^{\mathrm{i}m_l\phi}$ in the expression (5.7), we see that

$$\frac{\partial}{\partial\phi}\psi_{n,l,m_l} = \mathrm{i}m_l\psi_{n,l,m_l}, \tag{5.10}$$

so that ψ_{n,l,m_l} is also an eigenfunction of equation (5.9). Our choice of eigenfunctions was therefore very fortunate, for had we chosen linear combinations of the functions (5.7) with given n and l, which would have been equally good eigenfunctions of equation (5.6), we should have found that they were not eigenfunctions of (5.9). From (5.6), (5.9) and (5.10), we find

$$\varepsilon = \varepsilon^0 + \frac{e\hbar H}{2mc} m_l, \tag{5.11}$$

so that the eigenfunctions ψ_{n,l,m_l} of (5.9) are not degenerate, but each value of m_l corresponds to a different energy, and there are $2l+1$ separate levels, at intervals of $e\hbar H/2mc$, with given n and l. It should be noted that, if the electron is in an s state, there should be no splitting of the energy level in a magnetic field, due to the orbital magnetic moment, for l and m_l are zero.

In order to apply these ideas to many-electron atoms, we make use of the one-electron approximation described in the previous chapter. For a closed shell or sub-shell of electrons the z-components of the total orbital angular momentum and magnetic moment are clearly zero, for to every electron with a given positive value of m_l there is an electron with an equal negative value of m_l. A magnetic field should therefore have no effect upon the closed shells and sub-shells of an atom. An atom such as that of silver, which consists of closed shells and sub-shells, apart from one electron which is in a 5s state, and so without orbital magnetic moment, should therefore be unaffected by a magnetic field. The fact that this is not so is one of the reasons for introducing the concept of *electron spin*, which we shall discuss in the following section.

Beginners are often worried by the fact that the z-axis seems to have arbitrarily been singled out as the axis along which the angular momentum is quantized. It should be realized that this is not arbitrary, but is due to the fact that the magnetic field has been taken to be in the z-direction. The wave functions (5.7) are eigenfunctions of L_z, and they are only eigenfunctions of equation (5.9) also because the magnetic field is in the z-direction. If we had taken the magnetic field to be in the x-direction, say, the eigenfunctions of the corresponding Schrödinger equation would have been found to be simultaneously eigenfunctions of L_x, not L_z, and the values of L_x would have been quantized. The splitting of the energy levels, however, would have been unaltered.

5.2. Electron Spin

The theory we have presented so far fails to account for several known experimental facts. In the first place, where the theory would predict a single line in the spectrum of an atom, a group of closely-spaced lines is often observed — this is known as the *fine structure of spectra.* A well-known example is that of the so-called sodium D-lines — two prominent lines occur in the spectrum of sodium, corresponding to the wavelengths 5890 Å and 5896 Å, where only one should be observed. Such a pair of lines is called a *doublet*, a group of three lines is called a *triplet*, and in general a group of several lines is called a *multiplet*.

Again, in the presence of a magnetic field, where the normal Zeeman effect would give rise to a triplet, generally a larger number of lines is observed. This is known as the *anomalous Zeeman effect.*

Another striking example is provided by the results of the experiments of Stern and Gerlach on the splitting of beams of atoms in an inhomogeneous magnetic field. It is known from classical electromagnetic theory that an atom with magnetic moment $\boldsymbol{\mu}$ in a magnetic field $\boldsymbol{H}$ will experience a force $(\boldsymbol{\mu} \cdot \nabla)\boldsymbol{H}$, or

$$\left(\mu_x \frac{\partial}{\partial x} + \mu_y \frac{\partial}{\partial y} + \mu_z \frac{\partial}{\partial z}\right) \boldsymbol{H},$$

the derivatives being evaluated at the position of the atom. In particular, if the field is in the z-direction, and varying with z only, as we will assume, the total force will be $\mu_z \mathrm{d}H/\mathrm{d}z$ in the z-direction. If the field is homogeneous, or uniform, the force is zero, since $\mathrm{d}H/\mathrm{d}z$ is zero — this is quite obvious if we picture the atom as an elementary magnet, for in a uniform magnetic field the forces on the two poles would be equal and opposite. A beam of atoms would therefore not be deflected on passing through a uniform magnetic field. From the discussion of the previous section we should, however, expect a beam of atoms generally to be split into several beams on passing through an *inhomogeneous* magnetic field. If, for example, they are hydrogenic atoms, all in the same state with azimuthal quantum number l, we should expect the beam to be split into $2l+1$ beams, corresponding to the $2l+1$ values of μ_z. The same splitting is expected if the atoms have several closed shells and sub-shells of electrons and one additional electron in a state with azimuthal quantum number l. It is clear, however, that if this single electron is in an s state no splitting is expected, since $l = 0$. An example of this is the normal silver atom, which has 46 electrons in closed shells and sub-shells and one additional electron in a 5s state. None the less, Stern and Gerlach found that a beam of silver atoms was split by an inhomogeneous magnetic field into *two* separate beams. The same effect has been found with beams of other 'one-electron' atoms, including those of hydrogen, lithium, and sodium.

An explanation of all these facts was provided by the suggestion of Goudsmit and Uhlenbeck, in 1925, that an electron possesses an intrinsic angular momentum or *spin* momentum $\boldsymbol{S}$ and corresponding magnetic moment $\boldsymbol{M}$. In other words, an electron is in some sense to be regarded as a charged particle spinning about an axis — although we shall see that this picture must not be taken too seriously. We assume that, in the presence of a magnetic field in the z-direction, S_z is quantized in the same way as L_z, and the quantized values may be deduced from the results of Stern and Gerlach. It follows from our previous discussion that if, as a result of the orbital angular momentum, a beam were split into $2l+1$ beams, we should deduce that the quantized values of L_z were $-l\hbar$, $(-l+1)\hbar, \ldots l\hbar$. In the same way, since a beam of 'one-electron' atoms is split into *two* beams as a result of the spin momentum (and $2l+1 = 2$ gives $l = \frac{1}{2}$), we may deduce that the quantized values of S_z are $-\frac{1}{2}\hbar$ and $\frac{1}{2}\hbar$. Also, the amount of the separation of the beams shows that the corresponding values of M_z must be $e\hbar/2mc$ and $-e\hbar/2mc$. Thus, the ratio of the z-components of spin magnetic moment and spin angular momentum is

$$\frac{M_z}{S_z} = -\frac{e}{mc}. \tag{5.12}$$

We see, however, from equation (5.3), that the ratio of the z-components of orbital magnetic moment and orbital angular momentum is

$$\frac{\mu_z}{L_z} = -\frac{e}{2mc}. \tag{5.13}$$

The fact that these two ratios are different indicates that the picture of an electron as a spinning charged particle cannot be a true one, for this would lead to the latter ratio — none the less, it is a useful intuitive guide.

The quantity $e\hbar/2mc$ is called the *Bohr magneton* and is often denoted by μ_B. Thus, in the presence of a magnetic field H the energy of an electron will be changed, as a result of its spin, by $\pm\mu_B H$, corresponding to the values $\pm\frac{1}{2}\hbar$ of S_z.

5.3. Spin Wave Functions

Electron spin appears quite naturally in the relativistic quantum mechanics of Dirac, and the correct value of the magnetic moment is obtained. Again, without invoking relativity, electron spin can be grafted on to the previously developed theory by means of the *Pauli spin matrices*. However, in all the problems we shall meet, electron spin does not appear in the Hamiltonian — at least, as a very good approximation — and this permits us to dispense with both of these elaborate theories.

It will be sufficient for our purposes if we recognize that for each one-electron state that we have considered so far we now have two states, in one of which the electron has, say, *positive* spin, and, in the other, *negative* spin — the former corresponding to $S_z = \frac{1}{2}\hbar$ and the latter to $S_z = -\frac{1}{2}\hbar$. To incorporate the spin into our mathematical formalism we simply have to introduce a *spin quantum number* m_s and a *spin variable* ζ, so that a complete designation of a one-electron state becomes

$$\phi_{n, l, m_l, m_s}(x, y, z, \zeta).$$

In future we shall always use ϕ to denote a function of both the positional and spin coordinates of an electron — there should be no confusion with the angular coordinate ϕ — and shall retain ψ to denote an orbital function, that is, a function of the positional coordinates only.

By analogy with the magnetic quantum number m_l, we define m_s so that $S_z = m_s\hbar$, which means that the possible values of m_s are $\pm\frac{1}{2}$. Also, it is found that the success of the theory demands that the spin variable ζ be permitted to assume only *two* values, which we will arbitrarily take to be ± 1. This seems a little artificial, and indeed it is, but it is necessary if we are to obtain the desired results without completely changing our mathematical treatment. We have seen that it is not strictly possible to regard an electron as a spinning charged particle, and it would be meaningless to ascribe an angle of rotation to it. There is, in fact, no satisfactory physical picture of the spin variable ζ, and it is not necessary to have one, but if it is found helpful ζ may be regarded as the cosine of the angle which the axis of spin makes with the z-axis — this angle can only have the values 0 and π, however.

Corresponding to each one-electron state we have considered previously, then, we now have two:

$$\phi_{n,l,m_l,\frac{1}{2}}(x, y, z, \zeta) \quad \text{and} \quad \phi_{n,l,m_l,-\frac{1}{2}}(x, y, z, \zeta).$$

We know that an electron which is not in an s state has a magnetic moment due to its orbital motion as well as its spin magnetic moment, and there must be an interaction between the two — we may picture the electron as an elementary magnet moving in the magnetic field created by its orbital motion. This is called *spin-orbit coupling*, and it means that the orbital motion of the electron, and its energy, depend upon the direction of its spin, even in the absence of an external magnetic field. In fact, the spin magnetic moment of the electron is forced to be in the same direction as the orbital magnetic moment, or in the opposite direction. This gives rise to the fine structure of spectra mentioned earlier. However, it may be shown, and this is borne out by the observed fine structure splitting, that the energy due to this effect is very small — it is smaller than the energy required to remove the electron from the atom by a factor of the order of $(e^2/\hbar c)^2$, and $e^2/\hbar c$ has the value 1/137. As far as the calculation of the energy of an atom is concerned, therefore, the spin-orbit coupling can generally be neglected. Then each of the above wave functions may be written as the product of an orbital function and a spin function, the orbital functions being the same:

$$\psi_{n,l,m_l}(x, y, z)\chi_{\frac{1}{2}}(\zeta) \quad \text{and} \quad \psi_{n,l,m_l}(x, y, z)\chi_{-\frac{1}{2}}(\zeta).$$

It is customary to denote the function $\chi_{\frac{1}{2}}$ by α and $\chi_{-\frac{1}{2}}$ by β, so that we have

$$\phi_{n,l,m_l,\frac{1}{2}}(x, y, z, \zeta) = \psi_{n,l,m_l}(x, y, z)\alpha(\zeta),$$
$$\phi_{n,l,m_l,-\frac{1}{2}}(x, y, z, \zeta) = \psi_{n,l,m_l}(x, y, z)\beta(\zeta).$$

The meaning of the spin states is as follows: if an electron is in the positive spin state α, then S_z is *certain* to have the value $\hbar/2$, while, if it is in the negative spin state β, S_z is *certain* to have the value $-\hbar/2$. In other words, when a magnetic field H is switched on in the z-direction, the energy of an electron in the state α will be increased by $\mu_B H$, and the energy of an electron in the state β will be increased by $-\mu_B H$. It will be seen below that this meaning is completely expressed, in a manner consistent with our previous interpretation of wave functions, if we permit the spin functions to have only the two values 0 and 1: thus,

$$\alpha(1) = 1, \qquad \alpha(-1) = 0,$$
$$\beta(1) = 0, \qquad \beta(-1) = 1.$$

The spin coordinate ζ can only have the two values ± 1, so that the spin 'space' consists of only two points. An integration of a function of ζ over such a space would give a zero result. It is therefore necessary to replace an integration with respect to ζ by a summation over the two values of ζ. For example,

$$\int |\alpha(\zeta)|^2 \mathrm{d}\zeta \equiv \sum_{\zeta=\pm 1} |\alpha(\zeta)|^2 = |\alpha(1)|^2 + |\alpha(-1)|^2 = 1. \tag{5.14}$$

It follows that the functions α and β as defined above are normalized. They are also orthogonal, for the functions are real and

$$\int \alpha(\zeta)\beta(\zeta)\mathrm{d}\zeta \equiv \sum_{\zeta=\pm 1} \alpha(\zeta)\beta(\zeta) = \alpha(1)\beta(1) + \alpha(-1)\beta(-1) = 0. \tag{5.15}$$

We must also interpret $|\alpha(\zeta)|^2$ as the probability that, in the state α, the spin coordinate has the value ζ. This is entirely consistent with the meaning we have given to the spin states, for

$$|\alpha(1)|^2 = 1 \quad \text{and} \quad |\alpha(-1)|^2 = 0,$$

which means that, in the state α, ζ is *certain* to have the value 1 — in other words, the spin momentum is certain to be in the z-direction, so that $S_z = \hbar/2$.

Finally, we wish to introduce a new notation which will prove very convenient. In the previous work we have written an orbital function $\psi(x, y, z)$ concisely as $\psi(\boldsymbol{r})$. We shall in future let the vector $\boldsymbol{x}$ stand for the four coordinates (x, y, z, ζ), so that a one-electron wave function including spin may be written $\phi(\boldsymbol{x})$ instead of $\phi(x, y, z, \zeta)$ or $\phi(\boldsymbol{r}, \zeta)$. Such a function of the positional and spin coordinates, incidentally, is often referred to as a *spin-orbital*. Similarly, we shall let $\mathrm{d}\boldsymbol{x}$ denote a volume element of configuration space including spin, so that

$$\mathrm{d}\boldsymbol{x} \equiv \mathrm{d}\boldsymbol{r}\,\mathrm{d}\zeta.$$

In this convention, then, if $f(\boldsymbol{x})$ is any function of the positional and spin coordinates, we have

$$\int f(\boldsymbol{x})\mathrm{d}\boldsymbol{x} \equiv \int f(\boldsymbol{r}, \zeta)\mathrm{d}\boldsymbol{r}\,\mathrm{d}\zeta \equiv \sum_{\zeta=\pm 1} \int f(\boldsymbol{r}, \zeta)\mathrm{d}\boldsymbol{r}. \tag{5.16}$$

As an example, we will consider the normalization of a spin orbital $\phi(\boldsymbol{x})$. Suppose that

$$\phi(\boldsymbol{x}) = \psi(\boldsymbol{r})\alpha(\zeta).$$

Then the normalizing condition

$$\int \phi^*(\boldsymbol{x})\phi(\boldsymbol{x})\mathrm{d}\boldsymbol{x} = 1$$

means, simply,

$$\sum_{\zeta=\pm 1} \int |\psi(\boldsymbol{r})|^2\,|\alpha(\zeta)|^2\,\mathrm{d}\boldsymbol{r} = 1.$$

Putting in the two values of α, we see that this equation reduces to

$$\int |\psi(\boldsymbol{r})|^2\,\mathrm{d}\boldsymbol{r} = 1.$$

Hence, if the orbital function is normalized, so is the spin-orbital — which could have been deduced immediately from the fact that the spin functions are normalized.

This completes the formal theory of electron spin as far as we shall require it in the remainder of the book.

5.4. The Pauli Principle and the Symmetry of Wave Functions

In the case of a many-electron atom it may be deduced from the experimental data that, if two electrons are in the same orbital state, they must have opposite spins. For example, an atom of helium in its ground state is found to have no magnetic moment, so that the two electrons, which are both in 1s orbitals, must have their spin magnetic moments opposed.

If the spin is included in the specification of a one-electron state, therefore, the Pauli principle may be expressed as follows:

not more than one electron may occupy any state.

This is clearly equivalent to our previous statement in terms of orbital states only. It is still incomplete, however, in that it refers to the one-electron *approximation.* Before giving a more general statement of the principle we must consider the symmetry of many-electron wave functions with respect to the electronic coordinates.

We first note that electrons are *indistinguishable.* In experiments on many-electron systems it is impossible to label the electrons. Thus, we may observe that there is a certain number of electrons in a given set of states, but we can never know *which* electron is in any particular state. This means that an observable quantity which depends upon the electronic coordinates must be *symmetric* with respect to those coordinates — in other words, any interchange of the coordinates of the electrons, including the spin coordinates, must leave the observable quantity unchanged.

Now the wave function Ψ is not itself a physically observable quantity, but $|\Psi|^2$ is. Thus, any interchange of the coordinates of two electrons must leave the value of $|\Psi|^2$ unaltered. For example, interchanging the coordinates $\boldsymbol{x}_1$ and $\boldsymbol{x}_2$, which include the spin coordinates, we must have

$$|\Psi(\boldsymbol{x}_1, \boldsymbol{x}_2, \ldots \boldsymbol{x}_N)|^2 = |\Psi(\boldsymbol{x}_2, \boldsymbol{x}_1, \ldots \boldsymbol{x}_N|^2,$$

for an N-electron system. In general, if the operator P represents any one of the $N!$ different permutations of the electronic coordinates, then

$$|\Psi(\boldsymbol{x}_1, \boldsymbol{x}_2, \ldots \boldsymbol{x}_N)|^2 = |\mathsf{P}\Psi(\boldsymbol{x}_1, \boldsymbol{x}_2, \ldots \boldsymbol{x}_N)|^2. \tag{5.17}$$

Now let us examine the implications of this for the wave function Ψ. If the operator P_{12} represents the interchange of $\boldsymbol{x}_1$ and $\boldsymbol{x}_2$, it follows from equation (5.17) that

$$\begin{aligned}\Psi(\boldsymbol{x}_2, \boldsymbol{x}_1, \ldots \boldsymbol{x}_N) &= \mathsf{P}_{12}\Psi(\mathbf{x}_1, \boldsymbol{x}_2, \ldots \boldsymbol{x}_N)\\ &= \mathrm{e}^{\mathrm{i}\gamma_{12}}\,\Psi(\boldsymbol{x}_1, \boldsymbol{x}_2, \ldots \boldsymbol{x}_N),\end{aligned} \tag{5.18}$$

where γ_{12} is a real constant to be determined. Equation (5.18) is seen to correspond with equation (5.17) if we take the moduli of both sides, for $|e^{i\gamma_{12}}| = 1$. If we apply the operator P_{12} again to equation (5.18), we find

$$\mathsf{P}_{12}\Psi(\boldsymbol{x}_2, \boldsymbol{x}_1, \ldots \boldsymbol{x}_N) = \Psi(\boldsymbol{x}_1, \boldsymbol{x}_2, \ldots \boldsymbol{x}_N)$$

$$= \mathsf{P}_{12}\mathsf{P}_{12}\Psi(\boldsymbol{x}_1, \boldsymbol{x}_2, \ldots \boldsymbol{x}_N) = e^{2i\gamma_{12}}\Psi(\boldsymbol{x}_1, \boldsymbol{x}_2, \ldots \boldsymbol{x}_N). \quad (5.19)$$

Thus,

$$e^{2i\gamma_{12}} = 1, \quad \text{or} \quad e^{i\gamma_{12}} = \pm 1,$$

so that

$$\Psi(\boldsymbol{x}_2, \boldsymbol{x}_1, \ldots \boldsymbol{x}_N) = \pm\Psi(\boldsymbol{x}_1, \boldsymbol{x}_2, \ldots \boldsymbol{x}_N), \quad (5.20)$$

and the same result holds true for the interchange of the coordinates of any pair of electrons. In other words, the function Ψ must be either *symmetric* (if it does not change sign) or *antisymmetric* (if it changes sign) with respect to the interchange of the coordinates of any pair of electrons.

It can also easily be seen that Ψ cannot be antisymmetric with respect to one pair of electrons and symmetric with respect to another pair, for this leads to inconsistency. Thus, suppose Ψ were antisymmetric with respect to $\boldsymbol{x}_1$ and $\boldsymbol{x}_2$, and symmetric with respect to $\boldsymbol{x}_2$ and $\boldsymbol{x}_3$; we should then have

$$\Psi(\boldsymbol{x}_1, \boldsymbol{x}_2, \boldsymbol{x}_3) = -\Psi(\boldsymbol{x}_2, \boldsymbol{x}_1, \boldsymbol{x}_3) = -\Psi(\boldsymbol{x}_3, \boldsymbol{x}_1, \boldsymbol{x}_2)$$

$$= \Psi(\boldsymbol{x}_3, \boldsymbol{x}_2, \boldsymbol{x}_1) = \Psi(\boldsymbol{x}_2, \boldsymbol{x}_3, \boldsymbol{x}_1) = -\Psi(\boldsymbol{x}_1, \boldsymbol{x}_3, \boldsymbol{x}_2)$$

$$= -\Psi(\boldsymbol{x}_1, \boldsymbol{x}_2, \boldsymbol{x}_3). \quad (5.21)$$

It therefore follows from the indistinguishability of electrons that Ψ must be either symmetric in all the coordinates or antisymmetric in all of them, but, in order to decide which, we must appeal to experiment. In fact, what may be regarded as the generalization of the Pauli principle simply states that

for a system of electrons, the total wave function must be antisymmetric in the electronic coordinates, including spin.

We shall show in the following section that when this antisymmetry principle is applied to the one-electron approximation it leads to the Pauli principle in the form given previously, whereas this would not be so if a symmetric total wave function were assumed. It is found that systems of protons and neutrons also must have anti-symmetric wave functions, while a system of photons, for example, must have a symmetric wave function.

5.5. Determinantal Wave Functions

Let us suppose that a set of one-electron wave functions of a system of N electrons has been obtained, by the Hartree method for instance, and that these are, with the appropriate spin functions included,

$$\phi_1(\boldsymbol{x}_1),\ \phi_2(\boldsymbol{x}_2), \ldots \phi_N(\boldsymbol{x}_N),$$

where, for example,

$$\phi_1(\boldsymbol{x}_1) = \psi_1(\boldsymbol{r}_1)\alpha(\zeta_1).$$

The only approximate total wave function we have so far considered in detail has been of the simple product type:

$$\phi_1(\boldsymbol{x}_1)\phi_2(\boldsymbol{x}_2) \ldots \phi_N(\boldsymbol{x}_N).$$

Clearly any such product, with the electronic coordinates rearranged in any order, would be equally acceptable and would give the same energy. None of these single product functions obeys the antisymmetry rule, however.

A more general function may be constructed by taking a linear combination of all such products; thus

$$\sum_{\mathsf{P}} a_{\mathsf{P}} \mathsf{P} \phi_1(\boldsymbol{x}_1)\phi_2(\boldsymbol{x}_2) \ldots \phi_N(\boldsymbol{x}_N), \tag{5.22}$$

where the a_{P} are constants and the sum is over the $N!$ permutations P of the electronic coordinates. This function is antisymmetric, as required, if all the a_{P} have the same absolute magnitude and positive or negative sign according as P is an even or an odd permutation, that is, according as P corresponds to an even or an odd number of interchanges of pairs of electrons. So long as Ψ is not required to be normalized we may take the magnitude of a_{P} to be unity, and write concisely

$$\Psi = \sum_{\mathsf{P}} (-1)^p \mathsf{P} \phi_1(\boldsymbol{x}_1)\phi_2(\boldsymbol{x}_2) \ldots \phi_N(\boldsymbol{x}_N), \tag{5.23}$$

where p is the number of interchanges in the permutation P. For example, $p = 2$ for the permutation which changes (123) into (312), for this permutation is equivalent to interchanging 1 and 2, and then 2 and 3 — or 1 and 3, and then 1 and 2.

The wave function (5.23) may be written in the determinantal form (see Appendix 3)

$$\Psi = \begin{vmatrix} \phi_1(\boldsymbol{x}_1) & \phi_1(\boldsymbol{x}_2) \dots \phi_1(\boldsymbol{x}_N) \\ \phi_2(\boldsymbol{x}_1) & \phi_2(\boldsymbol{x}_2) \dots \phi_2(\boldsymbol{x}_N) \\ \cdot & \cdot \quad \cdot \quad \cdot \quad \cdot \\ \phi_N(\boldsymbol{x}_1) & \phi_N(\boldsymbol{x}_2) \dots \phi_N(\boldsymbol{x}_N) \end{vmatrix}. \tag{5.24}$$

This makes it clear that Ψ is antisymmetric in the electronic coordinates, for if we interchange any pair, say $\boldsymbol{x}_1$ and $\boldsymbol{x}_2$, we interchange two columns of the determinant and hence change its sign. It can be proved, in fact, that this determinantal function is the *only* antisymmetric function of the form (5.22), but the proof requires group theory and we will omit it.

The Pauli principle follows immediately, for, if two of the one-electron functions ϕ_i are the same, then two rows of the determinant are the same and its value is identically zero. This is not permissible for a wave function, and so we have the fact that no two electrons may be in the same one-electron state. It is easily seen that a *symmetric* function of the form (5.22), which is obtained by letting all the a_{P} have the same magnitude and the same sign, does not lead to the Pauli principle, for if two of the one-electron functions are the same in this case the total wave function does not vanish — indeed, for those systems of particles which are described by symmetric wave functions, *all* the particles may be in the same one-particle state.

5.6. The Expectation Value of a Symmetric Operator and the Normalization of a Determinantal Wave Function

The wave function Ψ given in equation (5.24) is not normalized even when the one-electron functions ϕ_i are normalized. The normalizing constant depends upon the ϕ_i, in general, but can easily be evaluated if these functions are orthogonal as well as normalized, that is, if

$$\int \phi_i^*(\boldsymbol{x})\phi_j(\boldsymbol{x})\mathrm{d}\boldsymbol{x} = \delta_{ij}. \tag{5.25}$$

In this case, as we shall prove below, the normalizing constant is $1/\sqrt{N!}$, so that the normalized determinantal wave function is

$$\Psi = \frac{1}{\sqrt{N!}} \sum_{\mathrm{P}} (-1)^p \mathrm{P} \phi_1(\boldsymbol{x}_1)\phi_2(\boldsymbol{x}_2) \dots \phi_N(\boldsymbol{x}_N). \tag{5.26}$$

Before proving this it will be useful to present a simple theorem relating to the expectation value of a symmetric operator F, which is defined as

$$\langle F \rangle = \int \Psi^* F \Psi \, d\tau', \tag{5.27}$$

the prime on the volume element indicating that a summation over the values of the spin variables is included in the integration throughout the configuration space of the system; thus,

$$d\tau' \equiv d\boldsymbol{x}_1 \, d\boldsymbol{x}_2 \ldots d\boldsymbol{x}_N .$$

A symmetric operator is one which is symmetric in the electronic coordinates, so that $\mathsf{P}F = F$, where P is a permutation operator as previously defined — the Hamiltonian is an example of a symmetric operator. The theorem is as follows:

for a symmetric operator F and normalized determinantal wave function Ψ, we may write

$$\int \Psi^* F \Psi \, d\tau' = \sqrt{N!} \int \Psi^* F \, \phi_1(\boldsymbol{x}_1)\phi_2(\boldsymbol{x}_2) \ldots \phi_N(\boldsymbol{x}_N) d\tau'. \tag{5.28}$$

In other words, in the expression for $\langle F \rangle$ we may replace the determinant Ψ by $\sqrt{N!}$ times the product of its diagonal elements. It is assumed, of course, that the ϕ_i are orthonormal, as in (5.25). The proof is straightforward. We have, using (5.26),

$$\begin{aligned}
\int \Psi^* F \Psi \, d\tau' &= \frac{1}{\sqrt{N!}} \int \Psi^* F \sum_{\mathsf{P}} (-1)^p \mathsf{P} \phi_1(\boldsymbol{x}_1)\phi_2(\boldsymbol{x}_2) \ldots \phi_N(\boldsymbol{x}_N) d\tau' \\
&= \frac{1}{\sqrt{N!}} \sum_{\mathsf{P}} (-1)^p \mathsf{P} \int (\mathsf{P}^{-1} \Psi^*) F \phi_1(\boldsymbol{x}_1)\phi_2(\boldsymbol{x}_2) \ldots \phi_N(\boldsymbol{x}_N) d\tau' \\
&= \frac{1}{\sqrt{N!}} \sum_{\mathsf{P}} \mathsf{P} \int \Psi^* F \phi_1(\boldsymbol{x}_1)\phi_2(\boldsymbol{x}_2) \ldots \phi_N(\boldsymbol{x}_N) d\tau' \\
&= \sqrt{N!} \int \Psi^* F \phi_1(\boldsymbol{x}_1)\phi_2(\boldsymbol{x}_2) \ldots \phi_N(\boldsymbol{x}_N) d\tau'.
\end{aligned} \tag{5.29}$$

In the second line of this equation we have transferred the summation over P, and the operator P, to the left of the integral sign, and this necessitates our annulling the effect of P upon Ψ^* by introducing the operator P^{-1} (which is to operate upon Ψ^* only). The fact that P now operates upon F

is of no consequence, since $\mathsf{P}F = F$, which is the reason for specifying a symmetric operator. Now the number of interchanges in P^{-1} is just p, the same as in P, since the two operators affect the same interchanges in reverse order. Hence

$$\mathsf{P}^{-1}\Psi^* = (-1)^p \Psi^*, \tag{5.30}$$

for P^{-1} merely produces p interchanges of pairs of columns of the determinant. Since there is a factor $(-1)^p$ already present, and $(-1)^{2p} = 1$, we obtain line three of equation (5.29). Finally, we note that the value of a definite integral is independent of the symbols used for the variables of integration. Hence, the integral in line three has the same value for every permutation P, and there are $N!$ permutations in all. So we arrive at the required expression.

We shall find this theorem particularly useful when calculating the energy of a metal, in the following chapter. Meanwhile, we may use it to show very easily that the function Ψ given in (5.26) is normalized. The operator F is in this case unity, and is symmetric in the electronic coordinates, for it does not depend upon any of them. Thus,

$$\begin{aligned}\int \Psi^*\Psi \,\mathrm{d}\tau' &= \sqrt{N!}\int \Psi^* \phi_1(\boldsymbol{x}_1)\phi_2(\boldsymbol{x}_2)\ldots\phi_N(\boldsymbol{x}_N)\mathrm{d}\tau' \\ &= \int [\sum_{\mathsf{P}}(-1)^p \mathsf{P}\phi_1^*(\boldsymbol{x}_1)\ldots\phi_N^*(\boldsymbol{x}_N)]\,\phi_1(\boldsymbol{x}_1)\ldots\phi_N(\boldsymbol{x}_N)\mathrm{d}\tau' \\ &= \int |\phi_1(\boldsymbol{x}_1)|^2|\phi_2(\boldsymbol{x}_2)|^2\ldots|\phi_N(\boldsymbol{x}_N)|^2\mathrm{d}\tau' \\ &= \int |\phi_1(\boldsymbol{x}_1)|^2\mathrm{d}\boldsymbol{x}_1\ldots\int|\phi_N(\boldsymbol{x}_N)|^2\mathrm{d}\boldsymbol{x}_N = 1,\end{aligned} \tag{5.31}$$

all the other terms of Ψ^* giving zero contribution owing to the orthogonality of the ϕ_i.

5.7. The Ground State and the Excited States of the Helium Atom

As a simple example of the inclusion of electron spin and the use of a determinantal wave function, let us consider again the application of the one-electron approximation to the helium atom. It will be recalled that the Hamiltonian of this system is

$$H = -\frac{\hbar^2}{2m}(\nabla_1^2+\nabla_2^2) - \frac{2e^2}{r_1} - \frac{2e^2}{r_2} + \frac{e^2}{r_{12}}, \tag{5.32}$$

and, if the electronic interaction term e^2/r_{12} is neglected, the Schrödinger equation separates into two hydrogenic equations of the form

$$\left(-\frac{\hbar^2}{2m}\nabla^2-\frac{2e^2}{r}\right)\psi = \varepsilon\psi. \tag{5.33}$$

For simplicity, in the following work, we will choose our one-electron orbitals to be eigenfunctions of this equation, and treat the term e^2/r_{12} by first-order perturbation theory. Our procedure will therefore be similar to that of § 3.6.1, except that we will now consider excited states also and will use properly antisymmetrized wave functions. Although we have seen that first-order perturbation theory gives a reasonable result for the ground state, we have also seen that the Hartree method gives a better one, so that it would be more reasonable to use the Hartree orbitals in constructing our determinantal wave functions. Indeed, the general procedure is the same whatever type of orbitals is used, but the advantage of using the eigenfunctions of equation (5.33) is that they are orthogonal, whereas the Hartree functions are not, and this orthogonality makes it easier to normalize the total wave function. We are more concerned with demonstrating the general effects of using a determinantal wave function than with obtaining an accurate energy value.

(i) *Ground state.* In the ground state we know that both electrons occupy the same 1s orbital, whose normalized wave function $\psi(\boldsymbol{r})$ we are assuming to be the eigenfunction of equation (5.33) corresponding to its lowest eigenvalue, -4 ryd. It follows that the electrons must have opposite spins, and the two one-electron states may be written

$$\phi_1(\boldsymbol{x}) = \psi(\boldsymbol{r})\alpha(\zeta), \qquad \phi_2(\boldsymbol{x}) = \psi(\boldsymbol{r})\beta(\zeta).$$

The normalized total wave function, from equation (5.26), is thus

$$\begin{aligned}\Psi_0 &= \frac{1}{\sqrt{2}}\begin{vmatrix}\phi_1(\boldsymbol{x}_1) & \phi_1(\boldsymbol{x}_2)\\ \phi_2(\boldsymbol{x}_1) & \phi_2(\boldsymbol{x}_2)\end{vmatrix}\\ &= \frac{1}{\sqrt{2}}[\phi_1(\boldsymbol{x}_1)\phi_2(\boldsymbol{x}_2)-\phi_1(\boldsymbol{x}_2)\phi_2(\boldsymbol{x}_1)]\\ &= \frac{1}{\sqrt{2}}\psi(\boldsymbol{r}_1)\psi(\boldsymbol{r}_2)[\alpha(\zeta_1)\beta(\zeta_2)-\alpha(\zeta_2)\beta(\zeta_1)].\end{aligned} \tag{5.34}$$

The energy of the ground state, given by this wave function, is

$$\iint \Psi_0^* H \Psi_0 \,\mathrm{d}\boldsymbol{x}_1 \mathrm{d}\boldsymbol{x}_2 = \tfrac{1}{2} \sum_{\zeta_1, \zeta_2 = \pm 1} \iint \psi^*(\boldsymbol{r}_1)\psi^*(\boldsymbol{r}_2) H \psi(\boldsymbol{r}_1)\psi(\boldsymbol{r}_2) \mathrm{d}\boldsymbol{r}_1 \mathrm{d}\boldsymbol{r}_2 \times [\alpha(\zeta_1)\beta(\zeta_2) - \alpha(\zeta_2)\beta(\zeta_1)]^2$$
$$= \iint \psi^*(\boldsymbol{r}_1)\psi^*(\boldsymbol{r}_2) H \psi(\boldsymbol{r}_1)\psi(\boldsymbol{r}_2) \mathrm{d}\boldsymbol{r}_1 \mathrm{d}\boldsymbol{r}_2, \tag{5.35}$$

since the spin factor is unity when ζ_1 and ζ_2 have opposite signs, and vanishes when they have the same sign. Thus, the energy in this case is the same as that given by the simple product wave function $\psi(\boldsymbol{r}_1)\psi(\boldsymbol{r}_2)$, which was used in § 3.6.1. This is always true, even for excited states of the atom, if both electrons are in the same orbital, but it is not true for excited states in general, as we shall see.

Since the electrons must have opposite spins, states in which both electrons are in the same orbital can be described by a single determinantal wave function only, and are thus non-degenerate. When the determinant is expressed as a product of an orbital function and a spin function, as in equation (5.34), we see that the orbital part is *symmetric* in the positional coordinates, while the spin part is antisymmetric in the spin coordinates of the electrons. Non-degenerate states are known as *singlets.*

(ii) *Excited states.* Let us now consider an excited state in which the two orbitals are different, the normalized wave functions $\psi_a(\boldsymbol{r})$ and $\psi_b(\boldsymbol{r})$ being eigenfunctions of equation (5.33) corresponding to the different eigenvalues ε_a and ε_b. In this case the electrons need not have opposite spins, so that there are four possible determinantal wave functions corresponding to the four ways of associating spin functions with the orbitals. These are as follows:

$$\Psi_1 = \frac{1}{\sqrt{2}} \begin{vmatrix} \psi_a(\boldsymbol{r}_1)\alpha(\zeta_1) & \psi_a(\boldsymbol{r}_2)\alpha(\zeta_2) \\ \psi_b(\boldsymbol{r}_1)\alpha(\zeta_1) & \psi_b(\boldsymbol{r}_2)\alpha(\zeta_2) \end{vmatrix}$$
$$= \frac{1}{\sqrt{2}} [\psi_a(\boldsymbol{r}_1)\psi_b(\boldsymbol{r}_2) - \psi_a(\boldsymbol{r}_2)\psi_b(\boldsymbol{r}_1)]\alpha(\zeta_1)\alpha(\zeta_2),$$

$$\Psi_2 = \frac{1}{\sqrt{2}} \begin{vmatrix} \psi_a(\boldsymbol{r}_1)\beta(\zeta_1) & \psi_a(\boldsymbol{r}_2)\beta(\zeta_2) \\ \psi_b(\boldsymbol{r}_1)\beta(\zeta_1) & \psi_b(\boldsymbol{r}_2)\beta(\zeta_2) \end{vmatrix}$$
$$= \frac{1}{\sqrt{2}} [\psi_a(\boldsymbol{r}_1)\psi_b(\boldsymbol{r}_2) - \psi_a(\boldsymbol{r}_2)\psi_b(\boldsymbol{r}_1)]\beta(\zeta_1)\beta(\zeta_2),$$

$$\Psi_3 = \frac{1}{\sqrt{2}} \begin{vmatrix} \psi_a(\boldsymbol{r}_1)\alpha(\zeta_1) & \psi_a(\boldsymbol{r}_2)\alpha(\zeta_2) \\ \psi_b(\boldsymbol{r}_1)\beta(\zeta_1) & \psi_b(\boldsymbol{r}_2)\beta(\zeta_2) \end{vmatrix}$$

$$= \frac{1}{\sqrt{2}} [\psi_a(\boldsymbol{r}_1)\psi_b(\boldsymbol{r}_2)\alpha(\zeta_1)\beta(\zeta_2) - \psi_a(\boldsymbol{r}_2)\psi_b(\boldsymbol{r}_1)\alpha(\zeta_2)\beta(\zeta_1)],$$

$$\Psi_4 = \frac{1}{\sqrt{2}} \begin{vmatrix} \psi_a(\boldsymbol{r}_1)\beta(\zeta_1) & \psi_a(\boldsymbol{r}_2)\beta(\zeta_2) \\ \psi_b(\boldsymbol{r}_1)\alpha(\zeta_1) & \psi_b(\boldsymbol{r}_2)\alpha(\zeta_2) \end{vmatrix}$$

$$= \frac{1}{\sqrt{2}} [\psi_a(\boldsymbol{r}_1)\psi_b(\boldsymbol{r}_2)\alpha(\zeta_2)\beta(\zeta_1) - \psi_a(\boldsymbol{r}_2)\psi_b(\boldsymbol{r}_1)\alpha(\zeta_1)\beta(\zeta_2)].$$

The wave functions are all normalized, since ψ_a and ψ_b are orthonormal. When interaction between the electrons is neglected — that is, for the unperturbed system — the four wave functions are degenerate, each of them corresponding to the unperturbed energy $\varepsilon_a + \varepsilon_b$. Instead of using Ψ_3 and Ψ_4, therefore, we may construct linear combinations of them, as follows:

$$\Psi_3 + \Psi_4 = \frac{1}{\sqrt{2}} [\psi_a(\boldsymbol{r}_1)\psi_b(\boldsymbol{r}_2) - \psi_a(\boldsymbol{r}_2)\psi_b(\boldsymbol{r}_1)][\alpha(\zeta_1)\beta(\zeta_2) + \alpha(\zeta_2)\beta(\zeta_1)],$$

$$\Psi_3 - \Psi_4 = \frac{1}{\sqrt{2}} [\psi_a(\boldsymbol{r}_1)\psi_b(\boldsymbol{r}_2) + \psi_a(\boldsymbol{r}_2)\psi_b(\boldsymbol{r}_1)][\alpha(\zeta_1)\beta(\zeta_2) - \alpha(\zeta_2)\beta(\zeta_1)].$$

These functions are no longer normalized, but become so if we multiply each by a further factor $1/\sqrt{2}$, as may easily be verified. They have the advantage that the orbital and spin functions are separated, as in Ψ_1 and Ψ_2, and a further advantage which we will now discuss.

Since the unperturbed state is four-fold degenerate, the first-order perturbation energies must be obtained by setting up, and solving, the secular equation for the perturbation e^2/r_{12} or for the whole Hamiltonian H, as explained in § 3.7. Now, the fourth-order secular determinant may be constructed in terms of Ψ_1, Ψ_2, Ψ_3, and Ψ_4, and this will lead to the correct perturbed levels. If, however, we construct the secular determinant in terms of the normalized wave functions

$$\Psi_1,\ \Psi_2,\ \frac{1}{\sqrt{2}}(\Psi_3 + \Psi_4),\ \frac{1}{\sqrt{2}}(\Psi_3 - \Psi_4), \tag{5.36}$$

as is perfectly permissible, we find that the off-diagonal elements all vanish, so that the perturbed energy levels are given immediately by the equation

$$E = \int \Psi^* H \Psi \, \mathrm{d}\tau', \tag{5.37}$$

where Ψ stands for any one of the functions (5.36). That this is so may be easily understood if it is noticed that the spin factors of these functions are orthogonal, for each off-diagonal element contains the integral of the product of two of them.

The wave functions (5.36) are therefore the best linear combinations of the determinantal functions to represent approximately the perturbed states of the system. It may be seen that the function

$$\Psi_1, \ \Psi_2, \text{ and } \frac{1}{\sqrt{2}}(\Psi_3+\Psi_4),$$

all have the antisymmetric orbital factor

$$\frac{1}{\sqrt{2}}[\psi_a(\boldsymbol{r}_1)\psi_b(\boldsymbol{r}_2)-\psi_a(\boldsymbol{r}_2)\psi_b(\boldsymbol{r}_1)],$$

while the remaining function

$$\frac{1}{\sqrt{2}}(\Psi_3-\Psi_4)$$

has the symmetric orbital factor

$$\frac{1}{\sqrt{2}}[\psi_a(\boldsymbol{r}_1)\psi_b(\boldsymbol{r}_2)+\psi_a(\boldsymbol{r}_2)\psi_b(\boldsymbol{r}_1)].$$

On the other hand, the spin factors of the first three functions are symmetric in the spin coordinates, while the spin factor of the last function is antisymmetric, so that the four wave functions are antisymmetric in *all* the electronic coordinates, as required.

Now, the normalized spin factors do not affect the energy values given by equation (5.37) — for example,

$$\begin{aligned}\int \Psi_1^* H \Psi_1 \,\mathrm{d}\tau' &= \tfrac{1}{2} \sum_{\zeta_1, \zeta_2 = \pm 1} \iint [\psi_a^*(\boldsymbol{r}_1)\psi_b^*(\boldsymbol{r}_2)-\psi_a^*(\boldsymbol{r}_2)\psi_b^*(\boldsymbol{r}_1)] \\ &\qquad \times H[\psi_a(\boldsymbol{r}_1)\psi_b(\boldsymbol{r}_2)-\psi_a(\boldsymbol{r}_2)\psi_b(\boldsymbol{r}_1)]|\alpha(\zeta_1)|^2|\alpha(\zeta_2)|^2 \,\mathrm{d}\boldsymbol{r}_1\,\mathrm{d}\boldsymbol{r}_2 \\ &= \tfrac{1}{2}\iint [\psi_a^*(\boldsymbol{r}_1)\psi_b^*(\boldsymbol{r}_2)-\psi_a^*(\boldsymbol{r}_2)\psi_b^*(\boldsymbol{r}_1)] \\ &\qquad \times H[\psi_a(\boldsymbol{r}_1)\psi_b(\boldsymbol{r}_2)-\psi_a(\boldsymbol{r}_2)\psi_b(\boldsymbol{r}_1)]\,\mathrm{d}\boldsymbol{r}_1\,\mathrm{d}\boldsymbol{r}_2.\end{aligned}$$

Thus, there are only two perturbed energy levels, corresponding to the symmetric and antisymmetric orbital functions respectively:

$$\begin{aligned}E = \tfrac{1}{2}\iint &[\psi_a^*(\boldsymbol{r}_1)\psi_b^*(\boldsymbol{r}_2)\pm\psi_a^*(\boldsymbol{r}_2)\psi_b^*(\boldsymbol{r}_1)] \\ &\times H[\psi_a(\boldsymbol{r}_1)\psi_b(\boldsymbol{r}_2)\pm\psi_a(\boldsymbol{r}_2)\psi_b(\boldsymbol{r}_1)]\,\mathrm{d}\boldsymbol{r}_1\,\mathrm{d}\boldsymbol{r}_2. \qquad (5.38)\end{aligned}$$

Using equation (5.32) and remembering that ψ_a and ψ_b are the orthonormal eigenfunctions of equation (5.33), with eigenvalues ε_a and ε_b, we find

$$E = \varepsilon_a+\varepsilon_b+\frac{1}{2}\iint\frac{e^2}{r_{12}}\,[|\psi_a(\boldsymbol{r}_1)|^2\,|\psi_b(\boldsymbol{r}_2)|^2+|\psi_a(\boldsymbol{r}_2)|^2\,|\psi_b(\boldsymbol{r}_1)|^2$$

$$\pm\{\psi_a^*(\boldsymbol{r}_1)\psi_b^*(\boldsymbol{r}_2)\psi_a(\boldsymbol{r}_2)\psi_b(\boldsymbol{r}_1)+\psi_a(\boldsymbol{r}_1)\psi_b(\boldsymbol{r}_2)\psi_a^*(\boldsymbol{r}_2)\psi_b^*(\boldsymbol{r}_1)\}]\,\mathrm{d}\boldsymbol{r}_1\,\mathrm{d}\boldsymbol{r}_2. \quad (5.39)$$

The contributions to the integral from the first two terms in the square brackets are equal, and also the contributions from the two terms in the curly brackets are equal, for the terms of each pair have the same form — they differ only by the interchange of $\boldsymbol{r}_1$ and $\boldsymbol{r}_2$, and this does not affect the value of the double integral. Hence,

$$E = \varepsilon_a+\varepsilon_b+C\pm J, \quad (5.40)$$

where

$$C = \iint\frac{e^2}{r_{12}}\,|\psi_a(\boldsymbol{r}_1)|^2\,|\psi_b(\boldsymbol{r}_2)|^2\,\mathrm{d}\boldsymbol{r}_1\,\mathrm{d}\boldsymbol{r}_2, \quad (5.41)$$

and

$$J = \iint\frac{e^2}{r_{12}}\,\psi_a^*(\boldsymbol{r}_1)\psi_b^*(\boldsymbol{r}_2)\psi_a(\boldsymbol{r}_2)\psi_b(\boldsymbol{r}_1)\,\mathrm{d}\boldsymbol{r}_1\,\mathrm{d}\boldsymbol{r}_2. \quad (5.42)$$

The interpretation of C is straightforward: it is the energy due to the Coulomb interaction between the charge clouds of the electrons. This term would occur even if a simple product type of wave function were used. The integral J, however, appears only because an antisymmetric total wave function has been used. This antisymmetry ensures that the total charge density remains unchanged when the two electrons are exchanged, and J is called the *exchange integral*, the last term in (5.40) being the *exchange energy*.

The integrand of C is always positive, so that the integral is positive. The integrand of J will in general be positive for some values of $\boldsymbol{r}_1$ and $\boldsymbol{r}_2$ and negative for others. None the less, the integral J is positive, as may roughly be understood in the following way.† When $\boldsymbol{r}_1$ and $\boldsymbol{r}_2$ are very nearly the same the integrand of J has almost the same value as that of C, which is then very large and positive owing to the small value of r_{12}. On the other hand, if the integrand of J is negative, either $\psi_a(\boldsymbol{r}_1)$ and $\psi_a(\boldsymbol{r}_2)$ or $\psi_b(\boldsymbol{r}_1)$ and $\psi_b(\boldsymbol{r}_2)$ must have opposite signs, which implies that $\boldsymbol{r}_1$ and

† We assume, for simplicity, that the wave functions are real.

$\boldsymbol{r}_2$ are in general quite different in this case, so that r_{12} is large and the integrand is small. The contributions to the integral from regions where the integrand is positive thus outweigh those from regions where the integrand is negative, making the integral positive.

The *lower* energy level is, therefore,

$$E_t = \varepsilon_a + \varepsilon_b + C - J. \tag{5.43}$$

and is triply degenerate — it is called a *triplet*. The three wave functions, all having the same antisymmetric orbital factor, are

$$\frac{1}{\sqrt{2}}[\psi_a(\boldsymbol{r}_1)\psi_b(\boldsymbol{r}_2) - \psi_a(\boldsymbol{r}_1)\psi_b(\boldsymbol{r}_2)]\begin{Bmatrix} \alpha(\zeta_1)\alpha(\zeta_2) \\ \beta(\zeta_1)\beta(\zeta_2) \\ \frac{1}{\sqrt{2}}[\alpha(\zeta_1)\beta(\zeta_2)+\alpha(\zeta_2)\beta(\zeta_1)] \end{Bmatrix}, \tag{5.44}$$

the orbital and spin factors being separately normalized. These three states are, of course, degenerate only if there is no external magnetic field — we are consistently neglecting spin-orbit coupling. In the first state both electrons have positive spins, in the second both have negative spins, and the third is a linear combination of states in which the spins of the electrons are opposed, the corresponding values of the *total* z-component of the spin momentum being $\hbar$, $-\hbar$, 0. In other words, if a magnetic field H is switched on in the positive z-direction, the energies of the three states will be increased by $2\mu_B H$, $-2\mu_B H$ and 0, respectively, so that the degeneracy will be removed.

The *higher* energy level,

$$E_s = \varepsilon_a + \varepsilon_b + C + J, \tag{5.45}$$

is non-degenerate, and is therefore a *singlet*, as is the ground state. The wave function

$$\frac{1}{\sqrt{2}}[\psi_a(\boldsymbol{r}_1)\psi_b(\boldsymbol{r}_2) + \psi_a(\boldsymbol{r}_2)\psi_b(\boldsymbol{r}_1)]\frac{1}{\sqrt{2}}[\alpha(\zeta_1)\beta(\zeta_2) - \alpha(\zeta_2)\beta(\zeta_1)] \tag{5.46}$$

has a symmetric orbital factor. The spins of the electrons are opposed, so that the total z-component of the spin momentum is zero, and the energy of the singlet state is unchanged in a magnetic field.

It must be realized that ψ_a and ψ_b are eigenfunctions of a hydrogenic equation, and all eigenvalues ε_a, ε_b are degenerate, except the lowest. For any unperturbed level $\varepsilon_a + \varepsilon_b$, therefore, apart from the ground level, there will be a larger number of determinantal wave functions than we have considered — we have only dealt with the possibilities arising from a particular choice of ψ_a and ψ_b. This is sufficient for our purpose, which was not to obtain all the energy levels of helium, but merely to give an example of the use of determinantal wave functions. When we come to calculate the energy of a metal we shall consider only the ground state, which is non-degenerate, so that there will be just one determinantal wave function to contend with.

5.8. The Hydrogen Molecule

The only examples we have considered so far have been systems containing a single centre of force — the nucleus — apart from the interactions among the electrons themselves. Before going on to consider metallic systems, which contain very many atoms, it will be instructive to consider a simpler example, the hydrogen molecule, which consists of two protons and two electrons. It is not our intention, however, to give anything like a full account of the theory of molecular structure, of which there is a considerable literature. Admittedly, a metal may be regarded as a large molecule, but many of the methods which are applicable to small molecules are not appropriate to metals, and it would be merely confusing to describe them. None the less, the hydrogen molecule provides a simple illustration of the use of two different kinds of approximate orbitals, both of which are encountered in the theory of metals.

In our treatment of a free atom we have assumed as a good approximation that the nucleus is at rest, but in a molecule the motion of the nuclei relative to one another gives rise to important effects which cannot be neglected. Fortunately, again owing to their much greater mass, the nuclei move very slowly compared with the electrons, and, as shown originally by Born and Oppenheimer, this makes it possible to deal with the electronic and nuclear motions separately. In our present case, we may solve the Schrödinger equation for the hydrogen molecule on the assumption that the protons are fixed at a distance R from each other, and so obtain the energy E, which does not include the kinetic energy of the protons, as a function of R. This energy $E(R)$ may then be used as the potential energy function in a Schrödinger equation for the nuclear motion only. We will, however, confine ourselves to describing the calculation of $E(R)$.

If we assume that the protons are fixed at a distance R apart, and label the protons A, B and the electrons 1, 2, the Hamiltonian operator is

$$H = -\frac{\hbar^2}{2m}(\nabla_1^2+\nabla_2^2)-e^2\left(\frac{1}{r_{A1}}+\frac{1}{r_{A2}}+\frac{1}{r_{B1}}+\frac{1}{r_{B2}}-\frac{1}{r_{12}}-\frac{1}{R}\right). \quad (5.47)$$

the distance r_{A1}, r_{B1}, etc., being those shown in Figure 5.2.

(i) *Atomic orbitals.* Let us first consider the case in which the internuclear distance R is very large, when the ground state of the system is that of two normal hydrogen atoms. The one-electron wave functions will then be hydrogen atom functions centred on the two protons, so that in the ground state they will both be 1s functions of the form e^{-r/a_0}, where r is the distance from the appropriate nucleus and a_0 is the Bohr radius. Thus, if we denote the two functions by ψ_A and ψ_B, and the position vectors of the two electrons with respect to some origin by $\boldsymbol{r}_1$ and $\boldsymbol{r}_2$, we have

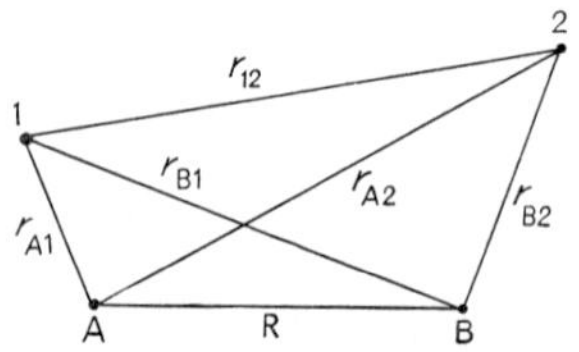

Fig. 5.2. The hydrogen molecule.

$$\psi_A(\boldsymbol{r}_1) = e^{-r_{A1}/a_0}, \qquad \psi_A(\boldsymbol{r}_2) = e^{-r_{A2}/a_0}$$
$$\psi_B(\boldsymbol{r}_1) = e^{-r_{B1}/a_0}, \qquad \psi_B(\boldsymbol{r}_2) = e^{-r_{B2}/a_0},$$

These functions are not normalized, of course.

The total wave function of the system may then be one of four determinants of the type

$$\begin{vmatrix} \psi_A(\boldsymbol{r}_1)\chi_A(\zeta_1) & \psi_A(\boldsymbol{r}_2)\chi_A(\zeta_2) \\ \psi_B(\boldsymbol{r}_1)\chi_B(\zeta_1) & \psi_B(\boldsymbol{r}_2)\chi_B(\zeta_2) \end{vmatrix},$$

where the spin functions χ_A, χ_B can be either α or β. These functions are of the same form as those we obtained for the excited state of the helium atom. Also, if the hydrogen atoms are so far apart that the interaction between them is negligible, the four functions are degenerate, so that we may combine them linearly, again as for the helium atom, to obtain three functions which have the antisymmetric orbital factor

$$\Psi_- = \psi_A(\boldsymbol{r}_1)\psi_B(\boldsymbol{r}_2) - \psi_A(\boldsymbol{r}_2)\psi_B(\boldsymbol{r}_1),$$

and one which has the symmetric orbital factor

$$\Psi_+ = \psi_A(\boldsymbol{r}_1)\psi_B(\boldsymbol{r}_2) + \psi_A(\boldsymbol{r}_2)\psi_B(\boldsymbol{r}_1).$$

The spin factors are such as to make the complete wave function antisymmetric in each case — they are given in equations (5.44) and (5.46).

Of course, when R is so large that there is virtually no interaction between the two atoms, the calculation of the total energy presents no difficulty — it is just twice the ground state energy of the hydrogen atom. However, these same wave functions Ψ_+ and Ψ_- may be used as a first approximation in calculating the energy for small values of R, when the interactions of the electrons with each other and with both nuclei have to be taken into account. This is known as the *Heitler-London method*, or the method of *atomic* or *localized orbitals*.

Ψ_+ and Ψ_- now correspond to different energies, and these may be calculated in the usual way by means of the formula

$$E_\pm = \frac{\int \Psi_\pm H \Psi_\pm \,\mathrm{d}\tau}{\int \Psi_\pm^2 \,\mathrm{d}\tau}. \tag{5.48}$$

It should be noted that the functions ψ_A and ψ_B are not orthogonal, so that the normalizing constant, which has not been included in Ψ_+ and Ψ_-, is not just $1/\sqrt{2}$, as for helium, even when ψ_A and ψ_B are normalized, but is a function of the internuclear distance R. Equation (5.48) is, of course, correct whether the wave functions are normalized or not.

Using the fact that both ψ_A and ψ_B satisfy equations of the type

$$\left(-\frac{\hbar^2}{2m}\nabla_1^2 - \frac{e^2}{r_{A1}}\right)\psi_A(\boldsymbol{r}_1) = \varepsilon\psi_A(\boldsymbol{r}_1),$$

where ε is the ground state energy of a hydrogen atom, it is found after some manipulation that

$$E_\pm = 2\varepsilon + \frac{e^2}{R} + \frac{E_{11} \pm E_{12}}{S_{11}^2 \pm S_{12}^2}, \tag{5.49}$$

where

$$S_{11} = \int \psi_A^2(\boldsymbol{r}_1)\mathrm{d}\boldsymbol{r}_1 = \int \psi_B^2(\boldsymbol{r}_1)\mathrm{d}\boldsymbol{r}_1,$$

$$S_{12} = \int \psi_A(\boldsymbol{r}_1)\psi_B(\boldsymbol{r}_1)\mathrm{d}\boldsymbol{r}_1,$$

$$E_{11} = e^2 \iint \psi_A^2(\boldsymbol{r}_1)\psi_B^2(\boldsymbol{r}_2)\left(\frac{1}{r_{12}} - \frac{1}{r_{A2}} - \frac{1}{r_{B1}}\right)\mathrm{d}\boldsymbol{r}_1\,\mathrm{d}\boldsymbol{r}_2,$$

$$E_{12} = e^2 \iint \psi_A(\boldsymbol{r}_1)\psi_A(\boldsymbol{r}_2)\psi_B(\boldsymbol{r}_1)\psi_B(\boldsymbol{r}_2)\left(\frac{1}{r_{12}} - \frac{1}{r_{A2}} - \frac{1}{r_{B1}}\right)\mathrm{d}\boldsymbol{r}_1\,\mathrm{d}\boldsymbol{r}_2.$$

All these integrals may be evaluated with a little difficulty, and the resulting energy is shown as a function of R in Figure 5.3. We see that only $E_+(R)$, the energy of the symmetric state Ψ_+, has a minimum, so that only this state gives rise to a stable molecule. In the antisymmetric state Ψ_- the hydrogen atoms repel each other at all distances. If we consider the spin functions which correspond to these orbital functions, as we did for the helium atom, we deduce that, if the electrons in two hydrogen atoms have parallel spins, the atoms will repel each other, whereas, if the spins are antiparallel (opposite), the atoms will attract each other and form a stable molecule. The *binding energy* of the molecule, which is the depth of the minimum of E_+ below the energy of two free hydrogen atoms, is given by this method as 3.14 eV, compared with the experimental value 4.72 eV. The equilibrium internuclear distance is found to be 0.87 Å, compared with the experimental value 0.74 Å.

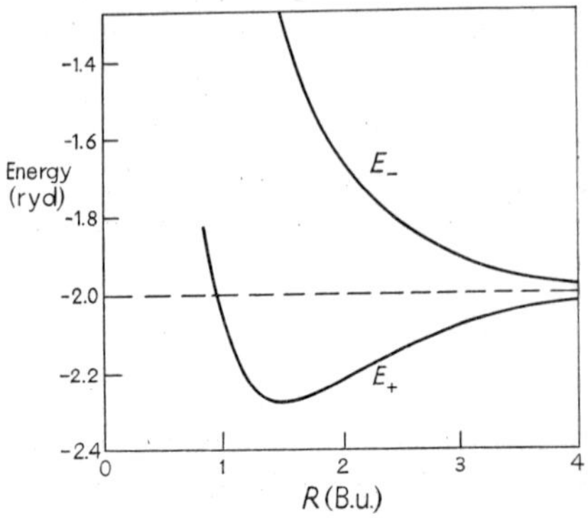

Fig. 5.3. Energy curves for the hydrogen molecule (Heitler-London method).

(ii) *Molecular orbitals.* Although the Heitler-London method is certainly correct at very large internuclear distances, it is equally certainly not correct at small internuclear distances, when the atomic wave functions centred on the two nuclei overlap considerably. An alternative method, which suggests itself in the latter circumstances, is to calculate the one-electron orbitals on the assumption that each electron is shared equally by both nuclei. That is to say, in the ground state, both electrons will occupy the *same* orbital but with opposite spins, as in the ground state of the helium atom, and this orbital, instead of being centred on a particular nucleus, will extend symmetrically around both (see Figure 5.4). Such orbitals are called *molecular orbitals* or *extended orbitals* or, in the electron theory of metals, *Bloch orbitals.*

In principle, molecular orbitals may be calculated by the Hartree method. Each electron, in the present case, would be assumed to move in the field due to the nuclei and the average charge distribution of the other electron, and the procedure would be as described for the helium atom in § 4.4. In practice, however, self-consistent field calculations are very difficult for molecules, owing to the lack of spherical symmetry of the potential function, so that generally approximate methods are used to construct molecular orbitals. The simplest approximate method is that known as the method of Linear Combinations of Atomic Orbitals, or LCAO, which we will now describe.

In the immediate vicinity of each nucleus we should expect the molecular orbital to be not very different from what it would be if the nuclei were completely isolated from each other. In other words, in the vicinity of each nucleus, we should expect the molecular orbital to resemble an atomic orbital of the type discussed above. This suggests that we might obtain reasonable approximations to molecular orbitals by adding atomic orbitals centred on the different nuclei, with appropriate numerical coefficients — that is, by taking linear combinations of atomic orbitals. The numerical coefficients may be chosen by the variational method, as described in § 3.4. For the ground state of the hydrogen molecule, however, considerations of symmetry permit only two possible molecular orbitals, which we will denote by ψ_s and ψ_a; thus,

$$\psi_s(\boldsymbol{r}) = \psi_A(\boldsymbol{r})+\psi_B(\boldsymbol{r}),$$
$$\psi_a(\boldsymbol{r}) = \psi_A(\boldsymbol{r})-\psi_B(\boldsymbol{r}),$$

where $\boldsymbol{r}$ can be either $\boldsymbol{r}_1$ or $\boldsymbol{r}_2$ — we assume that *both* electrons occupy the same orbital.

Graphs of the functions ψ_A, ψ_B, ψ_s and ψ_a along a line through the nuclei are shown in Figure 5.4. The function ψ_s has no nodal surfaces, but ψ_a has a nodal plane through the mid-point of AB. We therefore expect ψ_s to correspond to the lower energy. Not only is this borne out by calculation, but it is found, in addition, that ψ_a does not even correspond to a stable molecule. We therefore reject ψ_a and accept ψ_s as the correct molecular orbital within the LCAO approximation. Since both electrons occupy ψ_s, with opposite spins, the orbital part of the total wave function is simply

$$\Psi = \psi_s(\boldsymbol{r}_1)\psi_s(\boldsymbol{r}_2) = [\psi_A(\boldsymbol{r}_1)+\psi_B(\boldsymbol{r}_1)][\psi_A(\boldsymbol{r}_2)+\psi_B(\boldsymbol{r}_2)]. \qquad (5.50)$$

This must, of course, be multiplied by an antisymmetric spin factor, just as in the ground state wave function of the helium atom given in equation (5.34).

The function Ψ is not normalized, but, as before, the energy is given by

$$E = \frac{\int \Psi H \Psi \, d\tau}{\int \Psi^2 \, d\tau}. \qquad (5.51)$$

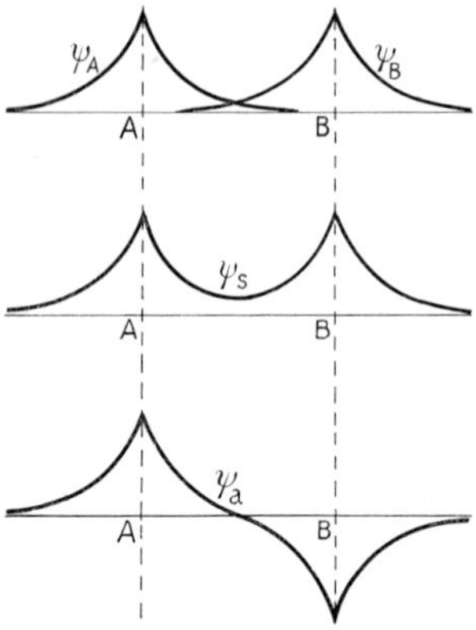

Fig. 5.4. Wave functions for the hydrogen molecule, along a line through the nuclei A, B. ψ_s and ψ_a are molecular orbitals obtained by taking symmetric and antisymmetric linear combinations, respectively, of the Heitler-London functions ψ_A and ψ_B.

We will not give details of the evaluation of E as a function of R, but merely state the results relating to its minimum value. The binding energy is found to be 2.68 eV, compared with the experimental value 4.72 eV, and the equilibrium internuclear distance is found to be 0.85 Å, compared with the experimental value 0.74 Å. The binding energy given by the LCAO method thus compares unfavourably in the present case with that given by the Heitler-London method, which was 3.14 eV. However, the calculated binding energy can be considerably improved by using molecular orbitals better than those constructed by LCAO — the best value is 3.60 eV.

It should be emphasized that the molecular orbital method is quite wrong at large internuclear distances. This may be seen by comparing the function Ψ with the Heitler-London function Ψ_+, which gives correct results at large internuclear distances. From equation (5.50) we obtain

$$\Psi = \psi_A(\boldsymbol{r}_1)\psi_B(\boldsymbol{r}_2)+\psi_A(\boldsymbol{r}_2)\psi_B(\boldsymbol{r}_1)+\psi_A(\boldsymbol{r}_1)\psi_A(\boldsymbol{r}_2)+\psi_B(\boldsymbol{r}_1)\psi_B(\boldsymbol{r}_2),$$

whereas

$$\Psi_+ = \psi_A(\boldsymbol{r}_1)\psi_B(\boldsymbol{r}_2)+\psi_A(\boldsymbol{r}_2)\psi_B(\boldsymbol{r}_1).$$

The functions differ in that Ψ contains two additional terms, $\psi_A(\boldsymbol{r}_1)\psi_A(\boldsymbol{r}_2)$ and $\psi_B(\boldsymbol{r}_1)\psi_B(\boldsymbol{r}_2)$, which represent states in which *both* electrons are on the same nucleus. We know, however, that the ground state at large internuclear distances is that in which *one* electron is on each nucleus, so it is clear that Ψ will not give the correct energy.

At very small internuclear distances, on the other hand, the molecular orbital method is superior. This is clear from the results quoted above, but may be seen without detailed calculation. If we take the extreme limiting case when R becomes zero and the two nuclei unite, then as far as the electronic wave functions are concerned we simply have a helium atom.

The Heitler-London method, however, will still give the one-electron functions as *hydrogen* atom functions, whereas the molecular orbital method (although not the LCAO approximation) will give the proper helium atom functions.

It should be pointed out that the Heitler-London method can itself be improved — for example, by using orbitals of the atomic type which are not hydrogen atom functions but, let us say, of the form e^{-cr}, the parameter c being calculated as a function of R by the variational method. In this way results can be obtained which are slightly better than those given by the best molecular orbital calculation. Of course, both the Heitler-London method and the method of molecular orbitals can be used as the basis of perturbation calculations in order to improve the results still further. In general, one cannot say that either method is *correct*, but one or the other will give better results in given circumstances and will be the more *convenient* as a basis for more accurate calculations. In dealing with metals it is found that molecular orbitals are more convenient, and we shall use these exclusively in the following work — in Chapter 8 we shall again meet the LCAO approximation, which is known in the theory of metals as the *approximation of tight binding*.

The difference between the Heitler-London and molecular orbital methods lies in their different treatments of *correlation* between the motions of the electrons, a topic already mentioned in § 4.4 in connection with the Hartree method and one which will occupy us a good deal later in the book. The Heitler-London method includes a large degree of correlation in that the electrons are kept apart on separate nuclei, whereas in the molecular orbital method, as will be seen in the following chapter, the only correlation which appears is due to the Pauli principle, and this does not affect the energy of the hydrogen molecule since there are only two electrons and they may therefore occupy the same orbital, provided they have opposite spins. The reason why both methods give rather inaccurate results is because neither takes proper account of correlation.

In conclusion, it must be remarked that, owing to the relative simplicity of the hydrogen molecule, it has been found possible to apply the variational method directly, with analytical trial functions, of great complexity, which include the effects of correlation, and results have been obtained which agree almost exactly with experiment. This method is not applicable to more complicated systems, however, which is why we have concentrated on the approximate methods described above.

CHAPTER 6

METALLIC COHESION AND THE HARTREE-FOCK METHOD

6.1. The Cohesive Energy of a Metal

Solid metals have a crystalline structure. That is to say, the nuclei of the atoms which constitute a metal are arranged on a *space lattice* or *crystal lattice* — in other words, they are arranged in a regular spatial pattern which repeats itself throughout the volume of the metal. As a matter of fact, a lump of metal of macroscopic dimensions generally consists of a mass of tiny crystals tightly packed together, or at least has irregularities in its crystal structure. The mechanical properties of metals, from an engineering point of view, depend strongly upon these crystal imperfections, but for most theoretical purposes they are not important and it is sufficient to consider a metal as a perfect crystal. We shall describe the most important crystal structures of metals in Chapter 8.

Of course, metals are not the only crystalline solids. Indeed, we may say that all true solids are crystalline — so-called *amorphous*, or non-crystalline, solids, such as glasses, are more properly regarded as highly viscous liquids. The structure of non-metallic solids, however, particularly when more than one kind of atoms are present, may be more complicated than those of metals. The discussion of the present chapter can be applied, with slight modifications, to all solids. The true distinction between metals and other solids will appear later.

The nuclei are never static, even at the absolute zero of temperature, but undergo a vibrational motion. Owing to the relatively large masses of the nuclei, however, this vibrational motion is very slight, and as far as energy calculations go, particularly at low temperatures, it can generally be neglected. Only in a very accurate calculation of the energy of a light metal, such as lithium, is the vibrational energy of the nuclei of any significance. In all our future work, except where otherwise stated, we will assume that the temperature is absolute zero, and will ignore the *zero-point* vibrations of the nuclei.

The first step in calculating the energy of a metal is to set up the Hamiltonian operator for the system of nuclei and electrons, just as we have done for single atoms. This time, however, we have a large number of atoms — about 10^{23} per cubic centimetre. Let us say that the metal is composed of N atoms, each with Z electrons, so that there are ZN electrons, each with charge $-e$, and N nuclei, each with charge Ze.

As before we will neglect magnetic interactions, as they are of a very much smaller order of magnitude than the electrostatic interactions. The Hamiltonian operator is then

$$\mathscr{H} = -\sum_{i=1}^{ZN} \frac{\hbar^2}{2m} \nabla_i^2 - \sum_{i=1}^{ZN} \sum_{a=1}^{N} \frac{Ze^2}{|\boldsymbol{R}_a - \boldsymbol{r}_i|} + \tfrac{1}{2} \sum_{i \neq j}^{ZN} \sum^{ZN} \frac{e^2}{|\boldsymbol{r}_i - \boldsymbol{r}_j|} + \tfrac{1}{2} \sum_{a \neq b}^{N} \sum^{N} \frac{Z^2 e^2}{|\boldsymbol{R}_a - \boldsymbol{R}_b|}, \tag{6.1}$$

where $\boldsymbol{r}_i$ is the position vector of electron i, and $\boldsymbol{R}_a$ is that of nucleus a. The first term represents the kinetic energy of the electrons; the second is the potential energy of the electrons in the field of the nuclei; the third is the potential energy due to the Coulomb interaction of the electrons; and the last term is the potential energy due to the Coulomb interaction of the nuclei.

Although we shall be specifically concerned with metals, this basic Hamiltonian is, in fact, the same for all solids containing only one kind of atoms, and is only slightly more complicated if several kinds of atoms are present. No particular metallic properties have so far been required, although we assume that the crystal structure of the metal we are dealing with has already been incorporated in the positioning of the nuclei. The ideal procedure would be, of course, to assume random positions for the nuclei at first and then show that the minimum ground state energy is obtained when they are arranged on the correct crystal lattice. However, different lattice structures have very similar energies, so that, in view of the somewhat crude approximations which have to be made, such a calculation is at present hardly feasible.

We shall mainly be interested in the ground state energy, which is simply the lowest eigenvalue of the Schrödinger equation

$$\mathscr{H}\Psi = E\Psi. \tag{6.2}$$

The Hamiltonian $\mathscr{H}$ depends upon the internuclear distance, and consequently so do E and Ψ. However, if the internuclear distance is fixed, then Ψ may in principle be determined as a function of the electronic coordinates, both space and spin, and the corresponding energy found A different internuclear distance may now be chosen and the calculation repeated, and so on. In this way we can obtain the energy of the solid as a function of internuclear distance. The equilibrium internuclear distance will then clearly be that which gives the minimum ground state energy.

Perhaps it should be mentioned that here the zero of energy is taken to be that of the nuclei and electrons when widely dispersed and at rest, so that their kinetic energy is zero and their interactions negligible. The zero of energy is arbitrary, however, and later we shall choose a more convenient one.

We have remarked that a cubic centimetre of metal contains something like 10^{23} nuclei and Z times this number of electrons, so it is quite clear that the Schrödinger equation cannot be solved directly, and, not only this, but even a simple approximate method like that of Hartree, which is so successful in the case of isolated atoms, cannot be applied directly. None the less, although drastic approximations must be made, certain simplifying features of the electronic wave functions in a metal, which are not present in isolated atoms and molecules, sometimes permit quite accurate numerical results to be obtained.

We have been speaking so far of the *total* energy of the electrons and nuclei in the metal, but, in fact, we are usually not interested in this, but only in the amount by which it differs from the energy of a system of free atoms. This difference is called the *cohesive energy* of the solid, because it is a measure of the strength of the forces which bind the atoms together in the solid state — a stable solid exists only because its energy is *lower* than that of a system of free atoms at the same temperature. We will define the cohesive energy formally as follows:

the cohesive energy of a metal is the energy required to dissociate a given mass of the solid metal, at the absolute zero of temperature, into free atoms. In other words, it is the amount of heat which must be supplied to the metal, initially at 0°K, in order to vaporize it. If the effect of the surface of the metal is neglected, as it may be for most theoretical purposes, the energy is proportional to the number of atoms present. A convenient unit of mass to use is thus the gram-atomic weight or, what is the same thing for a metal, the gram-molecular weight, or mole, and cohesive energies are often quoted in kilo-calories per mole. It is sometimes more convenient to express the cohesive energy in electron-volts or rydbergs per atom, however.

If we are only interested in the cohesive energy, it is possible to recast the Hamiltonian (6.1) in a slightly simpler form, which takes into account the fact that some of the electrons have practically the same energy in the metal as they have in a free atom.

6.1.1. REFORMULATION OF THE HAMILTONIAN

We will now specifically consider a monovalent metal, although the general analysis is no more complicated for a metal of any valency. The

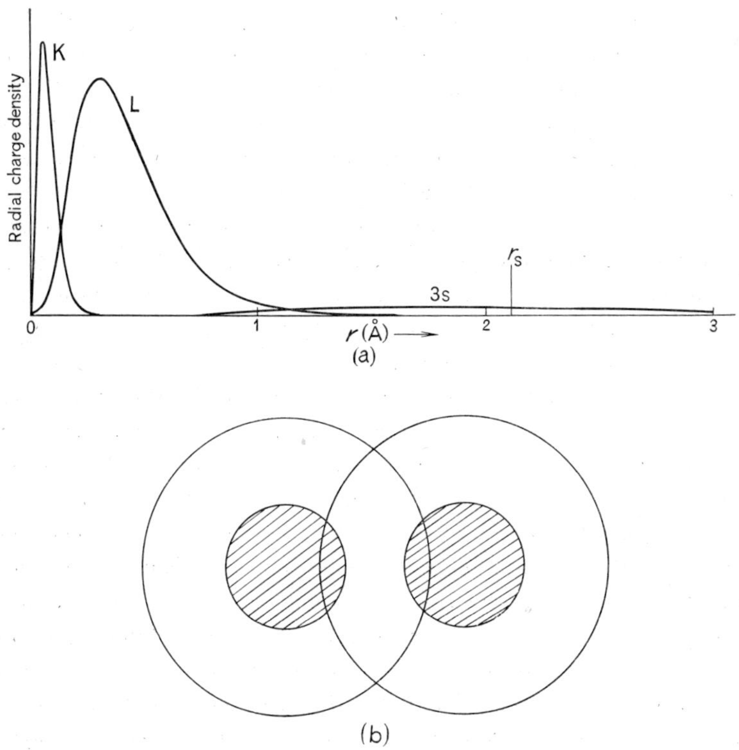

Fig. 6.1. (a) Radial charge densities of the K and L shells and of the 3s electron in a free atom of sodium. (b) Schematic representation of the charge clouds of the ion-cores (shaded circles) and of the valence electrons of two sodium atoms whose internuclear distance (3.67 Å) is that of nearest neighbouring atoms in the solid metal.

ideal metal from our point of view is *sodium*, for reasons which will become apparent — it is by no means an ideal metal from an experimental point of view.

The ground state configuration of a normal sodium atom is $(1s)^2(2s)^2(2p)^6(3s)$ — that is, one 3s electron and closed K and L shells. The Hartree method has been applied to a sodium atom, and the radial charge densities in the various shells are found to be as shown in Figure 6.1(a). The radial charge density of a given shell is defined as $4\pi r^2 \rho(r)$, where $\rho(r)$ is the total charge density of the electrons in the shell at a point distant r from the nucleus — the integral of the radial charge density with respect to r, from $r = 0$ to infinity, is thus the total charge in the shell.

The K and L shells are confined almost entirely within a radius of 1 Å from the nucleus, whereas the effective radius of the charge cloud of the 3s electron is several ångströms — of course, in principle, all charge clouds extend to infinity. The chemical properties of sodium depend mainly upon the 3s electron, which is called the *valence electron*. In general, for any metal, the valence electrons may be thought of loosely as those whose charge clouds are most widespread in a free atom. They are also known as *conduction electrons* because they are largely responsible for the electrical conductivity of the solid metal. The nucleus and all the electrons except the valence electrons are together referred to as the *ion-core* of the atom.

Figure 6.1(b) shows schematically the charge clouds of two sodium atoms whose internuclear distance (3.67 Å) is equal to that of nearest neighbouring atoms in the solid metal. We see that the shaded circles, which represent the ion-cores, are well separated, whereas the large circles, which represent the valence electron distributions, overlap considerably. It is therefore reasonable to suppose that, when a cloud of free atoms condenses to form a solid, the K and L shells do not alter significantly, but that the wave functions of the valence electrons undergo a great change. In fact, the atomic wave functions of the 3s electrons on neighbouring atoms of the solid overlap so much that it is no longer appropriate to regard a valence electron as being associated with a particular atom, but its wave function must extend throughout the metal, and it must be associated equally with all the atoms. A metal may, in fact, be regarded as a lattice of ion-cores, together with a *gas* of valence electrons which may move more or less freely through the lattice.

A useful quantity to bear in mind when considering the possible overlap of the ion-cores in the metal is the so-called *atomic radius* r_s. This is defined by

$$\frac{4\pi}{3} r_s^3 = \frac{v}{N}, \tag{6.3}$$

where v is the volume of the metal. In other words, it is the radius of a sphere whose volume is the mean volume per atom. If the effective radius of the ion-core is small compared with r_s, we may assume that the ion-core of an atom is virtually unchanged in the solid state. This is more or less true of the alkali metals, the alkaline earth metals, and aluminium. It is not true, for example, of copper — in this metal the 3d sub-shells of neighbouring ion-cores overlap significantly, and this must be taken into account in cohesive energy calculations. The atomic radius of sodium is 2.1 Å, as shown in Figure 6.1(a) — it is twice as great as the effective radius of the ion-core.

The cohesion of metallic sodium is thus due essentially to the redistribution of the valence electrons in the solid state. If we imagine a system of free atoms (arranged on a widely spaced lattice, for simplicity), then, as the internuclear distance is reduced, or the lattice is contracted, the valence electron wave functions begin to overlap and, as shown in Fig. 6.2, the energy begins to fall. This is due mainly to a lowering of the potential energy owing to the spreading of the wave functions over several atoms. However, the kinetic energy begins to increase †, so that a minimum in the energy curve is eventually reached, and at smaller internuclear distances the energy increases rapidly. The minimum in the energy curve corresponds to the equilibrium state of the solid, and the depth of the minimum below the energy of the free atoms is the cohesive energy of the metal.

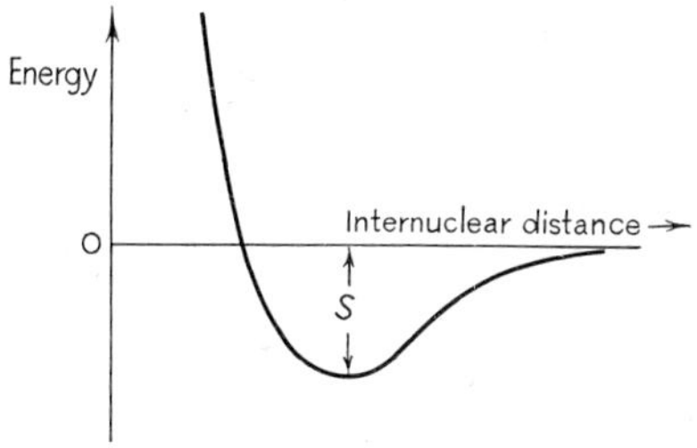

Fig. 6.2. Energy of a metal as a function of internuclear distance. The zero of energy here is the energy of a system of free atoms. S is the cohesive energy of the solid.

Since the ion-cores are to be regarded as being the same in the metal as in a free atom, the problem of calculating the cohesive energy may be slightly simplified by treating the system as one of valence electrons moving in a fixed lattice of ion-cores. Thus, if $V_a(\boldsymbol{r}_i)$ is the potential energy of electron i in the field of ion-core a,

† We have seen in § 2.3, equation (2.39), that for a particle in a box the kinetic energy increases as the size of the box decreases, and it is generally true that a particle has a larger kinetic energy the smaller the region in which it is confined.

the Hamiltonian operator becomes

$$H = -\sum_i^N \frac{\hbar^2}{2m}\nabla_i^2 + \sum_i^N \sum_a^N V_a(\boldsymbol{r}_i) + \tfrac{1}{2}\sum_{i\neq j}^N\sum^N \frac{e^2}{r_{ij}} + \tfrac{1}{2}\sum_{a\neq b}^N\sum^N \frac{e^2}{R_{ab}}. \tag{6.4}$$

We have used the more compact notation r_{ij} instead of $|\boldsymbol{r}_i - \boldsymbol{r}_j|$ and R_{ab} instead of $|\boldsymbol{R}_a - \boldsymbol{R}_b|$.

The last term in (6.4) represents the energy of interaction of the ion-cores: its simple form rests on the assumption that the ion-cores are far enough apart for their interaction to be considered as that of spheres each with a single positive charge e, the remaining charge of the nucleus being screened by the core electrons. This, of course, only applies to monovalent metals — for divalent metals the ion-cores would have charge $2e$, so that the last term in (6.4) would have to be multiplied by four, and so on.

It should be noted that the zero of energy is now that of a system of widely separated ion-cores and valence electrons at rest — this differs from the energy of a system of widely separated neutral atoms, the difference per atom being just I, the first ionization energy of a free atom, that is, the energy required to remove one electron from the neutral atom in its ground state.

Clearly, the Hamiltonian (6.4) is not simplified to such an extent that we can dispense with the one-electron approximation, and indeed we must still be content with some relatively crude form of this. For the time being, however, we will not go into details of how to obtain the one-electron functions, but will assume that the N functions which give the lowest energy consistent with the Pauli principle have been obtained, and will denote them by

$$\phi_1(\boldsymbol{x}_1),\ \phi_2(\boldsymbol{x}_2), \ldots \phi_N(\boldsymbol{x}_N),$$

including spin. We will also assume, for simplicity, that these functions are orthogonal and normalized, so that

$$\int \phi_i^*(\boldsymbol{x})\phi_j(\boldsymbol{x})\mathrm{d}\boldsymbol{x} = \delta_{ij}\,. \tag{6.5}$$

The effective extent of the wave functions beyond the surface of the metal is negligible, and so we will take all integrals throughout the volume of the metal, rather than throughout all space — we will later adopt boundary conditions consistent with this procedure.

6.1.2. SINGLE PRODUCT WAVE FUNCTION

First of all, and solely for purposes of comparison with our later results, we will calculate the total energy using a wave function consisting of a single product of one-electron functions, that is,

$$\Psi_0 = \phi_1(\boldsymbol{x}_1)\,\phi_2(\boldsymbol{x}_2)\ldots\phi_N(\boldsymbol{x}_N). \tag{6.6}$$

Owing to the normalization of the ϕ_i, Ψ_0 is also normalized, and the energy is given by

$$E_0 = \int \Psi_0^* H \Psi_0 \, \mathrm{d}\tau',$$

using the notation introduced in equation (5.27). Thus, with the Hamiltonian (6.4), we have

$$E_0 = \sum_i^N \int \Psi_0^* \left[-\frac{\hbar^2}{2m}\nabla_i^2 + \sum_a^N V_a(\boldsymbol{r}_i) \right] \Psi_0 \, \mathrm{d}\tau' + \tfrac{1}{2}\sum_{i \neq j}^N \sum^N \int \Psi_0^* \frac{e^2}{r_{ij}} \Psi_0 \, \mathrm{d}\tau' + \tfrac{1}{2}\sum_{a \neq b}^N \sum^N \frac{e^2}{R_{ab}}, \tag{6.8}$$

the last term being unchanged as it does not depend upon the electronic coordinates. Again, owing to the normalization of the ϕ_i, this becomes

$$E_0 = \sum_i^N \int \phi_i(\boldsymbol{x}_i) \left[-\frac{\hbar^2}{2m}\nabla_i^2 + \sum_a^N V_a(\boldsymbol{r}_i) \right] \phi_i(\boldsymbol{x}_i)\,\mathrm{d}\boldsymbol{x}_i + \tfrac{1}{2}\sum_{i \neq j}^N \sum^N \iint \frac{e^2}{r_{ij}} |\phi_i(\boldsymbol{x}_i)|^2 |\phi_j(\boldsymbol{x}_j)|^2 \, \mathrm{d}\boldsymbol{x}_i \mathrm{d}\boldsymbol{x}_j + \tfrac{1}{2}\sum_{a \neq b}^N \sum^N \frac{e^2}{R_{ab}}. \tag{6.9}$$

According to the notation of § 5.3, we write

$$\phi_i(\boldsymbol{x}) = \psi_i(\boldsymbol{r})\,\chi_i(\zeta), \tag{6.10}$$

where the spin function χ_i may be either α or β. We may then sum over the spin variables immediately, obtaining

$$E_0 = \sum_i^N \int \psi_i^*(\boldsymbol{r}_i) \left[-\frac{\hbar^2}{2m} \nabla_i^2 + \sum_a^N V_a(\boldsymbol{r}_i) \right] \psi_i(\boldsymbol{r}_i) \mathrm{d}\boldsymbol{r}_i$$
$$+ \tfrac{1}{2} \sum_{i \neq j}^N \sum^N \iint \frac{e^2}{r_{ij}} |\psi_i(\boldsymbol{r}_i)|^2 |\psi_j(\boldsymbol{r}_j)|^2 \mathrm{d}\boldsymbol{r}_i \mathrm{d}\boldsymbol{r}_j$$
$$+ \tfrac{1}{2} \sum_{a \neq b}^N \sum^N \frac{e^2}{R_{ab}} . \tag{6.11}$$

Finally, since the value of a definite integral is independent of the symbols used for the variables of integration, we may use, for example, $\boldsymbol{r}$ instead of $\boldsymbol{r}_i$ in the first term, and $\boldsymbol{r}_1$ and $\boldsymbol{r}_2$ instead of $\boldsymbol{r}_i$ and $\boldsymbol{r}_j$ in the second; thus,

$$E_0 = \sum_i^N \int \psi_i^*(\boldsymbol{r}) \left[-\frac{\hbar^2}{2m} \nabla^2 + \sum_a^N V_a(\boldsymbol{r}) \right] \psi_i(\boldsymbol{r}) \mathrm{d}\boldsymbol{r}$$
$$+ \tfrac{1}{2} \sum_{i \neq j}^N \sum^N \iint \frac{e^2}{r_{12}} |\psi_i(\boldsymbol{r}_1)|^2 |\psi_j(\boldsymbol{r}_2)|^2 \mathrm{d}\boldsymbol{r}_1 \mathrm{d}\boldsymbol{r}_2$$
$$+ \tfrac{1}{2} \sum_{a \neq b}^N \sum^N \frac{e^2}{R_{ab}} . \tag{6.12}$$

We do not expect the energy given by this expression to be very accurate, because the wave function (6.6) is not properly antisymmetric. We shall later calculate the error involved for the idealized case of a system of free electrons. Meanwhile, let us determine the equivalent expression using a determinantal wave function.

6.1.3. DETERMINANTAL WAVE FUNCTION

Using the same one-electron functions as in the previous section, we now construct the normalized, antisymmetric total wave function

$$\Psi = \frac{1}{\sqrt{N!}} \sum_{\mathrm{P}} (-1)^p \mathrm{P} \phi_1(\boldsymbol{x}_1) \phi_2(\boldsymbol{x}_2) \ldots \phi_N(\boldsymbol{x}_N), \tag{6.13}$$

which may be written in the determinantal form (5.24).

The Hamiltonian is a symmetric operator, for it is unchanged under any permutation of the electronic coordinates, so that in evaluating the total energy E we may make use of the theorem expressed in equation (5.28). Thus,

$$
\begin{aligned}
E &= \int \Psi^* H \Psi \, \mathrm{d}\tau' = \sqrt{N!} \int \Psi^* H \Psi_0 \, \mathrm{d}\tau' \\
&= \int [\sum_{\mathrm{P}} (-1)^p \mathrm{P} \phi_1^*(\boldsymbol{x}_1) \ldots \phi_N^*(\boldsymbol{x}_N)] \left[-\sum_i^N \frac{\hbar^2}{2m} \nabla_i^2 \right. \\
&\quad \left. + \sum_i^N \sum_a^N V_a(\boldsymbol{r}_i) + \tfrac{1}{2} \sum_{i \neq j}^N \sum^N \frac{e^2}{r_{ij}} \right] \phi_1(\boldsymbol{x}_1) \ldots \phi_N(\boldsymbol{x}_N) \mathrm{d}\tau' + \tfrac{1}{2} \sum_{a \neq b}^N \sum^N \frac{e^2}{R_{ab}} . \qquad (6.14)
\end{aligned}
$$

Because of the orthogonality and normalization of the ϕ_i, this expression becomes

$$
\begin{aligned}
E &= \sum_i^N \int \phi_i^*(\boldsymbol{x}_i) \left[-\frac{\hbar^2}{2m} \nabla_i^2 + \sum_a^N V_a(\boldsymbol{r}_i) \right] \phi_i(\boldsymbol{x}_i) \mathrm{d}\boldsymbol{x}_i \\
&\quad + \tfrac{1}{2} \sum_{i \neq j}^N \sum^N \iint [\phi_i^*(\boldsymbol{x}_i) \phi_j^*(\boldsymbol{x}_j) - \phi_i^*(\boldsymbol{x}_j) \phi_j^*(\boldsymbol{x}_i)] \frac{e^2}{r_{ij}} \phi_i(\boldsymbol{x}_i) \phi_j(\boldsymbol{x}_j) \mathrm{d}\boldsymbol{x}_i \mathrm{d}\boldsymbol{x}_j \\
&\quad + \tfrac{1}{2} \sum_{a \neq b}^N \sum^N \frac{e^2}{R_{ab}} . \qquad (6.15)
\end{aligned}
$$

In obtaining the first term, only the identity operator in the expression for Ψ^* — that which leaves the electronic coordinates unchanged — gives a non-zero result. All the other permutations give rise to factors like

$$
\int \phi_1^*(\boldsymbol{x}_1) \phi_2(\boldsymbol{x}_1) \mathrm{d}\boldsymbol{x}_1,
$$

which are zero by (6.5). In obtaining the second term, however, both the identity operator and the operator which interchanges $\boldsymbol{x}_i$ and $\boldsymbol{x}_j$, leaving the other coordinates unchanged, give non-zero results — this is due to the factor e^2/r_{ij} in the integrand. For the latter operator, $p = 1$, which accounts for the minus sign before the second term in the square brackets of the double integral.

Expanding the second term in (6.15), we obtain

$$
\begin{aligned}
E &= \sum_i^N \int \phi_i^*(\boldsymbol{x}_i) \left[-\frac{\hbar^2}{2m} \nabla_i^2 + \sum_a^N V_a(\boldsymbol{r}_i) \right] \phi_i(\boldsymbol{x}_i) \mathrm{d}\boldsymbol{x}_i \\
&\quad + \tfrac{1}{2} \sum_{i \neq j}^N \sum^N \iint \frac{e^2}{r_{ij}} |\phi_i(\boldsymbol{x}_i)|^2 |\phi_j(\boldsymbol{x}_j)|^2 \mathrm{d}\boldsymbol{x}_i \mathrm{d}\boldsymbol{x}_j \\
&\quad - \tfrac{1}{2} \sum_{i \neq j}^N \sum^N \iint \frac{e^2}{r_{ij}} \phi_i^*(\boldsymbol{x}_j) \phi_j^*(\boldsymbol{x}_i) \phi_i(\boldsymbol{x}_i) \phi_j(\boldsymbol{x}_j) \mathrm{d}\boldsymbol{x}_i \mathrm{d}\boldsymbol{x}_j + \tfrac{1}{2} \sum_{a \neq b}^N \sum^N \frac{e^2}{R_{ab}} . \qquad (6.16)
\end{aligned}
$$

Notice that this differs from expression (6.9) for E_0 only in the presence of the third term, which is called the *exchange energy*, because it is due to the exchange of electronic coordinates in the various terms of the expanded determinantal wave function [see equation (5.40) *et seq.*]. The second term, which represents the interaction of the charge clouds of the electrons, may be called the *Coulomb energy.*

As in the case of equation (6.9), the summation over the spin variables can be performed immediately for the first two terms in (6.16), the result being merely to replace ϕ_i by ψ_i and $\boldsymbol{x}_i$ by $\boldsymbol{r}_i$. The exchange energy must be considered in more detail.

First, if ϕ_i and ϕ_j have the same spin, their spin functions both being α, say, the integral in the exchange term becomes

$$\sum_{\zeta_i, \zeta_j = \pm 1} \iint \frac{e^2}{r_{ij}} \psi_i^*(\boldsymbol{r}_j)\psi_j^*(\boldsymbol{r}_i)\psi_i(\boldsymbol{r}_i)\psi_j(\boldsymbol{r}_j)\mathrm{d}\boldsymbol{r}_i\mathrm{d}\boldsymbol{r}_j|\alpha(\zeta_i)|^2\,|\alpha(\zeta_j)|^2$$

$$= \iint \frac{e^2}{r_{ij}} \psi_i^*(\boldsymbol{r}_j)\psi_j^*(\boldsymbol{r}_i)\psi_i(\boldsymbol{r}_i)\psi_j(\boldsymbol{r}_j)\mathrm{d}\boldsymbol{r}_i\mathrm{d}\boldsymbol{r}_j.$$

The same result follows if both spin functions are β.

Second, if ϕ_i and ϕ_j have opposite spins, the integral becomes

$$\sum_{\zeta_i, \zeta_j = \pm 1} \iint \frac{e^2}{r_{ij}} \psi_i^*(\boldsymbol{r}_j)\psi_j^*(\boldsymbol{r}_i)\psi_i(\boldsymbol{r}_i)\psi_j(\boldsymbol{r}_j)\mathrm{d}\boldsymbol{r}_i\mathrm{d}\boldsymbol{r}_j\alpha(\zeta_j)\beta(\zeta_i)\alpha(\zeta_i)\beta(\zeta_j) = 0.$$

The exchange energy is, therefore,

$$-\tfrac{1}{2} \sum_{\substack{i \neq j \\ (\| \text{ spins})}}^{N} \sum^{N} \iint \frac{e^2}{r_{ij}} \psi_i^*(\boldsymbol{r}_j)\psi_j^*(\boldsymbol{r}_i)\psi_i(\boldsymbol{r}_i)\psi_j(\boldsymbol{r}_j)\mathrm{d}\boldsymbol{r}_i\mathrm{d}\boldsymbol{r}_j$$

$$= -\tfrac{1}{2} \sum_{\substack{i \neq j \\ (\| \text{ spins})}}^{N} \sum^{N} \iint \frac{e^2}{r_{12}} \psi_i^*(\boldsymbol{r}_1)\psi_j^*(\boldsymbol{r}_2)\psi_i(\boldsymbol{r}_2)\psi_j(\boldsymbol{r}_1)\mathrm{d}\boldsymbol{r}_1\,\mathrm{d}\boldsymbol{r}_2,$$

the double sum being over those functions ψ_i and ψ_j associated with the same spin functions, that is, over electrons with parallel spins only.

The expression for the total energy in terms of orbital functions only is, thus,

$$E = \sum_{i}^{N} \int \psi_i^*(\boldsymbol{r}) \left[-\frac{\hbar^2}{2m} \nabla^2 + \sum_{a}^{N} V_a(\boldsymbol{r}) \right] \psi_i(\boldsymbol{r}) \mathrm{d}\boldsymbol{r}$$
$$+\tfrac{1}{2} \sum_{i \neq j}^{N} \sum^{N} \iint \frac{e^2}{r_{12}} |\psi_i(\boldsymbol{r}_1)|^2 |\psi_j(\boldsymbol{r}_2)|^2 \mathrm{d}\boldsymbol{r}_1 \mathrm{d}\boldsymbol{r}_2$$
$$-\tfrac{1}{2} \underset{(\| \text{ spins})}{\sum_{i \neq j}^{N} \sum^{N}} \iint \frac{e^2}{r_{12}} \psi_i^*(\boldsymbol{r}_1) \psi_j^*(\boldsymbol{r}_2) \psi_i(\boldsymbol{r}_2) \psi_j(\boldsymbol{r}_1) \mathrm{d}\boldsymbol{r}_1 \mathrm{d}\boldsymbol{r}_2$$
$$+\tfrac{1}{2} \sum_{a \neq b}^{N} \sum^{N} \frac{e^2}{R_{ab}}, \tag{6.17}$$

using the same notation as in (6.12). It should be noticed that, in deriving this expression for the energy, no assumption has been made about the form of the functions ψ_i — the expression is the same whether these are of localized (Heitler-London) type or of extended (Bloch) type, as discussed in § 5.8. We shall, in fact, use functions of the latter type, but we shall leave their description and the method of calculating them until later chapters — it will suffice for our present purposes to say that we assume there is the same chance of finding a given electron in the neighbourhood of any ion in the metal.

If i is put equal to j, the integrands in the second and third terms of (6.17) become the same. Since these terms have opposite signs, therefore, we can omit the condition $i \neq j$ from each of them. Changing the variable of integration from $\boldsymbol{r}$ to $\boldsymbol{r}_1$ in the first term which will prove convenient in the following work, we have, finally,

$$E = \sum_{i}^{N} \int \psi_i^*(\boldsymbol{r}_1) \left[-\frac{\hbar^2}{2m} \nabla_1^2 + \sum_{a}^{N} V_a(\boldsymbol{r}_1) \right] \psi_i(\boldsymbol{r}_1) \mathrm{d}\boldsymbol{r}_1$$
$$+\tfrac{1}{2} \sum_{i}^{N} \sum_{j}^{N} \iint \frac{e^2}{r_{12}} |\psi_i(\boldsymbol{r}_1)|^2 |\psi_j(\boldsymbol{r}_2)|^2 \mathrm{d}\boldsymbol{r}_1 \mathrm{d}\boldsymbol{r}_2$$
$$-\tfrac{1}{2} \underset{(\| \text{ spins})}{\sum_{i}^{N} \sum_{j}^{N}} \iint \frac{e^2}{r_{12}} \psi_i^*(\boldsymbol{r}_1) \psi_j^*(\boldsymbol{r}_2) \psi_i(\boldsymbol{r}_2) \psi_j(\boldsymbol{r}_1) \mathrm{d}\boldsymbol{r}_1 \mathrm{d}\boldsymbol{r}_2$$
$$+\tfrac{1}{2} \sum_{a \neq b}^{N} \sum^{N} \frac{e^2}{R_{ab}}. \tag{6.18}$$

This expression has been obtained, of course, for a monovalent metal. If the valency were q, say, so that the total number of valence electrons were Nq, the sums over i and j would be from one to Nq, and the last term would be multiplied by q^2.

6.2. The Hartree-Fock Method

We have seen in Chapter 4 that, according to the variation principle, Hartree's equations give the best one-electron functions to be used in a single-product type of wave function for the ground state. This is not so when a determinantal type of wave function is used. Application of the variation principle using a determinantal wave function results in equations for the one-electron functions ψ_i which are similar to those of Hartree but which contain an additional term — the 'exchange' term. These equations are called the Fock, or Hartree-Fock, equations.

We will not apply the variational method directly, as this is a somewhat complicated process, but will attempt to give a plausible derivation of Fock's equations by a method similar to that used in deriving Hartree's equations in § 4.6. The only terms in the expression (6.18) which depend upon the particular function ψ_i are the following

$$\int \psi_i^*(\boldsymbol{r}_1)\left[-\frac{\hbar^2}{2m}\nabla_1^2+\sum_a^N V_a(\boldsymbol{r}_1)\right]\psi_i(\boldsymbol{r}_1)\mathrm{d}\boldsymbol{r}_1$$
$$+\sum_j^N \iint \frac{e^2}{r_{12}}|\psi_i(\boldsymbol{r}_1)|^2|\psi_j(\boldsymbol{r}_2)|^2\mathrm{d}\boldsymbol{r}_1\mathrm{d}\boldsymbol{r}_2$$
$$-\sum_{\substack{j \\ (\text{spin } j \\ =\text{ spin } i)}}^N \iint \frac{e^2}{r_{12}}\psi_i^*(\boldsymbol{r}_1)\psi_j^*(\boldsymbol{r}_2)\psi_i(\boldsymbol{r}_2)\psi_j(\boldsymbol{r}_1)\mathrm{d}\boldsymbol{r}_1\mathrm{d}\boldsymbol{r}_2. \tag{6.19}$$

The factors $\frac{1}{2}$ have disappeared because the number i occurs in both sums of the double summations.

The expression (6.19) may be written in the form

$$\int \psi_i^*(\boldsymbol{r}_1)H_i\psi_i(\boldsymbol{r}_1)\mathrm{d}\boldsymbol{r}_1, \tag{6.20}$$

where the operator H_i is given by

$$H_i = -\frac{\hbar^2}{2m}\nabla_1^2+\sum_a^N V_a(\boldsymbol{r}_1)+e^2\sum_j^N\int\frac{|\psi_j(\boldsymbol{r}_2)|^2}{r_{12}}\mathrm{d}\boldsymbol{r}_2$$
$$-e^2\sum_{\substack{j \\ (\text{spin } j \\ =\text{ spin } i)}}^N \int \frac{\psi_j^*(\boldsymbol{r}_2)\psi_i(\boldsymbol{r}_2)\psi_j(\boldsymbol{r}_1)}{r_{12}\psi_i(\boldsymbol{r}_1)}\mathrm{d}\boldsymbol{r}_2, \tag{6.21}$$

as may immediately be verified by substitution.

For the ground state we wish to choose those one-electron functions which make the energy E an absolute minimum. Since the only terms of E which contain ψ_i are represented by (6.20), we must choose the function ψ_i which minimizes this expression. The variation principle tells us that the required ψ_i is the eigenfunction of the equation

$$H_i \psi_i = \varepsilon_i \psi_i,$$

with its lowest eigenvalue ε_i. This is the Fock equation for the function ψ_i. Written in full the equation is

$$\left[-\frac{\hbar^2}{2m} \nabla_1^2 + \sum_a^N V_a(\boldsymbol{r}_1) + e^2 \sum_j^N \int \frac{|\psi_j(\boldsymbol{r}_2)|^2}{r_{12}} \mathrm{d}\boldsymbol{r}_2 \right] \psi_i(\boldsymbol{r}_1)$$
$$- e^2 \sum_{\substack{j \\ (\text{spin } j \\ = \text{ spin } i)}}^N \left[\int \frac{\psi_j^*(\boldsymbol{r}_2)\psi_i(\boldsymbol{r}_2)\psi_j(\boldsymbol{r}_1)}{r_{12}\psi_i(\boldsymbol{r}_1)} \mathrm{d}\boldsymbol{r}_2 \right] \psi_i(\boldsymbol{r}_1) = \varepsilon_i \psi_i(\boldsymbol{r}_1). \qquad (6.22)$$

The operator in the first square brackets is just the Hartree operator, and may be compared with the operator in equation (4.29) for a single atom — the fact that $j = i$ is not excluded from the third term is of no importance in a metallic system, since the omission of one electron in 10^{23} can hardly have an appreciable effect upon the potential. This is, of course, only provided that the one-electron wave functions are extended ones, so that the removal of a single electron causes only a negligible change in the average charge density at any point of the metal. The remaining term on the left-hand side of the equation, the exchange term, may equally well be written

$$- e^2 \sum_{\substack{j \\ (\text{spin } j \\ = \text{ spin } i)}}^N \left[\int \frac{\psi_j^*(\boldsymbol{r}_2)\psi_i(\boldsymbol{r}_2)}{r_{12}} \mathrm{d}\boldsymbol{r}_2 \right] \psi_j(\boldsymbol{r}_1). \qquad (6.23)$$

There is an equation of the same form for each of the different one-electron functions, and these equations must be solved simultaneously. For a single atom this can be done by a method of successive approximations, until self-consistency of the required degree of accuracy is reached, as was described for the Hartree equations. In metals the problem is too complicated and a cruder approximate form of the equations must be used. In the idealized case of a free-electron gas, however, which is of some interest in metal theory, the equations can be solved analytically, and we shall do this in the following chapter.

Of course, although we have said that ψ_i is the eigenfunction of equation (6.22) corresponding to its *lowest eigenvalue*, in practice this must be modified to its *lowest eigenvalue permitted by the Pauli principle*. We know that, according to the Pauli principle, not more than two electrons may be in a given orbital state, and these must have opposite spins; a fact which must be borne in mind when solving the equations. In the ground state of a non-ferromagnetic metal at 0°K, which is the only case we shall consider in detail, all the orbital states of lowest energy are occupied by two electrons. In a ferromagnetic metal, on the other hand, the state of lowest energy is one in which there are more electrons with one kind of spin than there are with the other, so that some orbital states are occupied by only one electron.

Although equation (6.22) is correct, it must not be pretended that our derivation of it has been rigorous. The principal objection to it is that the operator H_i itself depends upon ψ_i, so that it is not obvious that the variation principle can be applied directly to (6.20) as we have done. None the less, this derivation is sufficient for our purposes, being more informative than a mere statement of the equation, yet avoiding complicated calculations which lie outside the scheme of this book.

It is easily seen that the total energy of the electrons is not simply the sum of the Fock eigenvalues ε_i. If we use equation (6.22) in conjunction with (6.18), we find immediately

$$\begin{aligned} E = \sum_i^N \varepsilon_i - \tfrac{1}{2} \sum_i^N \sum_j^N \iint \frac{e^2}{r_{12}} |\psi_j(\mathbf{r}_2)|^2 |\psi_i(\mathbf{r}_1)|^2 \mathrm{d}\mathbf{r}_1 \mathrm{d}\mathbf{r}_2 \\ + \tfrac{1}{2} \sum_{\substack{i \\ (\| \text{ spins})}}^N \sum_j^N \iint \frac{e^2}{r_{12}} \psi_i^*(\mathbf{r}_1)\psi_j^*(\mathbf{r}_2)\psi_i(\mathbf{r}_2)\psi_j(\mathbf{r}_1) \mathrm{d}\mathbf{r}_1 \mathrm{d}\mathbf{r}_2 \\ + \tfrac{1}{2} \sum_{a \neq b}^N \sum^N \frac{e^2}{R_{ab}} . \end{aligned} \tag{6.24}$$

None the less, the eigenvalue ε_i has a simple interpretation for a metallic system when the one-electron functions are of the extended type: it is the negative of the energy required to remove from the solid an electron in the state ψ_i. As we have already mentioned, if the average charge distribution of every electron is spread throughout the metal, and there are something like 10^{23} electrons, then the removal of a single one of them will hardly affect the Fock Hamiltonian H_i. We may thus assume that the functions ψ_i are virtually unchanged after the removal of a single electron.

Now we have seen that a given ψ_i only appears in the expression for E through the terms shown in (6.19). If an electron in the state ψ_i is removed from the metal, then, the total energy must be reduced by the value of the expression (6.19), namely, ε_i. The energy which must be supplied in order to remove the electron is therefore $-\varepsilon_i$, as we wished to prove. This result is generally known as *Koopmans's theorem.*

6.3. Coulomb Correlations and the Fermi Hole

Electrons repel one another, so that they do not move independently but in such a way as to avoid each other as far as possible. In other words, the effect of the Coulomb force is to couple, or correlate, the individual electronic motions so as to reduce the probability of two electrons closely approaching each other. Such correlations among the electronic motions, or positions, may be called *Coulomb correlations.*

In the Hartree method Coulomb correlations are completely ignored, each electron being supposed to move in the *average* charge distribution of the other electrons. The total wave function is a single product of one-electron functions, so that the probability of a given configuration depends only upon the one-electron functions and not directly upon the distances between pairs of electrons.

The Hartree-Fock method again neglects proper Coulomb correlations, as defined above, but includes correlations of another sort. These are correlations among the positions of electrons with parallel spins only, and are due, not to the Coulomb force, but to the Pauli principle, as embodied in the use of a determinantal wave function. The latter is of the form

$$\Psi = \begin{vmatrix} \phi_1(\boldsymbol{x}_1) & \phi_1(\boldsymbol{x}_2) \dots \phi_1(\boldsymbol{x}_N) \\ \phi_2(\boldsymbol{x}_1) & \phi_2(\boldsymbol{x}_2) \dots \phi_2(\boldsymbol{x}_N) \\ \cdot\ \cdot\ \cdot & \cdot\ \cdot\ \cdot\ \cdot\ \cdot\ \cdot \\ \phi_N(\boldsymbol{x}_1) & \phi_N(\boldsymbol{x}_2) \dots \phi_N(\boldsymbol{x}_N) \end{vmatrix}$$

where it must be remembered that

$$\phi(\boldsymbol{x}) = \psi(\boldsymbol{r})\,\chi(\zeta),$$

the spin function χ being either α or β. It can easily be seen that with such a total wave function there is zero probability of two electrons with parallel spins † being in the same place. For example, suppose that electrons 1 and 2 have parallel spins, so that $\zeta_1 = \zeta_2$, and are in the same place, so that $\boldsymbol{r}_1 = \boldsymbol{r}_2$. This implies that $\boldsymbol{x}_1 = \boldsymbol{x}_2$, and the first two columns of the determinant are the same, so that the value of the determinant, and consequently the probability density $|\Psi|^2$, is zero. If the electrons have anti-parallel spins, that is, if $\zeta_1 \neq \zeta_2$, this does not apply, for now $\boldsymbol{x}_1 \neq \boldsymbol{x}_2$ even when $\boldsymbol{r}_1 = \boldsymbol{r}_2$.

The use of a determinantal wave function not only implies zero probability of finding two electrons with parallel spins in the same place, but also that there is only a small probability of finding two such electrons within a short distance of each other. It is as if, during its motion, each electron were surrounded by a 'hole' in the distribution of electrons with parallel spins. This is called the *exchange hole* or *Fermi hole*. We shall see in the following chapter, after discussing the free-electron approximation, that the Fermi hole may be regarded roughly as a sphere of radius r_s, but meanwhile the idea can be made plausible by means of the Fock equation (6.22). It must be remarked in advance that, in spite of the footnote on this page, we will at first assume that the electron at position $\boldsymbol{r}_1$ is in the particular one-electron state ϕ_i — this is because we shall be arguing by analogy with the Hartree method, for which this is a permissible statement.

The exchange term in equation (6.22) may be written

$$A_i(\boldsymbol{r}_1)\psi_i(\boldsymbol{r}_1),$$

where

$$A_i(\boldsymbol{r}_1) = -e^2 \sum_{\substack{j \\ (\text{spin } j \\ = \text{spin} i)}}^{N} \int \frac{\psi_j^*(\boldsymbol{r}_2)\psi_i(\boldsymbol{r}_2)\psi_j(\boldsymbol{r}_1)}{r_{12}\psi_i(\boldsymbol{r}_1)} \mathrm{d}\boldsymbol{r}_2.$$

Just as the Hartree potential energy of the electron at $\boldsymbol{r}_1$, namely,

$$e^2 \sum_j^N \int \frac{|\psi_j(\boldsymbol{r}_2)|^2}{r_{12}} \mathrm{d}\boldsymbol{r}_2,$$

is that due to a charge distribution whose density at $\boldsymbol{r}_2$ is

$$-e \sum_j^N |\psi_j(\boldsymbol{r}_2)|^2,$$

† The meaning of this is that the two electrons have the same spin *directions*, or coordinates, not that they are in specific one-electron states having the same spin functions. When a determinantal wave function is used it is not strictly correct to think of any given electron as being in a particular one-electron state, but each electron must be regarded as partially in all of the states.

so the function $A_i(\boldsymbol{r}_1)$ may be interpreted as the potential energy of the electron at $\boldsymbol{r}_1$ due to a fictitious *exchange charge distribution*, whose density at $\boldsymbol{r}_2$ is

$$e \sum_{\substack{j \\ (\text{spin } j \\ = \text{ spin } i)}}^{N} \frac{\psi_j^*(\boldsymbol{r}_2)\psi_i(\boldsymbol{r}_2)\psi_j(\boldsymbol{r}_1)}{\psi_i(\boldsymbol{r}_1)} . \tag{6.25}$$

The total exchange charge is

$$e \sum_{\substack{j \\ (\text{spin } j \\ = \text{ spin } i)}}^{N} \int \frac{\psi_j^*(\boldsymbol{r}_2)\psi_i(\boldsymbol{r}_2)\psi_j(\boldsymbol{r}_1)}{\psi_i(\boldsymbol{r}_1)} \mathrm{d}\boldsymbol{r}_2 = e,$$

since

$$\int \psi_j^*(\boldsymbol{r}_2)\psi_i(\boldsymbol{r}_2)\mathrm{d}\boldsymbol{r}_2 = \delta_{ij},$$

owing to the orthogonality and normalization of the one-electron functions — see equation (6.5). This is a *positive* charge equal to that of a proton.

Furthermore, the exchange charge density at $\boldsymbol{r}_1$, obtained by putting $\boldsymbol{r}_2 = \boldsymbol{r}_1$ in (6.25), is

$$e \sum_{\substack{j \\ (\text{spin } j \\ = \text{ spin } i)}}^{N} |\psi_j(\boldsymbol{r}_1)|^2, \tag{6.26}$$

which is equal in magnitude, but opposite in sign, to the average charge density of electrons with spins parallel to that of the electron at $\boldsymbol{r}_1$ — this is supposed to be in the orbital state ψ_i and some spin state χ, and the sum is over all the orbitals associated with the same function χ. Since the total exchange charge is only e, the exchange charge density must decrease rapidly from the value (6.26) as the distance r_{12} increases.

Apart from the exchange term, the potential energy appearing in the Fock equation (6.22) is that of an electron in the field of the ion-cores and the charge cloud of *all* the valence electrons. The foregoing discussion suggests that, in addition, and due to the exchange term, the electron may be regarded as surrounded by a positive charge cloud of total charge e and of limited extent. This effectively cancels the average charge distribution of electrons with parallel spins in the neighbourhood of the given electron and gives rise to the Fermi hole described above.

It should be pointed out that, in general, the exchange charge density as defined by (6.25) is not spherically symmetrical about $\boldsymbol{r}_1$; it is not the same for different ψ_i; and it need not be a real function — as we shall see in the case of free electrons. It would, in fact, be more realistic, particularly in view of the footnote on p. 150, to *average* the exchange charge density over all the ψ_i. When we do this for free electrons, in § 7.6, we shall obtain an average Fermi hole which is spherically symmetrical and which otherwise accords with the description given.

Although these parallel spin correlations which appear in the Hartree-Fock theory are not due to the Coulomb interaction, they affect the energy in the same way as Coulomb correlations. The total energy given by the Hartree-Fock method is thus an improvement on that of the Hartree method, which neglects all correlations — the principal difference is due to the appearance of the exchange energy, which we shall find to be large and negative, in the Hartree-Fock expression. Antiparallel spin correlations are still completely neglected, of course, and we shall see that this has some unfortunate consequences. It might be expected that, in a more accurate theory, each electron would be surrounded by a hole, similar to the Fermi hole, in the distribution of electrons with anti-parallel spins also. We shall, in fact, make use of this concept of a *correlation hole* in the distribution of *all* electrons in Chapter 9, leaving its justification until Chapter 10.

CHAPTER 7

THE FREE-ELECTRON APPROXIMATION

7.1. The Periodic Field in a Metal

The total charge distribution of a closed shell of electrons in a free atom is spherically symmetrical about the nucleus, and it follows that the potential energy of a valence electron in the field of the ion-core is also a spherically symmetrical function. This function $V(r)$ for a sodium atom is compared with the corresponding function $-e^2/r$ for a hydrogen atom in Figure 7.1 — r being the distance from the nucleus. The nuclear charge of sodium is $11e$, so that at points very close to the nucleus the function $V(r)$ is practically $-11e^2/r$, the electrons there having negligible effect. At points lying outside the effective radius of the ion-core, however, $V(r)$ is very nearly $-e^2/r$, because the field of the nucleus is screened by the ten core electrons so that it becomes virtually the field of a single proton. At intermediate points the function cannot be estimated in a simple manner.

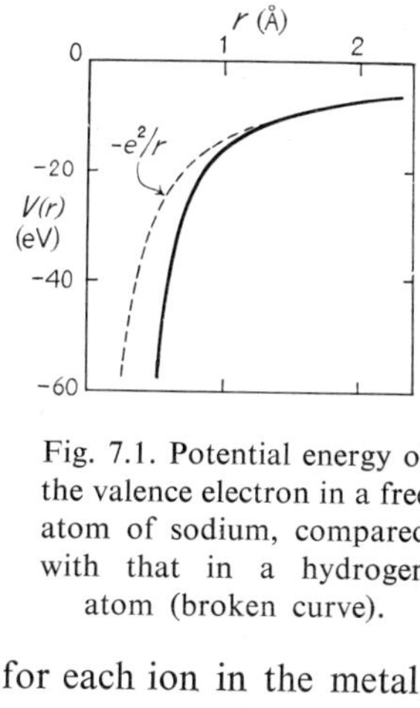

Fig. 7.1. Potential energy of the valence electron in a free atom of sodium, compared with that in a hydrogen atom (broken curve).

The potential energy of an electron in a solid metal, of course, is not obtained simply by summing such potential energy functions, one for each ion in the metal, even when we assume that the structure of the core remains unchanged in the solid state. The interactions of the valence electrons among themselves must be taken into account. The potential energy of any electron due to the *average* charge distribution of the valence electron gas may be found by the Hartree method. However, if more accurate account is to be taken of electronic correlations, as discussed in § 6.3, then the Hartree-Fock method or modifications of it must be used. We shall consider this problem in more detail later. Whatever method is used, the effect of the other electrons is such as to screen a given electron from the field of all the ion-cores except those in its immediate vicinity, so that the potential energy is numerically much less than it would be if only the ion-cores were present.

The potential energy of a valence electron as a function of position along a line of nuclei in the metal is shown schematically in Figure 7.2 (a). Along a parallel line, which does not pass through any nuclei, the function would be as shown in Figure 7.2 (b). There is a potential barrier at the surface, of course, since the electrons cannot pass freely out of the metal. However, except in a few atomic layers at the surface, the potential energy is an almost exactly periodic function with the period of the lattice. Since, in a cubic centimetre of metal, only about one atom in a million is at the surface, the effect of the surface is unimportant when calculating bulk properties of the metal, such as the cohesive energy. We therefore assume that the electrostatic field in which a valence electron moves in a metal is strictly periodic.

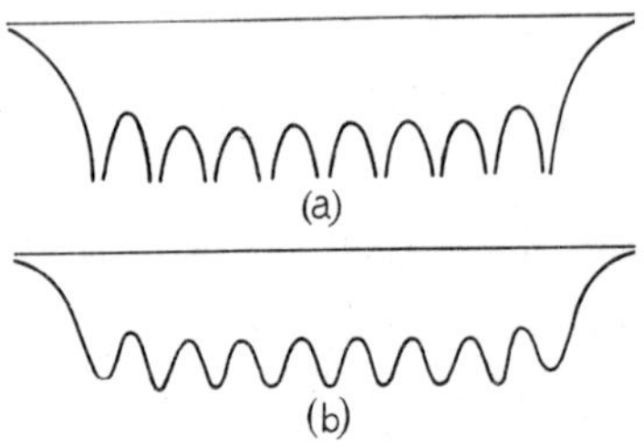

Fig. 7.2. Potential energy of an electron in a metal: (a) along a line of nuclei, (b) along a parallel line.

7.2. The Sommerfeld Model

The earliest application of quantum mechanics to the electrons in a metal was made in 1928 by Sommerfeld, who simplified the problem by taking the potential energy of each electron to be constant within the metal. That is to say, he assumed that the total field of the electrons and ion-cores at any point in the metal could be taken to be zero as a good approximation. Although this model seems to be a highly idealized one, we shall see that it is not unreasonable for the calculation of at least some of the physical properties of a number of metals.

The value assumed for the constant potential energy will clearly be of great importance in calculating such quantities as cohesive energy and work function (the energy required to remove an electron from the metal). In many calculations, however, only the distribution of energy levels relative to the lowest level is important and not their positions relative to some external zero. In such cases we may arbitrarily take the potential inside the metal to be zero, and as a slight further approximation the potential outside the metal may be taken to be infinite. We shall adopt a more sophisticated viewpoint in § 7.4, but meanwhile the problem is simply that of virtually non-interacting particles in a potential box of the type we have considered in § 2.3. Assuming that the metal is in the form of a cube of side L, we have immediately that the normalized wave functions of the stationary states (neglecting spin) are

$$\psi_{n_x n_y n_z} = \sqrt{\frac{8}{L^3}} \sin\frac{n_x \pi x}{L} \sin\frac{n_y \pi y}{L} \sin\frac{n_z \pi z}{L}, \tag{7.1}$$

within the metal, and zero outside, and the energy levels are

$$\varepsilon_{n_x n_y n_z} = \frac{\hbar^2 \pi^2}{2mL^2}(n_x^2 + n_y^2 + n_z^2), \tag{7.2}$$

where n_x, n_y, and n_z are positive integers.

According to the Pauli principle not more than two electrons may occupy any orbital state, so that, at the absolute zero of temperature, two electrons will go into the ground state, two into each state of next higher energy, and so on, until all the electrons are allocated to states of lowest possible energy. Since the number of electrons is very large, it is thus understandable that, even at the absolute zero of temperature, some electrons have kinetic energies of several electron volts. For a piece of metal of macroscopic dimensions, say a centimetre cube, the energy of the ground state ($n_x = n_y = n_z = 1$) is of the order of 10^{-15} eV and hence may be taken to be zero for all practical purposes. Also the maximum spacing between consecutive energy levels is less than 10^{-6} eV, so that the distribution of energy may be regarded as almost continuous — it is sometimes described as 'quasi-continuous'. In particular, it is possible, and useful, to define a *density of states in energy* $\mathcal{N}(\varepsilon)$ in the following way:

the number of orbital states with energies lying between ε *and* $\varepsilon + d\varepsilon$ *is* $\mathcal{N}(\varepsilon)d\varepsilon$.

Here it is assumed that $d\varepsilon$ is very small but still large enough for the interval to contain very many states — it is easy to see that this is possible, for the above considerations show that, if $d\varepsilon$ is only 10^{-3} eV, the interval will contain at least 1000 energy levels. It follows that the number of orbital states, $\nu(\varepsilon)$ say, with energies *less than* ε is

$$\nu(\varepsilon) = \int_0^{\varepsilon} \mathcal{N}(\varepsilon)d\varepsilon,$$

so that

$$\mathcal{N}(\varepsilon) = \mathrm{d}\nu/\mathrm{d}\varepsilon.$$

We shall use this in calculating $\mathcal{N}(\varepsilon)$.

Let us consider a system of rectangular Cartesian coordinates whose axes represent n_x, n_y, n_z. We note, first of all, that each orbital state is represented by a triad of positive integral values of n_x, n_y, n_z, and hence by a point in the positive octant of this '$\boldsymbol{n}$-space'. Also, if we divide the octant up into unit cubic cells, every point representing a state lies at a corner of a cell, so that unit volume contains just one representative point. Now, the equation

$$n_x^2 + n_y^2 + n_z^2 = \frac{2mL^2}{\hbar^2\pi^2}\,\varepsilon, \qquad (7.3)$$

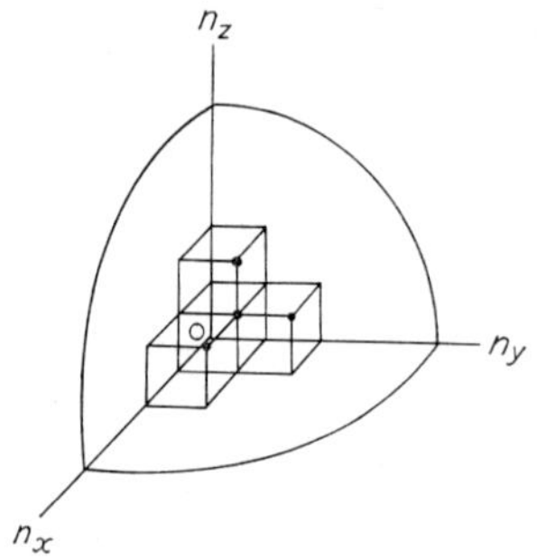

Fig. 7.3. The positive octant of $\boldsymbol{n}$-space. The dots represent states.

from (7.2), is that of a sphere in $\boldsymbol{n}$-space, the right hand side being the square of the radius. Thus, the number $\nu(\varepsilon)$ of states with energies less than ε is just the number of representative points lying within the positive octant of this sphere. Since there is one representative point per unit volume, therefore, this number is equal to the volume of the octant, that is

$$\nu(\varepsilon) = \frac{1}{8}\frac{4\pi}{3}\left(\frac{2mL^2}{\hbar^2\pi^2}\,\varepsilon\right)^{\frac{3}{2}} = \frac{v}{6\pi^2}\left(\frac{2m}{\hbar^2}\right)^{\frac{3}{2}}\varepsilon^{\frac{3}{2}}, \qquad (7.4)$$

where $v = L^3$, the volume of the metal. Differentiation with respect to ε gives the density of states

$$\mathcal{N}(\varepsilon) = \frac{v}{4\pi^2}\left(\frac{2m}{\hbar^2}\right)^{\frac{3}{2}}\varepsilon^{\frac{1}{2}} \qquad (7.5)$$

The graph of $\mathcal{N}(\varepsilon)$ is the parabola shown in Figure 7.4. It should be noted that here $\mathcal{N}(\varepsilon)$ is the density of *orbital* states for a metal of volume v — the density of states is sometimes defined with respect to states including spin, and for unit volume of metal, which would have the effect of replacing v by 2 in (7.5).

The above treatment ignores the fact that the surface of the sphere cuts through some of the unit cubic cells, but this is reasonable, since, except in the immediate neighbourhood of the origin, $\nu(\varepsilon)$ is very large. The approximation assumes, in fact, that $\nu(\varepsilon)$ is a continuous function of ε — this is not strictly true, of course, for we can never have a non-integral number of states, but it is equivalent to the assumption we made in defining $\mathcal{N}(\varepsilon)$.

At the absolute zero of temperature, as mentioned before, all the states with energies up to some maximum, which we will denote by ζ_0, will be occupied by two electrons with opposite spins. If N is the total number of electrons, we must have

$$N = 2\int_0^{\zeta_0} \mathcal{N}(\varepsilon)\mathrm{d}\varepsilon = \frac{v}{2\pi^2}\left(\frac{2m}{\hbar^2}\right)^{\frac{3}{2}} \tfrac{2}{3}\zeta_0^{\frac{3}{2}}. \tag{7.6}$$

This gives the highest occupied energy level as

$$\zeta_0 = \frac{\hbar^2}{2m}\left(\frac{3\pi^2 N}{v}\right)^{\frac{2}{3}}, \tag{7.7}$$

which has the value 3.2 eV for metallic sodium.

We have assumed that the potential energy is zero, so that all the energy

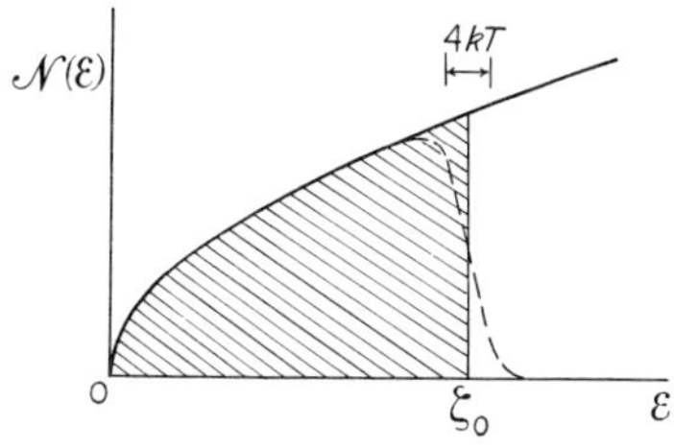

Fig. 7.4. Density of states in energy for a free-electron system. The shaded region represents the distribution of occupied states at the absolute zero of temperature: its area is $\frac{1}{2}N$. The broken curve shows the 'tailing off' of the top of the occupied region at a temperature of about 1000° K, assuming the electron density to be roughly that in metallic sodium.

is kinetic, and ζ_0 is the maximum kinetic energy at the absolute zero of temperature. The *total* kinetic energy of the electrons is given by

$$2\int_0^{\zeta_0} \mathcal{N}(\varepsilon)\varepsilon\,\mathrm{d}\varepsilon = \frac{v}{2\pi^2}\left(\frac{2m}{\hbar^2}\right)^{\frac{3}{2}} \tfrac{2}{5}\zeta_0^{\frac{5}{2}} = \tfrac{3}{5}N\zeta_0.$$

The *average* kinetic energy per electron, called the *Fermi energy*†, which we will denote by E_F, is, therefore,

$$E_F = \tfrac{3}{5}\zeta_0. \tag{7.8}$$

For a monovalent metal the *atomic radius* r_s, as defined in § 6.1.1, is given by

$$\frac{4\pi}{3} r_s^3 = \frac{v}{N}. \tag{7.9}$$

For polyvalent metals the number of electrons is not equal to the number of atoms, so that for N, in the above equation, we must substitute N/Z, where Z is the valency. In order to generalize the results it would be convenient to introduce another radius, r_e say, which is the radius of a sphere whose volume is equal to the average volume *per electron*, so that for all metals we should have

$$\frac{4\pi}{3} r_e^3 = \frac{v}{N} = \frac{1}{Z}\frac{4\pi}{3} r_s^3. \tag{7.10}$$

This gives $r_e = Z^{-\frac{1}{3}} r_s$ in general, and $r_e = r_s$ for a monovalent metal. In order to conform to the more general usage, however, we shall, unless otherwise stated, restrict ourselves to monovalent metals and use r_s as given in equation (7.9). None the less, it should be understood that all the results can be generalized to polyvalent metals merely by substituting r_e for r_s in the energy formulae. Of course, we have said nothing yet about the applicability of the approximations we are using to metals of different valencies, and we shall see, in fact, that the methods of the present chapter are more suited to monovalent metals.

Using equations (7.7), (7.8), and (7.9), we find

$$\zeta_0 = \frac{\hbar^2}{2m}\left(\frac{9\pi}{4}\right)^{\frac{2}{3}} \frac{1}{r_s^2}, \tag{7.11}$$

† No universal notation yet exists in the theory of metals. One-electron energies are often denoted by E, rather than ε, and the maximum kinetic energy of an electron, which we have denoted by ζ_0, is sometimes denoted by E_F or E_0, and it is sometimes also referred to as the *Fermi energy*. In the following work, except in one or two instances, we shall use the letter ε to denote an energy associated with a particular one-electron state, and the letter E to denote an *average energy per electron* of a system – appropriate subscripts will be used to denote the particular energy terms we are considering.

and

$$E_F = \frac{3\hbar^2}{10m}\left(\frac{9\pi}{4}\right)^{\frac{2}{3}}\frac{1}{r_s^2}. \tag{7.12}$$

For all metals r_s is of the order of an ångström unit, from which it follows that ζ_0 and E_F have values of several electron volts.

7.2.1. FERMI-DIRAC STATISTICS

The foregoing work, in which the temperature has been assumed to be absolute zero, is the simplest application to metals of the so-called *Fermi-Dirac statistics.* At higher temperatures the distribution of occupied states does not end abruptly at ζ_0, as does the shaded region in Figure 7.4, but tails off smoothly, as shown by the broken curve in the same figure. At absolute temperature T the number of electrons with energies lying between ε and $\varepsilon+\mathrm{d}\varepsilon$ is found to be

$$2\mathcal{N}(\varepsilon)f(\varepsilon)\,\mathrm{d}\varepsilon,$$

where $f(\varepsilon)$, known as the *Fermi-Dirac distribution function* †, is given by

$$f(\varepsilon) = \frac{1}{\mathrm{e}^{(\varepsilon-\zeta)/kT}+1}. \tag{7.13}$$

Here k is Boltzmann's constant and ζ is a function of T which is determined by the equation

$$2\int_0^\infty \mathcal{N}(\varepsilon)f(\varepsilon)\mathrm{d}\varepsilon = N, \tag{7.14}$$

expressing the fact that the total number of electrons is N.

We will now show that $\zeta(0)$, the value of ζ at 0°K, is just what we have denoted by ζ_0. It is easy to see that, with $\zeta(0)$ positive,

$$\lim_{T\to 0} \mathrm{e}^{(\varepsilon-\zeta)/kT} = 0, \quad \text{if} \quad \varepsilon < \zeta(0),$$

and

$$\mathrm{e}^{(\varepsilon-\zeta)/kT} \to \infty \text{ as } \; T \to 0, \quad \text{if} \quad \varepsilon > \zeta(0).$$

† See, for example, M. Born, *Atomic Physics*, 6th ed. (Blackie, 1957), Chapter VIII, for a simple derivation.

At the absolute zero of temperature, therefore, the function $f(\varepsilon)$ becomes

$$f(\varepsilon) = \begin{cases} 1, & \varepsilon < \zeta(0), \\ 0, & \varepsilon > \zeta(0), \end{cases} \tag{7.15}$$

so that equation (7.14) reduces to

$$2\int_0^{\zeta(0)} \mathcal{N}(\varepsilon)\mathrm{d}\varepsilon = N.$$

Comparing this with equation (7.6), we find that $\zeta(0) = \zeta_0$, as required, and the density of occupied orbital states $\mathcal{N}(\varepsilon)f(\varepsilon)$, with $f(\varepsilon)$ given by (7.15), is precisely what we found previously. At higher temperatures ζ is not equal to ζ_0 but, certainly at temperatures up to the melting points of most metals, it is very nearly so.

The general features of the function $f(\varepsilon)$ for any temperature T are easily obtained from equation (7.13). The value of $f(\zeta)$ is always 0.5. For values of ε much smaller than ζ, $f(\varepsilon)$ is nearly unity, and for values of ε much greater than ζ, $f(\varepsilon)$ is very nearly zero — indeed, at normal temperatures, $f(\varepsilon)$ differs appreciably from the function (7.15) only in a small region about ζ. In order to estimate the width of this region, let us evaluate $f(\varepsilon)$ when $\varepsilon = \zeta - 2kT$ and when $\varepsilon = \zeta + 2kT$.

$$f(\zeta - 2kT) = \frac{1}{\mathrm{e}^{-2}+1} = 0.88,$$

$$f(\zeta + 2kT) = \frac{1}{\mathrm{e}^{2}+1} = 0.12.$$

Thus, for practical purposes, we may assume that $f(\varepsilon)$ decreases from unity to zero in a region of width about $4kT$ about ζ. Now, at room temperature, 300°K, kT is equal to an energy of 0.026 eV, whereas we have seen that ζ_0, and hence ζ, has a value of several electron volts. It follows that, at normal temperatures,

$$kT \ll \zeta.$$

This means that the fall in value of $f(\varepsilon)$ near the energy ζ, or ζ_0 approximately, is so rapid that the distribution of electrons in energy is very little different from that at 0°K. The function $f(\varepsilon)$ at 0°K and at 1000°K is shown in Figure 7.5, the value of ζ_0 having been chosen for illustration to be 3.2 eV, as for sodium.

In the remainder of the book we shall make no explicit use of the Fermi-Dirac distribution function. Apart from a simple treatment of the electronic specific heat, in which we shall use the general results obtained above, we shall assume either that the temperature is absolute zero or that, at any temperature we may be considering, the distribution function does not differ appreciably from that at absolute zero.

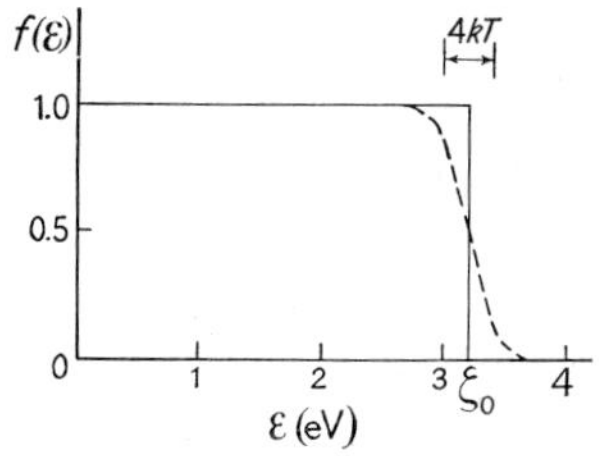

Fig. 7.5. The Fermi-Dirac distribution function $f(\varepsilon)$. The full curve is at 0°K and the broken curve at about 1000°K, assuming the electron density to be that in metallic sodium.

7.3. Periodic Boundary Conditions and Running Waves

(i) *One dimensional metal.* For simplicity, let us first consider a one-dimensional metal, which may be visualized as a thin wire of length L. We take the x-axis along the wire, with the origin at one end, and neglect all motion except that in the x-direction. If we apply the Sommerfeld theory to this case, that is, take the potential energy to be zero within the metal and infinite outside, we simply have the problem of a particle in a one-dimensional box, discussed in § 1.5. The energy levels are

$$\varepsilon_n = \frac{\hbar^2\pi^2}{2mL^2}\, n^2, \qquad n = 1, 2, 3, \ldots, \tag{7.16}$$

and the normalized wave functions are

$$\psi_n = \sqrt{\frac{2}{L}} \sin\frac{n\pi x}{L}. \tag{7.17}$$

We restrict the values of n to *positive* integers, because changing the sign of n does not give a different wave function — all wave functions are arbitrary to the extent of a multiplying factor of modulus unity.

The wave functions ψ_n represent standing waves — they describe the states of motion of an electron which is bouncing to and fro between the walls of the box. This can readily be understood from the fact that the average value of the momentum $\langle p_x \rangle$ is zero for all ψ_n. According to § 2.9, we have

$$\langle p_x \rangle = \int_0^L \psi_n^* \frac{\hbar}{\mathrm{i}} \frac{\mathrm{d}\psi_n}{\mathrm{d}x}\,\mathrm{d}x$$

$$= \frac{2n\pi\hbar}{L^2\mathrm{i}} \int_0^L \sin\frac{n\pi x}{L} \cos\frac{n\pi x}{L}\,\mathrm{d}x = 0.$$

This does not mean that the electron is stationary, but that a measurement of its momentum at any instant is equally likely to result in a positive or a negative value.

Such standing waves, although undoubtedly correct for the system we have described, are of no help in problems of conductivity, for which we require *running waves*, or functions which describe the motion of an electron in a definite direction. A function of this type is

$$\psi_k = \mathrm{e}^{\mathrm{i}kx}. \tag{7.18}$$

We have seen in § 2.8 that this function represents a free particle travelling in the x-direction with constant momentum $\hbar k$. It also satisfies the correct Schrödinger equation inside the metal, namely,

$$\frac{\mathrm{d}^2\psi}{\mathrm{d}x^2} + \frac{2m}{\hbar^2}\varepsilon\psi = 0,$$

provided that

$$\varepsilon = \frac{\hbar^2 k^2}{2m}.$$

However, it is clear that ψ_k does not satisfy the correct boundary conditions, for it does not vanish at $x = 0$ and at $x = L$. None the less, in the one-dimensional case, it is very easy to devise a physical situation for which the appropriate boundary conditions will permit ψ_k as a solution. In order that a continuous electric current might flow, we must have a closed circuit. Let us, therefore, simply bend our wire round until the two ends are touching, but still measure x along the wire. The Schrödinger equation inside the metal is then unchanged, but the infinite potential walls have been eliminated, and with them the necessity for the vanishing of the wave function at $x = 0$ and at $x = L$. The requirement that a wave function be smooth and continuous now imposes the boundary conditions

$$\psi(0) = \psi(L), \;\; \psi'(0) = \psi'(L). \tag{7.19}$$

Since the point $(x+L)$ is now the same as the point x, it follows, in fact, that ψ must be a periodic function of x with period L, that is,

$$\psi(x+L) = \psi(x), \tag{7.20}$$

for all x — this equation includes both of the conditions (7.19). These new boundary conditions, either (7.19) or (7.20), are called *periodic boundary conditions.*

Applying these conditions to the function ψ_k, we find

$$1 = e^{ikL},$$

so that,

$$k = \frac{2\pi n}{L}, \qquad n = 0, \pm 1, \pm 2, \ldots.$$

Notice that we now permit both positive and negative values of n, because e^{ikx} and e^{-ikx} represent different (but degenerate) states — they describe electrons travelling in opposite directions. The energy is

$$\varepsilon_k = \frac{\hbar^2 k^2}{2m} = \frac{\hbar^2 \pi^2}{2mL^2}(2n)^2. \tag{7.21}$$

Comparing (7.21) with (7.16) we see that the energy levels ε_k include only one half of the energy levels ε_n — they also include zero, but this is of no significance. None the less, the *density of states* is exactly the same in the two cases, because to each level ε_k, except zero, correspond *two* orbital states, with positive and negative values of n respectively. We have seen, in our work on the Sommerfeld model, that for a metallic system the number of electrons is so large, and the spacing between levels is so small, that the only quantity of real importance is the density of states, and the individual energy levels only matter in so far as they contribute to this. We may therefore conclude that the use of periodic boundary conditions and running waves leads, as far as the bulk properties of metals are concerned, to the same results as are obtained with standing waves — running waves are more useful, however, in that they are applicable to conduction problems, and they are mathematically more convenient, so that we shall use them exclusively from now on.

(ii) *Three-dimensional metal.* In applying the Sommerfeld theory to a cube of metal of side L, we assumed that the wave functions vanished on the surface of the cube, which led to the standing wave type of functions (7.1).

As explained above, it is generally more convenient, and in conduction problems necessary, to use functions representing running waves, which in the present case are of the type

$$\psi_{\boldsymbol{k}}(\boldsymbol{r}) = \mathrm{e}^{\mathrm{i}\boldsymbol{k}\cdot\boldsymbol{r}} = \mathrm{e}^{\mathrm{i}(k_1x+k_2y+k_3z)}, \tag{7.22}$$

describing the motion of a particle with constant momentum $\hbar\boldsymbol{k}$. These functions satisfy the Schrödinger equation in the metal but not the original boundary condition — instead, they are required to be triply periodic in x, y, and z, with period L, that is,

$$\psi_{\boldsymbol{k}}(x+L, y, z) = \psi_{\boldsymbol{k}}(x, y+L, z) = \psi_{\boldsymbol{k}}(x, y, z+L) = \psi_{\boldsymbol{k}}(x, y, z). \tag{7.23}$$

Equivalently, we may require that $\psi_{\boldsymbol{k}}$ and its gradient have the same values at corresponding points on opposite faces of the cube. We shall show in the following section, if it is not obvious from the work which has gone before, that these periodic boundary conditions lead to exactly the same density of states as we found previously — equation (7.5).

Notice that, in the present case, there is no question of justifying these conditions physically in the same way as for a one-dimensional metal — it is impossible to bend a cube so that all its pairs of opposite faces come into contact with each other. However, another physical justification is often given. We have already remarked that the bulk properties of a metal cannot depend appreciably upon surface effects, so that, if we are not particularly interested in the latter, there is no harm in imagining our cube of side L embedded in a very large, theoretically infinite, block of metal. If we also imagine that this block is constructed of cubes of side L, then we see that the periodic boundary conditions follow from the very reasonable assumption that all these cubes have exactly the same properties — this is known as a *cyclic system*. It is important to remember, however, that such devices are not strictly necessary — the real justification of the periodic boundary conditions is that they lead to the correct density of states.

Although we have so far considered only the Sommerfeld model of a metal, it is obvious that periodic boundary conditions will be even more appropriate when a periodic field is present, but we will defer this problem until the next chapter. It also need hardly be said that it is not essential to apply the boundary conditions to a cube — in the case of a rectangular parallelepiped of sides L_1, L_2, L_3, (7.23) would become

$$\psi_{\boldsymbol{k}}(x+L_1, y, z) = \psi_{\boldsymbol{k}}(x, y+L_2, z) = \psi_{\boldsymbol{k}}(x, y, z+L_3) = \psi_{\boldsymbol{k}}(x, y, z), \tag{7.24}$$

and again the same density of states would result, with $v = L_1L_2L_3$.

7.4. The Hartree Method Applied to a Free-Electron Gas

In the Sommerfeld theory the electrons are treated as completely free, that is to say, as non-interacting particles moving in zero external field. The term *free-electron gas* is generally applied to a system of electrons moving in zero external field even when the interactions of the electrons among themselves are explicitly taken into account. The effects of the electronic interactions, and Coulomb correlations in particular, upon the energy levels and total energy of a free-electron gas will occupy a good deal of our attention in the remainder of the book. This is mainly because the free-electron gas is the only model for which accurate results can be obtained with a reasonable amount of labour. Fortunately, it is not of purely academic interest, for we know that the electrons in several metals — the alkali metals, for example, sodium in particular, and also some polyvalent metals with small ion-cores, such as magnesium and aluminium — behave very much like free electrons. In the present section we will apply the Hartree theory to a free-electron gas and shall discover that the results are the same as those of the Sommerfeld theory — the Hartree model is a more sophisticated one, however, and we will take the opportunity of reframing our previous work in terms of the vector $\boldsymbol{k}$, appearing in the function (7.22).

If the electrons are assumed to interact, then, in order to stabilize the system — that is, in order to prevent the electron gas from dispersing — we must introduce a uniform distribution of positive charge just sufficient to neutralize the charge of the electrons. The approximation involved is thus simply one of replacing the actual charge distribution of the ion-cores by a uniform distribution of the same total charge. Let us then consider a cube of side L, containing N electrons and a uniform positive charge distribution of density eN/L^3. When periodic boundary conditions are applied, with running waves, the average electronic charge distribution is also uniform, so that the total Hartree field is zero — this will be seen below to be a self-consistent solution of the problem.

The Hartree equation is thus, simply,

$$-\frac{\hbar^2}{2m}\nabla^2\psi = \varepsilon\psi. \tag{7.25}$$

If $\boldsymbol{e}_1$, $\boldsymbol{e}_2$, $\boldsymbol{e}_3$ denote unit vectors along three mutually orthogonal cube edges, which we may take as axes (see Appendix 1), then

$$\boldsymbol{k} = k_1\boldsymbol{e}_1 + k_2\boldsymbol{e}_2 + k_3\boldsymbol{e}_3,$$

$$\boldsymbol{r} = x\boldsymbol{e}_1 + y\boldsymbol{e}_2 + z\boldsymbol{e}_3,$$

and

$$\boldsymbol{k} \cdot \boldsymbol{r} = k_1 x + k_2 y + k_3 z.$$

It follows that

$$\nabla^2 \mathrm{e}^{\mathrm{i}\boldsymbol{k}\cdot\boldsymbol{r}} = -k^2 \mathrm{e}^{\mathrm{i}\boldsymbol{k}\cdot\boldsymbol{r}},$$

and a solution of equation (7.25) is

$$\psi_{\boldsymbol{k}}(\boldsymbol{r}) = C\mathrm{e}^{\mathrm{i}\boldsymbol{k}\cdot\boldsymbol{r}}, \tag{7.26}$$

where C is any constant, provided that

$$\varepsilon \equiv \varepsilon(\boldsymbol{k}) = \frac{\hbar^2 k^2}{2m} = \frac{\hbar^2}{2m}(k_1^2 + k_2^2 + k_3^2). \tag{7.27}$$

Applying the periodic boundary conditions (7.23) to $\psi_{\boldsymbol{k}}$, we find

$$\mathrm{e}^{\mathrm{i}k_1 L} = \mathrm{e}^{\mathrm{i}k_2 L} = \mathrm{e}^{\mathrm{i}k_3 L} = 1,$$

so that

$$k_1 = \frac{2\pi n_1}{L}, \qquad k_2 = \frac{2\pi n_2}{L}, \qquad k_3 = \frac{2\pi n_3}{L}, \tag{7.28}$$

where n_1, n_2, n_3 may be positive or negative integers or zero. Hence,

$$\boldsymbol{k} = \frac{2\pi}{L}(n_1\boldsymbol{e}_1 + n_2\boldsymbol{e}_2 + n_3\boldsymbol{e}_3). \tag{7.29}$$

The vector $\boldsymbol{k}$ is known as the *wave vector* of the state whose wave function is $\psi_{\boldsymbol{k}}$, which is often referred to simply as the 'state $\boldsymbol{k}$'. The magnitude k is equal to $2\pi/\lambda$, where λ is the wavelength of the wave represented by $\psi_{\boldsymbol{k}}$ — for example, in the case of motion in the x-direction, it is easily seen that the function $\mathrm{e}^{\mathrm{i}k_1 x}$ is periodic in x with smallest period $2\pi/k_1$, since

$$\mathrm{e}^{\mathrm{i}k_1 x} = \mathrm{e}^{\mathrm{i}k_1(x + 2\pi/k_1)}.$$

In order to normalize the wave functions, we write

$$1 = \int |\psi_{\boldsymbol{k}}|^2 \mathrm{d}\boldsymbol{r} = C^2 \int \mathrm{d}\boldsymbol{r} = C^2 L^3,$$

the integrals being taken throughout the cube. The wave functions

$$\psi_{\boldsymbol{k}}(\boldsymbol{r}) = \frac{1}{\sqrt{L^3}}\, e^{i\boldsymbol{k}\cdot\boldsymbol{r}}, \tag{7.30}$$

are therefore normalized. We note that $|\psi_{\boldsymbol{k}}|^2 = 1/L^3$, so that the average charge distribution is uniform, and the average charge density of all the electrons is $-eN/L^3$ — the effect of this is exactly cancelled by the assumed uniform positive charge distribution, giving the self-consistent result that the Hartree field is zero.

The energy levels, from equations (7.27) and (7.28), are given by

$$\varepsilon(\boldsymbol{k}) = \frac{\hbar^2}{2m}\frac{4\pi^2}{L^2}(n_1^2+n_2^2+n_3^2).$$

Comparing this with (7.2), it may be seen that only one in eight of the original levels are now present — those corresponding to *even* integral values of n_x, n_y, n_z. However, owing to the fact that positive and negative values of n_1, n_2, n_3 now represent different states, the degeneracy of each level is eight times as great as before — in other words, there are now eight times as many states to each energy level. The density of states $\mathcal{N}(\varepsilon)$ therefore remains unchanged. We will now verify this by another method.

Instead of the '$\boldsymbol{n}$-space' which we introduced in § 7.2, it will be convenient to define a '$\boldsymbol{k}$-space', whose rectangular Cartesian axes represent k_1, k_2, and k_3. Equations (7.28) tell us that points in $\boldsymbol{k}$-space with coordinates

$$\left(\frac{2\pi}{L}n_1,\ \frac{2\pi}{L}n_2,\ \frac{2\pi}{L}n_3\right),$$

where n_1, n_2, and n_3 are integers, represent orbital states, and a cube of side $2\pi/L$ therefore contains one orbital state. It follows that the number of states per unit volume of $\boldsymbol{k}$-space is $L^3/8\pi^3$, or $v/8\pi^3$. We may therefore state that,

for a metal of volume v, the number of orbital states lying within a volume element $\mathrm{d}\boldsymbol{k}$ *of $\boldsymbol{k}$-space is* $v\mathrm{d}\boldsymbol{k}/8\pi^3$.

We assume, of course, that, although $\mathrm{d}\boldsymbol{k}$ may be chosen to be very small compared with the occupied volume of $\boldsymbol{k}$-space, it will none the less contain a large number of states — the approximations involved in the use of this formula are, in fact, the same as those we made in our previous calculation of $\mathcal{N}(\varepsilon)$.

Equation (7.27) shows that the surfaces of constant energy in $\boldsymbol{k}$-space are spheres, centred at the origin. At the absolute zero of temperature, the occupied region of **k**-space is thus a sphere, called the *Fermi sphere*, whose radius we will denote by k_0. Since each orbital state is occupied by two electrons, twice the number of states within the Fermi sphere must equal N, that is

$$2\frac{v}{8\pi^3}\frac{4\pi}{3}k_0^3 = N,$$

and

$$k_0 = \left(\frac{3\pi^2 N}{v}\right)^{\frac{1}{3}} = \left(\frac{9\pi}{4}\right)^{\frac{1}{3}}\frac{1}{r_s}. \tag{7.31}$$

We now find

$$\zeta_0 = \frac{\hbar^2 k_0^2}{2m} = \frac{\hbar^2}{2m}\left(\frac{9\pi}{4}\right)^{\frac{2}{3}}\frac{1}{r_s^2},$$

in agreement with equation (7.11).

Before finding the density of states for the present model, it will prove useful for our future work to obtain a general expression for $\mathcal{N}(\varepsilon)$ which applies to all cases in which the surfaces of constant energy in **k**-space are spheres, centred at the origin, whether ε is given by equation (7.27) or not. In other words, let us assume nothing more than that ε is a function of the magnitude k of the wave vector only, that is, $\varepsilon \equiv \varepsilon(k)$. Then the number of orbital states with energies less than ε is

$$\frac{4\pi}{3}k^3\frac{v}{8\pi^3} = \frac{v}{6\pi^2}k^3.$$

The density of states in energy is the derivative of this with respect to ε, so that

$$\begin{aligned}\mathcal{N}(\varepsilon) &= \frac{d}{d\varepsilon}\left(\frac{v}{6\pi^2}k^3\right)\\ &= \frac{d}{dk}\left(\frac{v}{6\pi^2}k^3\right)\Big/\frac{d\varepsilon}{dk}\\ &= \frac{vk^2}{2\pi^2}\Big/\frac{d\varepsilon}{dk}.\end{aligned} \tag{7.32}$$

We shall have occasion to use this formula later. In the present case of the Hartree method, we have

$$\varepsilon = \frac{\hbar^2}{2m} k^2, \qquad \frac{d\varepsilon}{dk} = \frac{\hbar^2}{m} k,$$

and

$$\mathcal{N}(\varepsilon) = \frac{v}{2\pi^2} \frac{m}{\hbar^2} k$$

$$= \frac{v}{4\pi^2} \left(\frac{2m}{\hbar^2}\right)^{\frac{3}{2}} \varepsilon^{\frac{1}{2}},$$

as in equation (7.5).

7.5. The Hartree-Fock Method Applied to a Free-Electron Gas

The Hartree-Fock equations for a monovalent metal were found in § 6.2, equation (6.22), to be of the form

$$\left[-\frac{\hbar^2}{2m} \nabla_1^2 + \sum_a^N V_a(\boldsymbol{r}_1) + e^2 \sum_j^N \int \frac{|\psi_j(\boldsymbol{r}_2)|^2}{r_{12}} \, d\boldsymbol{r}_2\right] \psi_i(\boldsymbol{r}_1)$$

$$-e^2 \sum_{\substack{j \\ (\text{spin } j \\ = \text{ spin } i)}}^N \left[\int \frac{\psi_j^*(\boldsymbol{r}_2)\psi_i(\boldsymbol{r}_2)\psi_j(\boldsymbol{r}_1)}{r_{12}\psi_i(\boldsymbol{r}_1)} \, d\boldsymbol{r}_2\right] \psi_i(\boldsymbol{r}_1) = \varepsilon_i \psi_i(\boldsymbol{r}_1). \tag{7.33}$$

We now wish to solve this equation for the free-electron system described in the previous section. We shall show that the normalized functions

$$\psi_{\boldsymbol{k}}(\boldsymbol{r}) = \frac{1}{\sqrt{v}} e^{i\boldsymbol{k}\cdot\boldsymbol{r}}, \tag{7.34}$$

which we found to be eigenfunctions of the Hartree equation, are also eigenfunctions of equation (7.33) — corresponding to different eigenvalues, however. Anticipating this fact, we may omit the second and third terms in the first square brackets, since these represent the Hartree field, which we know to be zero for the present model. Also, from now on, we will use the subscripts $\boldsymbol{k}$ and $\boldsymbol{k}'$ to distinguish between eigenfunctions, rather than the subscripts i and j used in equation (7.33). The Hartree-Fock equation for the state $\boldsymbol{k}$ thus becomes

$$-\frac{\hbar^2}{2m}\nabla_1^2\psi_k(r_1)-e^2\sum_{k'}\left[\int\frac{\psi_{k'}^*(r_2)\psi_k(r_2)\psi_{k'}(r_1)}{r_{12}\psi_k(r_1)}\,\mathrm{d}r_2\right]\psi_k(r_1)$$
$$=\varepsilon(k)\psi_k(r_1). \qquad (7.35)$$

The sum over k' is a sum over all the occupied orbital states, so that, at the absolute zero of temperature, when each of these states contains two electrons with opposite spins, the sum over k' is the same as a sum over all electrons with one kind of spin, and a sum over all electrons with the other kind of spin would be precisely the same. The specification "spin j = spin i", or "spin k' = spin k", thus need not be stated explicitly. The integrals are, of course, taken throughout the volume of the metal.

Now, if we use the functions ψ_k given in equation (7.34), the exchange term, which is the second term on the left-hand side of equation (7.35), becomes

$$-\frac{e^2}{v}\sum_{k'}\left[\int\frac{\mathrm{e}^{\mathrm{i}(k-k')\cdot(r_2-r_1)}}{r_{12}}\,\mathrm{d}r_2\right]\psi_k(r_1). \qquad (7.36)$$

The integral may be written

$$\mathrm{e}^{-\mathrm{i}(k-k')\cdot r_1}\int\frac{\mathrm{e}^{\mathrm{i}(k-k')\cdot r_2}}{r_{12}}\,\mathrm{d}r_2, \qquad (7.37)$$

and in order to evaluate it we make use of a device suggested by electrostatics. Suppose that $\phi(r)$ is the potential at the point r due to a distribution of charge whose density is given by the function $\mathrm{e}^{\mathrm{i}(k-k')\cdot r}$. This is not a physically real distribution, of course, but may be treated as such for purposes of calculation. Then $\phi(r)$ must satisfy Poisson's equation

$$\nabla^2\phi(r) = -4\pi\mathrm{e}^{\mathrm{i}(k-k')\cdot r},$$

the required solution of which, as may be verified by substitution, is

$$\phi(r) = \frac{4\pi\,\mathrm{e}^{\mathrm{i}(k-k')\cdot r}}{|k-k'|^2}. \qquad (7.39)$$

The potential at the point r_1, which is

$$\phi(r_1) = \int\frac{\mathrm{e}^{\mathrm{i}(k-k')\cdot r_2}}{r_{12}}\,\mathrm{d}r_2, \qquad (7.40)$$

must, according to (7.39), have the value

$$\frac{4\pi e^{i(\boldsymbol{k}-\boldsymbol{k}')\cdot \boldsymbol{r}_1}}{|\boldsymbol{k}-\boldsymbol{k}'|^2},$$

and the expression (7.37) must therefore be equal to †

$$\frac{4\pi}{|\boldsymbol{k}-\boldsymbol{k}'|^2}.$$

The exchange term (7.36) may thus be written

$$\varepsilon_x(\boldsymbol{k})\psi_{\boldsymbol{k}}(\boldsymbol{r}),$$

where

$$\varepsilon_x(\boldsymbol{k}) = -\frac{4\pi e^2}{v}\sum_{\boldsymbol{k}'}\frac{1}{|\boldsymbol{k}-\boldsymbol{k}'|^2}. \tag{7.41}$$

We will call $\varepsilon_x(\boldsymbol{k})$ *the exchange energy associated with the state* $\boldsymbol{k}$. This proves that the functions $\psi_{\boldsymbol{k}}$, as given in (7.34), are eigenfunctions of the Hartree-Fock equation, and the eigenvalues are given by

$$\varepsilon(\boldsymbol{k}) = \frac{\hbar^2 k^2}{2m} + \varepsilon_x(\boldsymbol{k}). \tag{7.42}$$

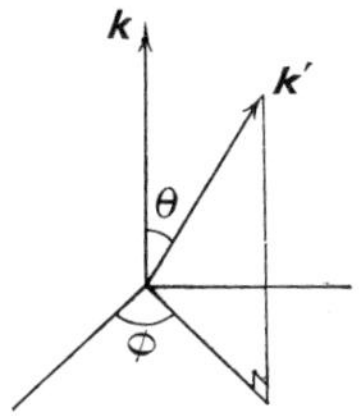

Fig. 7.6.

In order to evaluate $\varepsilon_x(\boldsymbol{k})$ we make use of the fact that a volume element $d\boldsymbol{k}$ of $\boldsymbol{k}$-space contains $v d\boldsymbol{k}/8\pi^3$ orbital states, and replace the sum in (7.41) by an integral, so that

$$\varepsilon_x(\boldsymbol{k}) = -\frac{4\pi e^2}{v}\frac{v}{8\pi^3}\int\frac{d\boldsymbol{k}'}{|\boldsymbol{k}-\boldsymbol{k}'|^2}.$$

The integral is taken throughout the Fermi sphere. If we use spherical polar coordinates (k', θ, ϕ), where θ is the angle between $\boldsymbol{k}'$ and $\boldsymbol{k}$ (see Figure 7.6), we find

† This result is not strictly accurate, since the value of the integral in (7.36) must depend to some extent upon the position of $\boldsymbol{r}_1$ — the integral is taken throughout the cube of side L, and its value when $\boldsymbol{r}_1$ is very close to a face of the cube must be different from its value when $\boldsymbol{r}_1$ is in the centre. The approximations involved in obtaining this result, independent of $\boldsymbol{r}_1$, however, are simply those which are implicit in the use of periodic boundary conditions.

$$\begin{aligned}\varepsilon_x(\boldsymbol{k}) &= -\frac{e^2}{2\pi^2}\int_0^{k_0} dk' \int_0^{\pi} d\theta \int_0^{2\pi} \frac{k'^2 \sin\theta \, d\phi}{|\boldsymbol{k}-\boldsymbol{k}'|^2} \\ &= -\frac{e^2}{\pi}\int_0^{k_0} dk' \int_{-1}^{1} \frac{k'^2 \, d(\cos\theta)}{k^2+k'^2-2kk'\cos\theta} \\ &= -\frac{e^2}{\pi k}\int_0^{k_0} k' \log\left|\frac{k+k'}{k-k'}\right| dk'. \end{aligned} \tag{7.43}$$

We note that the integrand becomes infinite when $k' = k$, so that, for $k < k_0$, the integral must be expressed as the sum of the integral from 0 to k and the integral from k to k_0, and the convergence of both integrals must be examined. In fact, both integrals converge, and (7.43) may be evaluated using elementary integration by parts. The result, which is true for both $k < k_0$ and $k > k_0$, is

$$\varepsilon_x(\boldsymbol{k}) = -\frac{e^2 k_0}{2\pi}\left[2+\frac{k_0^2-k^2}{kk_0}\log\left|\frac{k_0+k}{k_0-k}\right|\right]. \tag{7.44}$$

The Hartree-Fock energy associated with state $\boldsymbol{k}$, referred to the same zero as in our application of the Hartree theory, is thus

$$\varepsilon(\boldsymbol{k}) = \frac{\hbar^2 k^2}{2m} - \frac{e^2 k_0}{2\pi}\left[2+\frac{k_0^2-k^2}{kk_0}\log\left|\frac{k_0+k}{k_0-k}\right|\right]. \tag{7.45}$$

This is a spherically symmetrical function, that is, $\varepsilon(\boldsymbol{k}) \equiv \varepsilon(k)$, as in the Hartree case.

It may be verified that

$$\lim_{k\to 0} \frac{k_0^2-k^2}{kk_0}\log\left|\frac{k_0+k}{k_0-k}\right| = 2,$$

and

$$\lim_{k\to k_0} \frac{k_0^2-k^2}{kk_0}\log\left|\frac{k_0+k}{k_0-k}\right| = 0,$$

so that

$$\varepsilon(0) = -\frac{2e^2 k_0}{\pi} \quad \text{and} \quad \varepsilon(k_0) = \frac{\hbar^2 k_0^2}{2m} - \frac{e^2 k_0}{\pi}.$$

The *band width* for any metallic system may be defined as the difference between the highest and the lowest one-electron energies at 0°K. The Hartree-Fock band width for a free-electron gas is, therefore,

$$\varepsilon(k_0)-\varepsilon(0) = \frac{\hbar^2 k_0^2}{2m} + \frac{e^2 k_0}{\pi}$$
$$= \zeta_0 + \frac{e^2 k_0}{\pi}. \tag{7.46}$$

The band width according to the Hartree theory is, of course, just ζ_0. The additional band width, e^2k_0/π, in the case of the Hartree-Fock theory, is considerable — it amounts to 4.1 eV for sodium, while ζ_0 is only 3.2 eV for this metal. The true band width, which, as we shall see, can be roughly estimated from soft X-ray emission data, favours the Hartree rather than the Hartree-Fock theory.

The band width is the width of the occupied part of the distribution of states in energy, so it is perhaps not surprising that the shape of the $\mathcal{N}(\varepsilon)$ curve is quite different in the two theories. Since the surfaces of constant energy in **k**-space are again spheres, we may use formula (7.32) in the Hartree-Fock case also, giving

$$\mathcal{N}(\varepsilon) = \frac{vk^2}{2\pi^2}\Big/\frac{d\varepsilon}{dk}$$
$$= \frac{vk^2}{2\pi^2}\Big/\left[\frac{\hbar^2 k}{m} - \frac{e^2}{2\pi}\left\{\frac{2k_0}{k} - \left(1+\frac{k_0^2}{k^2}\right)\log\left|\frac{k_0+k}{k_0-k}\right|\right\}\right]. \tag{7.47}$$

Thè denominator, $d\varepsilon/dk$, becomes infinite when $k = k_0$, so that $\mathcal{N}(\varepsilon)$ falls to zero at the surface of the Fermi sphere.

Since we cannot obtain k as a simple function of ε, the $\mathcal{N}(\varepsilon)$ curve must be found numerically by calculating both $\mathcal{N}(\varepsilon)$ and ε for chosen values of k — the result, for the electron density occurring in metallic sodium, is compared with the Hartree curve in Figure 7.7. There is one important distinction between the two curves which is often overlooked. The parabolic Hartree $\mathcal{N}(\varepsilon)$ curve is the same for all temperatures and for all values of N — only the function $\mathcal{N}(\varepsilon)f(\varepsilon)$, which is the density of *occupied* states, changes. This is not so in the Hartree-Fock case — here the function $\mathcal{N}(\varepsilon)$ itself depends upon the occupation of states, since the exchange energy $\varepsilon_x(\boldsymbol{k})$ does. We have assumed the temperature to be 0°K: at higher temperatures, electrons would not simply be excited to states in the unoccupied part of the $\mathcal{N}(\varepsilon)$ curve, but the shape of the curve would be altered, owing to the change in $\varepsilon_x(\boldsymbol{k})$. Similarly, a larger value of N would not result in a filling up of unoccupied states lying beyond the sharp fall to zero in the $\mathcal{N}(\varepsilon)$ curve, but would result in a displacement of this zero — at 0°K the zero always occurs at the energy of the highest occupied state. It follows that the unshaded portion of the Hartree-Fock $\mathcal{N}(\varepsilon)$ curve in Figure 7.7

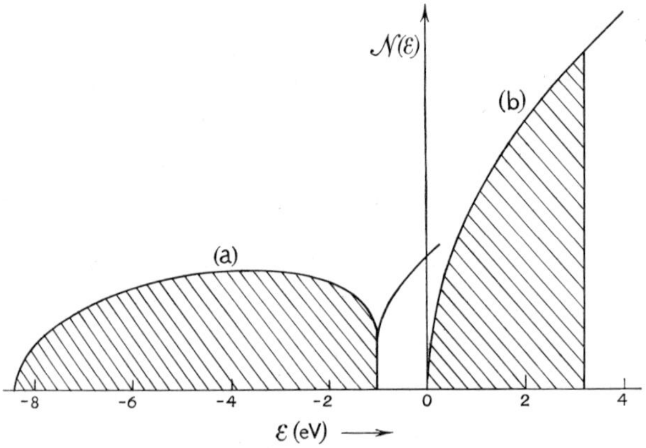

Fig. 7.7. Density of states $\mathcal{N}(\varepsilon)$ for a free-electron system with the same electron density as metallic sodium: (a) according to the Hartree-Fock theory at 0°K, (b) according to the Hartree theory, both referred to the same zero of energy. The shaded regions are occupied at 0°K.

has no meaning in a rigorous sense — however, it does show to a good approximation the density of possible states of an electron shot into the metal from outside, since the presence of one additional electron cannot appreciably affect the $\mathcal{N}(\varepsilon)$ curve. Similarly, we expect the curve to have *roughly* the same shape at temperatures not too much above 0°K, even though the sharp zero no longer appears.

Many physical properties of metals depend upon the shape of the $\mathcal{N}(\varepsilon)$ curve, particularly near the highest occupied energy level. Such properties are the electronic specific heat, soft X-ray emission spectrum, and spin paramagnetic susceptibility, all of which we shall consider in some detail later. It is clear that, as far as these properties are concerned, the Hartree and Hartree-Fock methods will give very different results — and those of the Hartree method are found to be in better agreement with experiment.

We know that this superiority of the Hartree method must be purely fortuitous, however, for this method completely ignores Coulomb correlations. The Hartree-Fock method, on the other hand, as we have seen in § 6.3, takes some account of parallel spin correlations, while neglecting anti-parallel spin correlations. It would seem that, as far as the density of states is concerned, it is better to ignore all correlations than to include only some of them. None the less, the Hartree-Fock method gives a better *total* energy than the Hartree method. This will be proved below, but it is suggested by Figure 7.7 — the Hartree-Fock $\mathcal{N}(\varepsilon)$ curve is displaced considerably to the left of the Hartree curve, so that, in spite of the larger band width, the Hartree-Fock total energy is expected to be much lower than that of the Hartree method. We shall show in Chapter 9 that this lowering of the energy is very necessary, for the Hartree method itself gives a negative cohesive energy, that is to say, no cohesion at all, whereas the Hartree-Fock method does give a positive cohesive energy, although it is still much too small. It will be seen later, in Chapter 10, that, when proper account is taken of *all* Coulomb correlations, the density of states becomes very similar to that of the Hartree theory and the total energy is lowered still further, giving excellent agreement with the observed cohesive energies.

We will now calculate the total energy of a free-electron gas according to the Hartree-Fock theory. This is not obtained simply by summing the eigenvalues $\varepsilon(\boldsymbol{k})$ over all the electrons, which would, in fact, include the total exchange energy twice, but the correct expression may be deduced from either equation (6.18) or equation (6.24). Since there are no ion-cores in the free-electron model, but only a uniform distribution of positive charge which exactly cancels the average distribution of electronic charge, the second and fourth terms on the right of equation (6.24) disappear, and the total energy becomes

$$\sum_i^N \varepsilon_i + \tfrac{1}{2} \sum_i^N \sum_{\substack{j \\ (\parallel \text{ spins})}}^N \iint \frac{e^2}{r_{12}} \psi_i^*(\boldsymbol{r}_1)\psi_j^*(\boldsymbol{r}_2)\psi_i(\boldsymbol{r}_2)\psi_j(\boldsymbol{r}_1)\mathrm{d}\boldsymbol{r}_1\,\mathrm{d}\boldsymbol{r}_2,$$

in our earlier notation. We will denote this by NE_{HF}, where E_{HF} is the *average* Hartree-Fock energy per electron, and also translate it into the '$\boldsymbol{k}$-notation'. Remembering that a sum over $\boldsymbol{k}$ is a sum over orbital states, so that it must be multiplied by two to obtain a sum over electrons, we find

$$
\begin{aligned}
NE_{\mathrm{HF}} &= 2\sum_{\boldsymbol{k}} \varepsilon(\boldsymbol{k}) + \sum_{\boldsymbol{k}}\sum_{\boldsymbol{k}'} \int\!\!\int \frac{e^2}{r_{12}}\, \psi_{\boldsymbol{k}}^*(\boldsymbol{r}_1)\psi_{\boldsymbol{k}'}^*(\boldsymbol{r}_2)\psi_{\boldsymbol{k}}(\boldsymbol{r}_2)\psi_{\boldsymbol{k}'}(\boldsymbol{r}_1)\,\mathrm{d}\boldsymbol{r}_1\,\mathrm{d}\boldsymbol{r}_2 \\
&= 2\sum_{\boldsymbol{k}} \left[\frac{\hbar^2 k^2}{2m} + \varepsilon_{\mathrm{x}}(\boldsymbol{k})\right] - \sum_{\boldsymbol{k}} \varepsilon_{\mathrm{x}}(\boldsymbol{k}) \\
&= 2\sum_{\boldsymbol{k}} \frac{\hbar^2 k^2}{2m} + \sum_{\boldsymbol{k}} \varepsilon_{\mathrm{x}}(\boldsymbol{k}).
\end{aligned} \tag{7.48}
$$

The first term is the total kinetic energy, or NE_{F}, where E_{F} is the Fermi energy given by equation (7.12) — this is, in fact, the total energy in the Hartree approximation. The second term is the total exchange energy, which may be evaluated by replacing the sum by an integral over the Fermi sphere, as we did in evaluating $\varepsilon_{\mathrm{x}}(\boldsymbol{k})$. This gives

$$
\begin{aligned}
\sum_{\boldsymbol{k}} \varepsilon_{\mathrm{x}}(\boldsymbol{k}) &= -\frac{e^2}{2\pi}\sum_{\boldsymbol{k}} \left[2k_0 + \frac{k_0^2 - k^2}{k}\log\left(\frac{k_0+k}{k_0-k}\right)\right] \\
&= -\frac{e^2}{2\pi}\frac{v}{8\pi^3}\int_0^{k_0} \left[2k_0 + \frac{k_0^2-k^2}{k}\log\left(\frac{k_0+k}{k_0-k}\right)\right] 4\pi k^2\,\mathrm{d}k \\
&= -\frac{e^2 v}{4\pi^3}\int_0^{k_0} \left[2k_0 k^2 + k(k_0^2-k^2)\log\left(\frac{k_0+k}{k_0-k}\right)\right]\mathrm{d}k \\
&= \frac{e^2 v}{4\pi^3} k_0^4 = -\frac{e^2 v}{4\pi^3}\left(\frac{3\pi^2 N}{v}\right)^{\frac{4}{3}} \\
&= -\frac{3e^2 N}{4}\left(\frac{9}{4\pi^2}\right)^{\frac{1}{3}}\frac{1}{r_{\mathrm{s}}},
\end{aligned} \tag{7.49}
$$

using (7.31).

Denoting the *average* exchange energy per electron by E_{x}, then, we have

$$
E_{\mathrm{x}} = -\frac{3e^2}{4}\left(\frac{9}{4\pi^2}\right)^{\frac{1}{3}}\frac{1}{r_{\mathrm{s}}}. \tag{7.50}
$$

The average energy per electron in the Hartree-Fock method applied to free electrons is, therefore,

$$
\begin{aligned}
E_{\mathrm{HF}} &= E_{\mathrm{F}} + E_{\mathrm{x}} \\
&= \frac{3\hbar^2}{10m}\left(\frac{9\pi}{4}\right)^{\frac{2}{3}}\frac{1}{r_{\mathrm{s}}^2} - \frac{3e^2}{4}\left(\frac{9}{4\pi^2}\right)^{\frac{1}{3}}\frac{1}{r_{\mathrm{s}}}.
\end{aligned} \tag{7.51}
$$

It is convenient to use the 'atomic units' defined in § 3.3, that is, to express energies in rydbergs and lengths in Bohr units. In this case, we find

$$E_F = \frac{3\hbar^2}{10m}\left(\frac{9\pi}{4}\right)^{\frac{2}{3}}\frac{1}{r_s^2}\left(\frac{me^2}{\hbar^2}\right)^2\left(\frac{2\hbar^2}{me^4}\right)$$

$$= \frac{3}{5}\left(\frac{9\pi}{4}\right)^{\frac{2}{3}}\frac{1}{r_s^2} = \frac{2.21}{r_s^2}\ \text{ryd}, \tag{7.52}$$

and

$$E_x = -\frac{3e^2}{4}\left(\frac{9}{4\pi^2}\right)^{\frac{1}{3}}\frac{1}{r_s}\left(\frac{me^2}{\hbar^2}\right)\left(\frac{2\hbar^2}{me^4}\right)$$

$$= -\frac{3}{2}\left(\frac{9}{4\pi^2}\right)^{\frac{1}{3}}\frac{1}{r_s} = -\frac{0.916}{r_s}\ \text{ryd}. \tag{7.53}$$

The average energy per electron in the Hartree-Fock method is thus

$$E_{HF} = \frac{2.21}{r_s^2} - \frac{0.916}{r_s}\ \text{ryd}, \tag{7.54}$$

while in the Hartree method it is simply the Fermi energy E_F. For all the monovalent metals r_s lies between about 3 and 6 B.u., so that the exchange energy lowers the value of E_{HF} considerably — making it negative, in fact.

7.6. The Exchange Charge Density and the Fermi Hole in a Free-Electron gas

We will first calculate the exchange charge density in the free-electron gas discussed above. The general expression for the exchange charge density is given by (6.25). Translating this into our '$\boldsymbol{k}$-notation', we find that the exchange charge density at position $\boldsymbol{r}_2$ for an electron in state $\boldsymbol{k}$ at $\boldsymbol{r}_1$ is

$$e\sum_{\boldsymbol{k}'}\frac{\psi_{\boldsymbol{k}'}^*(\boldsymbol{r}_2)\psi_{\boldsymbol{k}}(\boldsymbol{r}_2)\psi_{\boldsymbol{k}'}(\boldsymbol{r}_1)}{\psi_{\boldsymbol{k}}(\boldsymbol{r}_1)}. \tag{7.55}$$

Using (7.34) and, as usual, replacing the sum in (7.55) by an integral throughout the Fermi sphere, this expression becomes

$$\frac{e}{8\pi^3}\int e^{i(\boldsymbol{k}'-\boldsymbol{k})\cdot(\boldsymbol{r}_1-\boldsymbol{r}_2)}d\boldsymbol{k}' = \frac{e}{8\pi^3}e^{-i\boldsymbol{k}\cdot(\boldsymbol{r}_1-\boldsymbol{r}_2)}\int e^{i\boldsymbol{k}'\cdot(\boldsymbol{r}_1-\boldsymbol{r}_2)}d\boldsymbol{k}'. \tag{7.56}$$

In order to evaluate the integral we use spherical polar coordinates (k', θ, ϕ), where θ is the angle between the vectors $\boldsymbol{r}_1 - \boldsymbol{r}_2$ and $\boldsymbol{k}'$. The exchange charge density is then

$$\frac{e}{8\pi^3}\,\mathrm{e}^{-i\boldsymbol{k}\cdot(\boldsymbol{r}_1-\boldsymbol{r}_2)}\int_0^{k_0} 2\pi k'^2\,\mathrm{d}k' \int_{-1}^{1} \mathrm{e}^{ik'r_{12}\cos\theta}\,\mathrm{d}\,(\cos\theta)$$

$$= \frac{e}{2\pi^2}\,\mathrm{e}^{-i\boldsymbol{k}\cdot(\boldsymbol{r}_1-\boldsymbol{r}_2)}\int_0^{k_0} \frac{k'\sin k'r_{12}}{r_{12}}\,\mathrm{d}k'$$

$$= \frac{e}{2\pi^2}\left(\frac{\sin k_0 r_{12} - k_0 r_{12}\cos k_0 r_{12}}{r_{12}^3}\right)\mathrm{e}^{-i\boldsymbol{k}\cdot(\boldsymbol{r}_1-\boldsymbol{r}_2)}. \tag{7.57}$$

The magnitude of the exchange charge density thus decreases rapidly as r_{12} increases, and it is easily verified that, in the limit as $r_{12} \to 0$, its value becomes $eN/2v$, which is equal in magnitude, but opposite in sign, to the average charge density of electrons with one kind of spin. We see, however, that (7.57) is not spherically symmetrical about $\boldsymbol{r}_1$, that it depends upon $\boldsymbol{k}$, and that it is a complex function.

A more useful picture is obtained by *averaging* the exchange charge density over all electrons with one kind of spin, or over all values of $\boldsymbol{k}$ within the Fermi sphere. This also provides a more correct picture, as far as our interpretation is concerned, for, as we remarked in § 6.3, when a determinantal wave function is used, it is not correct to regard the electron at $\boldsymbol{r}_1$ as being in a particular one-electron state, but it must be regarded as partially in all of them. Since there are $N/2$ electrons with one kind of spin, the *average exchange charge density* at $\boldsymbol{r}_2$ for an electron at $\boldsymbol{r}_1$ is

$$\frac{e}{2\pi^2}\left(\frac{\sin k_0 r_{12} - k_0 r_{12}\cos k_0 r_{12}}{r_{12}^3}\right)\frac{2}{N}\frac{v}{8\pi^3}\int \mathrm{e}^{-i\boldsymbol{k}\cdot(\boldsymbol{r}_1-\boldsymbol{r}_2)}\,\mathrm{d}\boldsymbol{k}$$

$$= \frac{evk_0^6}{2\pi^4 N}\left(\frac{\sin k_0 r_{12} - k_0 r_{12}\cos k_0 r_{12}}{k_0^3 r_{12}^3}\right)^2$$

$$= \frac{9eN}{2v}\left(\frac{\sin\xi - \xi\cos\xi}{\xi^3}\right)^2, \tag{7.58}$$

where

$$\xi = k_0 r_{12} = \left(\frac{9\pi}{4}\right)^{\frac{1}{3}}\frac{r_{12}}{r_s}.$$

Adding (7.58) to $-eN/2v$, we find that the average charge density, at distance ξ/k_0 from an electron at $\boldsymbol{r}_1$, of electrons with parallel spins is

$$-\frac{eN}{2v}F(\xi),$$

where

$$F(\xi) = 1-9\left(\frac{\sin\xi-\xi\cos\xi}{\xi^3}\right)^2. \tag{7.59}$$

The graph of the function $F(\xi)$ is shown in Figure 7.8. It is at once apparent that the description of the average Fermi hole, as a spherical hole of approximate radius r_s in the distribution of electrons with parallel spins, is a very reasonable one.

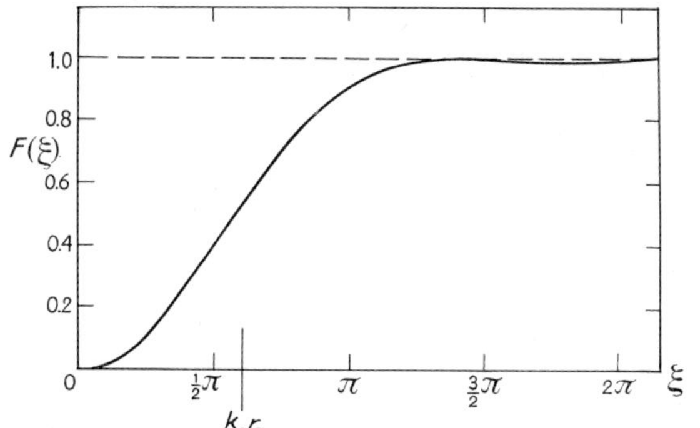

Fig. 7.8. Graph of the function $F(\xi)$. At distance ξ/k_0 from a given electron the average charge density of electrons with parallel spins is $-eN\,F(\xi)/2v$ (if the electronic motions were uncorrelated this would be just $-eN/2v$).

The basis of the foregoing work was the Hartree-Fock equation (7.35), and the treatment has been of a rather intuitive nature. It is instructive, and some may find it more satisfying, to obtain the same result directly, without explicit use of the Hartree-Fock equation, by showing that the probability of simultaneously finding two electrons with parallel spins in volume elements a distance r_{12} apart is proportional to $F(\xi)$. This may be derived, rather lengthily, from the probability density of the whole electron distribution, that is, the squared modulus of the total determinantal wave function, or more simply in the following way.

Let us consider at first only two free electrons, with parallel spins, in the states $\boldsymbol{k}$ and $\boldsymbol{k}'$. If we assume that the spins are positive, then the determinantal wave function for this system becomes

$$\frac{1}{v\sqrt{2}}\begin{vmatrix} e^{i\boldsymbol{k}\cdot\boldsymbol{r}_1} & e^{i\boldsymbol{k}\cdot\boldsymbol{r}_2} \\ e^{i\boldsymbol{k}'\cdot\boldsymbol{r}_1} & e^{i\boldsymbol{k}'\cdot\boldsymbol{r}_2} \end{vmatrix}\alpha(\zeta_1)\alpha(\zeta_2),$$

which is normalized in the volume v. The probability that $\boldsymbol{r}_1$ lies in the volume element $d\boldsymbol{r}_1$ and $\boldsymbol{r}_2$ in the volume element $d\boldsymbol{r}_2$ is, thus,

$$\begin{aligned}\frac{1}{2v^2}&|e^{i(\boldsymbol{k}\cdot\boldsymbol{r}_1+\boldsymbol{k}'\cdot\boldsymbol{r}_2)}-e^{i(\boldsymbol{k}\cdot\boldsymbol{r}_2-\boldsymbol{k}'\cdot\boldsymbol{r}_1)}|^2 d\boldsymbol{r}_1 d\boldsymbol{r}_2\\ &=\frac{1}{2v^2}|1-e^{i(\boldsymbol{k}'-\boldsymbol{k})\cdot(\boldsymbol{r}_1-\boldsymbol{r}_2)}|^2 d\boldsymbol{r}_1 d\boldsymbol{r}_2\\ &=\frac{1}{v^2}[1-\mathscr{R}e^{i(\boldsymbol{k}'-\boldsymbol{k})\cdot(\boldsymbol{r}_1-\boldsymbol{r}_2)}]d\boldsymbol{r}_1 d\boldsymbol{r}_2, \end{aligned}\tag{7.60}$$

where $\mathscr{R}$ stands for the *real part* of the function following it.

The same expression holds for all pairs of states $\boldsymbol{k}$ and $\boldsymbol{k}'$ associated with the same spin. In order to obtain the total probability, therefore, we average over all $\boldsymbol{k}$ and $\boldsymbol{k}'$ within the Fermi sphere. Hence, for our N-electron system, the probability that electron 1 is in $d\boldsymbol{r}_1$ and simultaneously electron 2, with parallel spin, is in $d\boldsymbol{r}_2$ is †

$$\begin{aligned}\frac{1}{v^2}\frac{4}{N^2}&\sum_{\boldsymbol{k}}\sum_{\boldsymbol{k}'}[1-\mathscr{R}e^{i(\boldsymbol{k}'-\boldsymbol{k})\cdot(\boldsymbol{r}_1-\boldsymbol{r}_2)}]d\boldsymbol{r}_1 d\boldsymbol{r}_2\\ &=\frac{4}{N^2}\frac{d\boldsymbol{r}_1 d\boldsymbol{r}_2}{(8\pi^3)^2}\iint[1-\mathscr{R}e^{i(\boldsymbol{k}'-\boldsymbol{k})\cdot(\boldsymbol{r}_1-\boldsymbol{r}_2)}]d\boldsymbol{k}d\boldsymbol{k}'\\ &=\frac{4}{N^2}\frac{d\boldsymbol{r}_1 d\boldsymbol{r}_2}{(8\pi^3)^2}\left[\left(\frac{4\pi}{3}k_0^3\right)^2-\mathscr{R}\int e^{i\boldsymbol{k}'\cdot(\boldsymbol{r}_1-\boldsymbol{r}_2)}d\boldsymbol{k}'\int e^{-i\boldsymbol{k}\cdot(\boldsymbol{r}_1-\boldsymbol{r}_2)}d\boldsymbol{k}\right]\\ &=\frac{4}{N^2}\frac{d\boldsymbol{r}_1 d\boldsymbol{r}_2}{(8\pi^3)^2}\left[\left(\frac{4\pi}{3}k_0^3\right)^2-16\pi^2\left(\frac{\sin k_0r_{12}-k_0r_{12}\cos k_0r_{12}}{r_{12}^3}\right)^2\right]\\ &=\frac{4}{N^2}\frac{d\boldsymbol{r}_1 d\boldsymbol{r}_2}{(8\pi^3)^2}\left(\frac{4\pi}{3}k_0^3\right)^2\left[1-9\left(\frac{\sin k_0r_{12}-k_0r_{12}\cos k_0r_{12}}{k_0^3r_{12}^3}\right)^2\right]\\ &=\frac{d\boldsymbol{r}_1 d\boldsymbol{r}_2}{v^2}F(\xi).\end{aligned}\tag{7.61}$$

† We know that two electrons with the same spin cannot occupy the same orbital state. It is unnecessary to take this into account in the double summation, because the value of (7.60) is zero anyway when $\boldsymbol{k}=\boldsymbol{k}'$. However, in order to obtain the correct average, we should really divide by the number of *different* pairs of $\boldsymbol{k}$ and $\boldsymbol{k}'$, namely, $\frac{1}{2}N(\frac{1}{2}N-1)$, instead of $\frac{1}{4}N^2$, as we have done, but N is so large that the difference between the two is negligible.

The integrals in the third line are equal in value and both real, as we have found above, so that the $\mathscr{R}$ does not affect the result.

The probability of finding a given electron in the volume element d$\boldsymbol{r}$, regardless of the positions of the other electrons, is d$\boldsymbol{r}/v$. It follows that, if electron 1 is known to be in d$\boldsymbol{r}_1$, the probability of electron 2, with parallel spin, being in d$\boldsymbol{r}_2$ is

$$F(\xi)\,\frac{\mathrm{d}\boldsymbol{r}_2}{v},$$

and the average charge density of electron 2 at $\boldsymbol{r}_2$ is, therefore,

$$-\frac{e}{v}\,F(\xi).$$

Hence, the average charge density at $\boldsymbol{r}_2$ due to all electrons with spins parallel to that of the electron at $\boldsymbol{r}_1$ is

$$-\frac{eN}{2v}\,F(\xi),$$

as we found previously.

If the motions of the electrons were completely uncorrelated, unity would be substituted for $F(\xi)$ everywhere, so that it is the second term of $F(\xi)$, equation (7.59), which represents the effects of correlations due to the Pauli principle. It should be noted that the Coulomb interaction of the electrons plays no part in the foregoing calculation — the probability (7.61) would be exactly the same if the electrons did not interact at all, provided only that the total wave function were of determinantal form. However, if the electrons did not interact, the correlated motion represented by (7.61) would not affect the energy of the system — in other words the exchange energy would be zero.

APPLICATIONS OF THE FREE-ELECTRON THEORY

7.7. Electronic Specific Heat at Low Temperatures

There are two distinct contributions to the specific heat of a metal: one from the thermal vibration of the ion-cores, which is called the *lattice specific heat*, and the other, called the *electronic specific heat*, from the thermal motion of the valence electrons. We only wish to consider the latter here. Fortunately, the two can be separated at low temperatures, because it is found that, at temperatures T near absolute zero, the lattice specific heat is proportional to T^3 while the electronic specific heat is proportional to T. The total specific heat at low temperatures is, thus,

$$C = \gamma T + AT^3, \tag{7.62}$$

where γ and A are constants, so that, if C/T is plotted against T^2, the result is a straight line which intersects the C/T axis in the value of γ, giving the electronic specific heat.

We will not obtain an explicit formula for the electronic specific heat, which involves the use of the Fermi-Dirac distribution function, but will be content to obtain the temperature dependence of it by general arguments. In particular, we will show that the Sommerfeld-Hartree method gives the correct temperature dependence, while the Hartree-Fock method does not. The actual values of the electronic specific heat, as given by the Sommerfeld-Hartree method are in reasonable agreement with the experimental values for the 'free-electron' metals.

At very low temperatures, as equation (7.62) shows, the electronic specific heat is larger than the lattice specific heat, but at normal temperatures the electronic specific heat is negligibly small compared with the other. This state of affairs could not be explained until quantum mechanics was applied to the problem. According to classical statistical mechanics, in a gas of free particles at temperature T°K each particle will have on the average an energy $\frac{3}{2}kT$. Since, in order to explain the conductivities of metals, it was necessary to assume that the number of conduction electrons was of the same order as the number of atoms, this meant that, according to the classical theory, the electronic and lattice specific heats should have similar magnitudes. That this is not so is easily understood from our work on the free-electron gas. We have seen that at normal temperatures all the one-electron states of low energy are filled, and that the only electrons which may accept energies of the order of kT are those occupying states near the Fermi surface. Thus, although the *excited* electrons have a normal specific heat, they are so few in number that their contribution is negligible compared with the lattice specific heat, which at ordinary temperatures is about $3k$ per atom.

(i) *Sommerfeld-Hartree theory.* According to this theory of a free-electron gas the graph of the density of states function $\mathcal{N}(\varepsilon)$, as shown in Figure 7.7, is a parabola, and, at low temperatures, $\mathcal{N}(\varepsilon)$ does not change much from $\mathcal{N}(\zeta_0)$ in an energy range of order kT about ζ_0. The number of electrons which can accept thermal energy of order kT is therefore proportional to $\mathcal{N}(\zeta_0)\, \hbar T$, and the increase in thermal energy when the temperature is raised from 0°K to T°K is proportional to $\mathcal{N}(\zeta_0)\,(\hbar T)^2$. Differentiating this with respect to T, we find, for the low temperature electronic specific heat C_v at constant volume,

$$C_v \propto T, \tag{7.63}$$

in agreement with experiment. The same result will always follow provided $\mathcal{N}(\varepsilon)$ does not vary rapidly near the Fermi surface.

(ii) *Hartree-Fock theory*. In this case we do not expect to obtain the correct temperature dependence of C_v, for we have seen that $\mathcal{N}(\varepsilon)$ falls rapidly to zero at the Fermi surface and then rises again — we may assume that the $\mathcal{N}(\varepsilon)$ curve, shown in Figure 7.7, is essentially the same at very low temperatures as at absolute zero. The electrons which can accept thermal energy are again those which lie within an energy range of about $\hbar T$ from the Fermi surface, but this time we cannot obtain an estimate of their number simply by multiplying $\hbar T$ by the value of $\mathcal{N}(\varepsilon)$ at the Fermi surface, since this is zero. In order to find the required number, we must first obtain the value of k for a state whose energy lies $\hbar T$ below the energy $\varepsilon(k_0)$ at the Fermi surface, T being very small — in other words, we must find k such that

$$\varepsilon(k_0) - \varepsilon(k) = \hbar T. \tag{7.64}$$

Then, if we write

$$k = (1-x)k_0,$$

the number of electrons which can accept energy $\hbar T$ is the number lying within a spherical shell of thickness xk_0 at the Fermi surface, that is,

$$\frac{2}{8\pi^3}\, 4\pi k_0^2 x k_0 = \frac{k_0^3}{\pi^2}\, x, \tag{7.65}$$

for unit volume of metal. The increase in thermal energy when the temperature is raised to T will be proportional to $\hbar T$ times this.

From equation (7.45) we have

$$\varepsilon(k) = \frac{\hbar^2 k^2}{2m} - \frac{e^2}{2\pi}\left[2k_0 + \frac{k_0^2 - k^2}{k}\log\left(\frac{k_0+k}{k_0-k}\right)\right]$$

and

$$\varepsilon(k_0) = \frac{\hbar^2 k_0^2}{2m} - \frac{e^2 k_0}{\pi}. \tag{7.66}$$

We may assume that x is small enough for its square to be neglected, and $2/x$ is thus very much greater than unity, so that, as a good approximation,

$$\varepsilon(k) = \frac{\hbar^2 k_0^2}{2m}(1-2x) - \frac{e^2}{2\pi}\left(2k_0 + 2xk_0 \log\frac{2}{x}\right).$$

Using this and (7.66) in (7.64), therefore, we obtain

$$\mathscr{k}T = \frac{\hbar^2 k_0^2}{m}x + \frac{e^2 k_0}{\pi}x \log\frac{2}{x}.$$

As x approaches zero, the first term on the right becomes negligible compared with the second, and we may write

$$\mathscr{k}T = \frac{e^2 k_0}{\pi}x \log\frac{2}{x},$$

approximately. The solution † of this equation is very nearly

$$x = \frac{\pi \mathscr{k}T}{e^2 k_0} \bigg/ \log\left(\frac{2e^2 k_0}{\pi \mathscr{k}T}\right). \tag{7.67}$$

From (7.65) and (7.67), ignoring constant factors, we find that the increase in thermal energy on raising the temperature from absolute zero to a very small temperature T is proportional to

$$T^2 \bigg/ \log\left(\frac{2e^2 k_0}{\pi \mathscr{k}T}\right).$$

Differentiating with respect to T, we find, for the low temperature specific heat,

$$C_v \propto \frac{2T}{\log\left(\dfrac{2e^2 k_0}{\pi \mathscr{k}T}\right)} + \frac{T}{\left[\log\left(\dfrac{2e^2 k_0}{\pi \mathscr{k}T}\right)\right]^2},$$

---

† This may be seen as follows:

Writing $\theta = \dfrac{\pi \mathscr{k}T}{e^2 k_0}$, we have $\theta = x \log\dfrac{2}{x}$, so that $x = \dfrac{\theta}{\log\dfrac{2}{x}}$ and $\dfrac{2}{x} = \dfrac{2}{\theta}\log\dfrac{2}{x}$.

This gives $x = \dfrac{\theta}{\log\dfrac{2}{\theta} + \log\log\dfrac{2}{x}} = \dfrac{\theta}{\log\dfrac{2}{\theta} + \log\log\dfrac{2}{\theta} + \log\log\log\dfrac{2}{x}}$, etc.

When θ is very small a good enough approximation is, clearly,

$$x = \theta \bigg/ \log\frac{2}{\theta}.$$

and the second term is negligible compared with the first. As a further simplification, we may write

$$\log\left(\frac{2e^2k_0}{\pi \ell T}\right) = \log\left(\frac{2e^2k_0}{\pi \ell}\right) - \log T$$

and neglect the first term on the right as T approaches zero. We then have, finally

$$C_v \propto T/\log T. \tag{7.68}$$

According to the Hartree-Fock theory, therefore, as T tends to zero, C_v/T also tends to zero, instead of to the finite value found experimentally and as given by the Sommerfeld-Hartree theory. We shall see, in Chapter 10, that the correct temperature dependence is restored when proper account is taken of Coulomb correlations.

7.8. Spin Paramagnetism

If a metal (or any other substance) is placed in a magnetic field $\boldsymbol{H}$, it becomes magnetized, the magnetic moment per unit volume $\boldsymbol{M}$ being related to $\boldsymbol{H}$ by the equation

$$\boldsymbol{M} = \chi \boldsymbol{H}, \tag{7.69}$$

where χ is the *magnetic susceptibility* of the metal. Defined in this way, χ is known as the *volume* susceptibility, but it should be noted that the susceptibility per unit mass and the susceptibility per atom, defined in terms of the magnetic moment per unit mass and per atom respectively, are frequently used.

If χ is negative, the metal is *diamagnetic*; if χ is small and positive, the metal is *paramagnetic*; and, if χ is large and positive, the metal is *ferromagnetic*. Most metals are weakly paramagnetic or diamagnetic — of the monovalent metals, for example, the alkali metals are paramagnetic, while the noble metals, copper, silver, and gold are diamagnetic. Excluding alloys, the only metals known to be ferromagnetic are iron, cobalt, nickel, and gadolinium, and we will omit these from consideration here.

Diamagnetism is due to the orbital motion of the electrons, whereas paramagnetism is due to the electron spin. It may be shown that, except in the case of some transition metals, the contribution to the susceptibility from the ion-cores is diamagnetic, so that any paramagnetic susceptibility must be due to the conduction electrons. We will now derive an expression for the paramagnetic susceptibility of the conduction electrons according to the Sommerfeld-Hartree theory of a free-electron gas. Although we will assume, for simplicity, that the temperature is absolute zero, it is not difficult to show, using the Fermi-Dirac distribution function, that the susceptibility is practically the same at all normal temperatures.

When there is no external magnetic field, all the orbital states of lowest energy are occupied by two electrons each, with opposite spins. We may thus draw two parabolic $\mathcal{N}(\varepsilon)$ curves, occupied up to the same energy, as in Figure 7.9 (a), one being for electrons with positive spin and one for electrons with negative spin. We know that, when a magnetic field $\boldsymbol{H}$ is switched on, an electron whose (spin) magnetic moment is parallel to the field will have its energy decreased by the amount $\mu_B H$, where μ_B is the Bohr magneton, given by

$$\mu_B = \frac{e\hbar}{2mc},$$

and an electron with its magnetic moment antiparallel to the field will have its energy increased by the same amount. Thus, in the presence of a magnetic field $\boldsymbol{H}$, the density of states curves for the electrons with spins parallel and antiparallel to the field respectively will become displaced relative to one another by an energy $2\mu_B H$, as shown in Figure 7.9 (b).

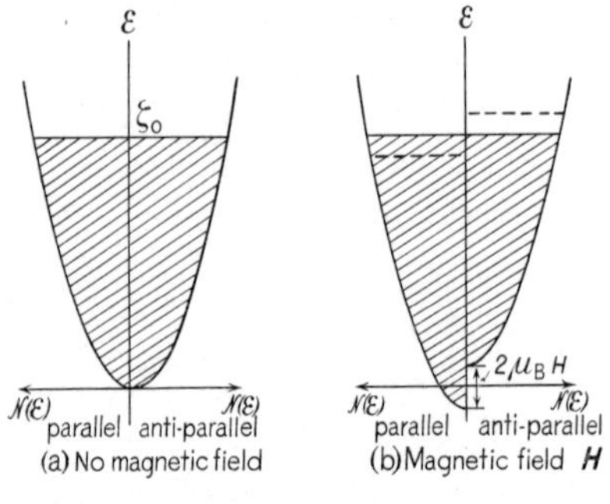

Fig. 7.9. Distribution at 0°K of free electrons with spin magnetic moments parallel and antiparallel to the direction of a magnetic field $\boldsymbol{H}$: (a) before, and (b) after the field is switched on. ε is the total one-electron energy, kinetic plus magnetic.

The number of electrons in each distribution will not remain the same, however, for this would mean that the maximum energy of the electrons with magnetic moments parallel to the field would be greater than that of the others, and a lower energy could be obtained by transferring some of the electrons from the higher distribution to the lower. The lowest energy is obtained when both distributions are filled up to the same energy (kinetic plus magnetic).

Now, even for fields of several hundred thousand gauss, $\mu_B H$ is only of the order of 10^{-3} eV, so that in an energy range whose width is $\mu_B H$, at ζ_0, we may take the density of states to be $\mathcal{N}(\zeta_0)$. The number of electrons which turn their magnetic moments parallel to the field is, thus,

$$\mu_B H \mathcal{N}(\zeta_0),$$

which means that the number of electrons with magnetic moments parallel to $\boldsymbol{H}$ is now

$$2\mu_B H \mathcal{N}(\zeta_0)$$

greater than the number with magnetic moments antiparallel to $\boldsymbol{H}$. The magnetic moment per unit volume is therefore

$$2\mu_B^2 H \mathcal{N}(\zeta_0)/v,$$

parallel to $\boldsymbol{H}$, so that, from equation (7.69), we find the paramagnetic susceptibility to be

$$\chi = 2\mu_B^2 \mathcal{N}(\zeta_0)/v. \tag{7.70}$$

From equations (7.5) and (7.7), we have

$$\mathcal{N}(\zeta_0) = \frac{vm}{2\pi^2\hbar^2}\left(\frac{3\pi^2 N}{v}\right)^{\frac{1}{3}},$$

so that, if $n = N/v$ is the electron density,

$$\chi = \frac{\mu_B^2 m}{\pi^2\hbar^2}(3\pi^2 n)^{\frac{1}{3}}. \tag{7.71}$$

This is the paramagnetic susceptibility of a gas of free electrons, calculated according to the Hartree approximation. The values given by the formula cannot easily be compared with experiment, even for those metals, such as sodium, for which the valence electrons are very nearly free. This is because the total susceptibility, which is what is generally observed, consists of the sum of three terms — in addition to the spin paramagnetism of the valence electrons, there is also a diamagnetic contribution from the valence electrons, due to the effect of the magnetic field upon their orbital motion, and a diamagnetic contribution from the ion-cores. The latter can be estimated, however, on the assumption that the ion-cores are the same as in a free atom, and it can also be shown that, for perfectly free electrons, the diamagnetic contribution is exactly $-\frac{1}{3}$ of the paramagnetic contribution. The total susceptibility calculated in this way is of the right order of magnitude for some simple metals, but the correspondence between the calculated and experimental values is not close. It should be pointed out, however, that the experimental values themselves are not very consistent, probably owing to the effects of ferromagnetic impurities.

If the Hartree-Fock method is used to calculate the paramagnetic susceptibility, it is clear from the density of states curves shown in Figure 7.7 that the value will be very different from that given by (7.70). The situation is complicated by the fact that a change in the number of electrons with either kind of spin will alter the exchange energy, which depends upon the numbers of electrons with parallel spins. Detailed calculation shows, in fact, that the inclusion of the exchange energy *increases* the calculated susceptibility considerably — in the case of sodium it multiplies the value given by (7.71) by a factor of about three, which is certainly too high. This, again, is due to the inclusion of parallel spin correlations while completely ignoring antiparallel spin correlations — when Coulomb correlations are properly taken into account, as in the method described in Chapter 10, the resulting susceptibility is little greater than that given by the Hartree method, and in better agreement with experiment.

We shall see in Chapter 9 that the effect of the periodic field of the ion-cores on the wave functions of the valence electrons can sometimes be taken into account by substituting for the electronic mass m an 'effective mass' m^*. If this is done in formula (7.71), the result is little different in the case of sodium, for which m/m^* is very nearly unity, but is in much better agreement with experiment in the case of lithium, for which m/m^* is 0.69.

7.9. Soft X-Ray Emission Spectra

If a piece of metal is irradiated with cathode rays, some of the ions will lose electrons; that is, vacancies will occur in some of the inner shells, or *bound* levels, and valence electrons may fall into these vacancies with the consequent emission of X-rays. If ε_1 is the energy of the valence electron before the transition, and ε_2 the energy of the bound level, the frequency ν of the emitted X-ray is given by

$$\varepsilon_1 - \varepsilon_2 = h\nu.$$

The *intensity* of X-rays with frequency ν will depend upon the density of valence electrons with energy ε_1, and, since there is a quasi-continuous distribution of valence electrons in energy, called the *conduction band*, the result is an X-ray spectrum of continuously varying intensity (see Figure 7.10). If everything else were equal, the intensity of the X-ray spectrum would exactly reflect the density of states $\mathcal{N}(\varepsilon)$ of the valence electrons.

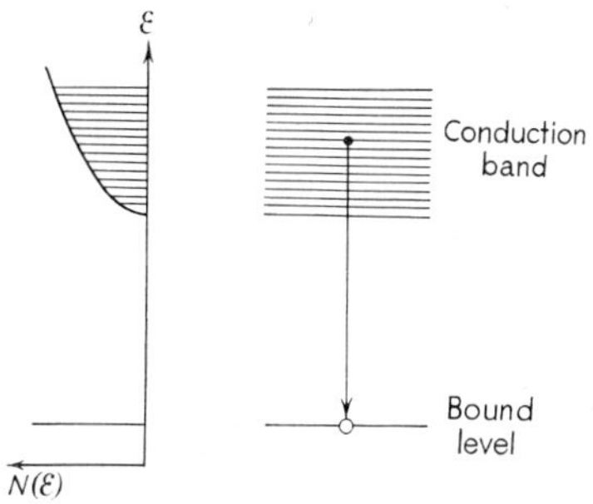

Fig. 7.10. Schematic diagram showing the transition of a valence electron from the conduction band to a vacant bound level, together with the density of states.

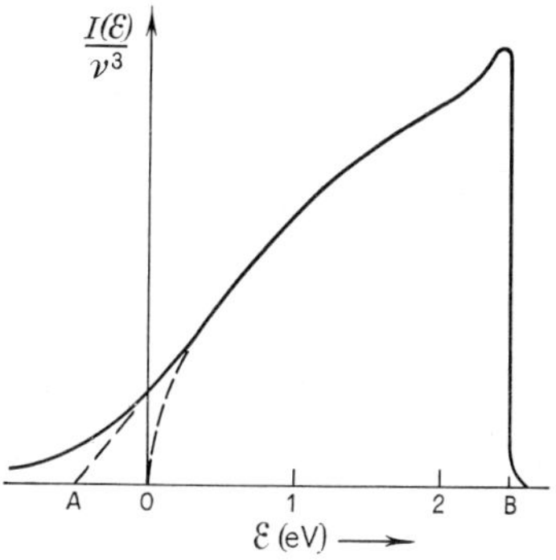

Fig. 7.11. Soft X-ray L_3 emission band for sodium (after Skinner, 1940). $I(\varepsilon)$ is the intensity and ν is the emitted frequency, the quantity $I(\varepsilon)/\nu^3$ is comparable with $\mathcal{N}(\varepsilon)$. AB is the 'empirical' band width, 3.0 eV, and OB is the 'reduced' band width, 2.5 eV.

Complications arise, however, owing to the fact that the probability of a transition is not constant for all valence electron energies, but depends both upon the wave function of the bound level and that of the valence electron. None the less, in some cases the soft X-ray emission spectrum is expected to give a reasonable picture of the $\mathcal{N}(\varepsilon)$ curve, and, even when the *shape* of the curve is in doubt, at least the *width* of the band should be given with reasonable accuracy. The L_3 spectrum of sodium, which is due to transitions from the conduction band to bound 2p levels, is shown in Figure 7.11.

It is difficult to fix the energy corresponding to the bottom of the band, owing to the presence of a long 'tail', which is not directly related to the $\mathcal{N}(\varepsilon)$ curve. However, this may be done roughly by a linear extrapolation, or, what would appear more reasonable if the Sommerfeld-Hartree $\mathcal{N}(\varepsilon)$ curve is a good approximation, a parabolic extrapolation of the main part of the intensity curve. Skinner, from whose work † the figure was taken, called the band width resulting from the linear extrapolation the *empirical* band width, and that resulting from the parabolic extrapolation the *reduced* band width. The empirical and reduced band widths found by Skinner from the L_3 spectra of the metals sodium, magnesium, and aluminium are compared with the Sommerfeld-Hartree theoretical band widths in Table 1, and the agreement is seen to be quite good. The calculated values are just the values of ζ_0 given by equation (7.11), remembering that the numbers of valence electrons per atom are one, two, and three respectively for sodium, magnesium and aluminium, and using the appropriate r_e, given by equation (7.10), instead of r_s.

TABLE 1

	Band widths		
	Na	Mg	Al
Calculated (ζ_0)	3.2	7.3	11.9
Empirical (Skinner)	3.0±0.2	7.2±0.2	13.2±0.4
Reduced (Skinner)	2.5±0.3	6.2±0.3	11.8±0.5

All values are in eV.

The Hartree-Fock band width, as given by equation (7.46), for these metals is about twice ζ_0, so that, although the experimental band width is uncertain to the extent of an electron-volt or so, it is quite clear that the Hartree-Fock result is badly in error. Once again, it will be seen in Chapter 10 that when proper account is taken of Coulomb correlations the band width returns to a value close to that of the Sommerfeld-Hartree theory.

7.10. The Thomas-Fermi Approximation

We will now describe a method, devised by Thomas and Fermi, which applies the ideas of the free-electron approximation to many-electron systems in which the potential energy of an electron is not constant. It has been used, with varying degrees of success, in calculating the electronic charge distributions in heavy atoms, molecules, and solids.

We have seen that, for a free-electron gas of volume v, an element $d\boldsymbol{k}$ of $\boldsymbol{k}$-space contains $v\, d\boldsymbol{k}/8\pi^3$ orbital states, and hence may accommodate

† Skinner, H. W. B., 1940, Phil. Trans. Roy. Soc. A, **239**, 95.

$2v\,\mathrm{d}\boldsymbol{k}/8\pi^3$ electrons. Also, the momentum $\boldsymbol{p}$ of a free electron is given by

$$\boldsymbol{p} = \hbar\boldsymbol{k}.$$

Thus, if we consider a momentum space, or $\boldsymbol{p}$-space, similar to $\boldsymbol{k}$-space, we see immediately that a volume element $\mathrm{d}\boldsymbol{p}$ may accommodate $2v\,\mathrm{d}\boldsymbol{p}/8\pi^3\hbar^3$, or $2v\,\mathrm{d}\boldsymbol{p}/h^3$, electrons. Also, at the absolute zero of temperature, the occupied portion of $\boldsymbol{p}$-space is a sphere of radius p_0, where $p_0 = \hbar k_0$. If the total number of electrons is N, therefore, we have

$$\frac{4\pi}{3}\,p_0^3\,\frac{2v}{h^3} = N,$$

and, if $n = N/v$ is the number of electrons per unit volume, this gives

$$n = \frac{8\pi}{3h^3}\,p_0^3.$$

The Thomas-Fermi approximation assumes that this relation remains true for the ground state of a system even when the electrons are not free, that is, when the potential energy is not constant. The electron density n and maximum momentum p_0 are now functions of the position vector $\boldsymbol{r}$, however, so that we have

$$n(\boldsymbol{r}) = \frac{8\pi}{3h^3}\,p_0^3(\boldsymbol{r}). \tag{7.72}$$

The approximation is clearly only valid if the electron density is so great that a volume element of real space in which the potential energy changes very little may still contain a large number of electrons.

Now, let us suppose that $-eV(\boldsymbol{r})$ is the potential energy of an electron due to the field of all the nuclei present and the whole of the electronic charge distribution. If we denote by $-eV_0$ the *total* energy, kinetic and potential, of the *fastest* electron, then the classical equation of energy tells us that

$$-eV_0 = \frac{p_0^2(\boldsymbol{r})}{2m} - eV(\boldsymbol{r}),$$

or

$$p_0(\boldsymbol{r}) = [2me(V - V_0)]^{\frac{1}{2}},$$

and substitution in (7.72) gives

$$n(\boldsymbol{r}) = \frac{8\pi}{3h^3}\,[2me(V - V_0)]^{\frac{3}{2}}. \tag{7.73}$$

V_0 is, of course, independent of $\boldsymbol{r}$, $-eV_0$ being simply the highest occupied energy level of the system.

Now, for consistency, the potential $V(\boldsymbol{r})$ must satisfy Poisson's equation, that is, since the electronic charge density is $-en(\boldsymbol{r})$,

$$\nabla^2 V = 4\pi e n,$$

or, using (7.73),

$$\nabla^2 V = \mu(V - V_0)^{\frac{3}{2}}, \tag{7.74}$$

where

$$\mu = \frac{32\pi^2 e}{3h^3}(2me)^{\frac{3}{2}}.$$

Equation (7.74) is the basic equation of the Thomas-Fermi theory and it must be solved, in general numerically, subject to appropriate boundary conditions. It should be noted that equations (7.73) and (7.74) are only valid so long as $V > V_0$; $n(\boldsymbol{r})$ must be zero in any region where $V < V_0$, that is, where the potential energy $-eV$ is higher than the maximum energy $-eV_0$ of any electron.

It is possible also to include the exchange energy in the theory, again using the free-electron formula, and various other generalizations have been made, but it would take us too far afield to consider these complications here.

7.10.1. FIELD DUE TO A POINT CHARGE IN AN ELECTRON GAS

As a simple application of the Thomas-Fermi theory let us find the field due to a point charge q introduced into a free-electron gas. Initially, before the introduction of q, the system consists of a uniform distribution of positive charge and an electron gas of uniform density, the total charge being zero. We may assume that the potential is then zero everywhere, so that

$$-eV_0 = \zeta_0, \tag{7.75}$$

and the initial electron density, which we will here distinguish by the symbol n_0, is

$$n_0 = \frac{8\pi}{3h^3}(2m\zeta_0)^{\frac{3}{2}}. \tag{7.76}$$

If the system is a large one it is reasonable to neglect any change in $-eV_0$ when q is introduced. Thus, if the final potential is $V(r)$, taking the origin at the position of q, the final electron density is, from (7.73) and (7.75),

$$n(r) = \frac{8\pi}{3h^3}\left[2me\left(V+\frac{\zeta_0}{e}\right)\right]^{\frac{3}{2}}$$

$$= n_0\left(1+\frac{eV}{\zeta_0}\right)^{\frac{3}{2}}. \tag{7.77}$$

Neglecting surface effects, for a sufficiently large system, we may take both $V(r)$ and $n(r)$ to be spherically symmetrical about q.

Since there is a uniform distribution of positive charge of density en_0, Poisson's equation now gives

$$\nabla^2 V = 4\pi e(n-n_0)$$

$$= 4\pi e n_0\left[\left(1+\frac{eV}{\zeta_0}\right)^{\frac{3}{2}}-1\right]. \tag{7.78}$$

The effect of the introduction of q will be to cause a redistribution of the electron gas, so as to increase or decrease the electron density around q, according to whether q is a positive or a negative charge. The electron gas will, in fact, 'screen' the charge q so that the field at large distances is zero, but this screening will have negligible effect close to q. The boundary conditions on $V(r)$ are, therefore,

$$\left.\begin{aligned} V(r) &\to 0 \quad \text{as } r\to\infty,\\ V(r) &\to \frac{q}{r} \quad \text{as } r\to 0. \end{aligned}\right\} \tag{7.79}$$

Equation (7.78), as it stands, can only be solved numerically, but if we assume that V is so small that the square of eV/ζ_0 can be neglected in comparison with unity then an approximate analytical solution may be obtained. This assumption is certainly not valid very close to q, since $V(r) \to \infty$ as $r \to 0$, and, furthermore, equation (7.78) itself does not hold when $eV/\zeta_0 < -1$. None the less, provided the assumption fails in only a very small region about q, we may hope to obtain at least a rough approximation to V in this way. We thus expand $(1+eV/\zeta_0)^{\frac{3}{2}}$ binomially and find, approximately,

$$\left(1+\frac{eV}{\zeta_0}\right)^{\frac{3}{2}}-1 = \frac{3eV}{2\zeta_0}.$$

Since $V(r)$ is spherically symmetrical, equation (7.78) becomes

$$\frac{\mathrm{d}^2 V}{\mathrm{d}r^2} + \frac{2}{r}\frac{\mathrm{d}V}{\mathrm{d}r} = \frac{6\pi e^2 n_0}{\zeta_0} V. \tag{7.80}$$

It may be verified by substitution that the solution of this equation which satisfies the boundary conditions (7.79) is

$$V(r) = \frac{q}{r}\,\mathrm{e}^{-r/\lambda}, \tag{7.81}$$

where λ is positive and given by

$$\lambda = \left(\frac{\zeta_0}{6\pi e^2 n_0}\right)^{\frac{1}{2}}. \tag{7.82}$$

The potential is thus a *screened Coulomb potential* and λ is called the *screening distance* — it is the distance in which the potential is reduced to about one third of its unscreened value, and is a rough measure of the effective range of the field due to q.

If we assume that the electron gas is that of the valence electrons in a monovalent metal, then, in terms of the atomic radius r_s, we have

$$n_0 = \frac{3}{4\pi r_s^3},$$

and

$$\zeta_0 = \frac{\hbar^2}{2m}\left(\frac{9\pi}{4}\right)^{\frac{2}{3}}\frac{1}{r_s^2},$$

so that

$$\lambda = \frac{1}{3}\left(\frac{9\pi}{4}\right)^{\frac{1}{3}}(a_0 r_s)^{\frac{1}{2}},$$

where $a_0 = \hbar^2/me^2$ is the Bohr radius. If r_s is measured in Bohr units, this gives

$$\lambda = 0.64\, r_s^{\frac{1}{2}}\ \text{B.u.} \tag{7.83}$$

For *sodium* r_s is about 4 B.u., so that

$$\lambda = 1.28\ \text{B.u.} = 0.68\ \text{Å},$$

which is much smaller than the average inter-electronic distance.

The calculation has application in estimating the potential due to an impurity atom in a metal, which is used in the theory of alloys. If an impurity atom of valency $z+1$ is dissolved in a monovalent metal, for instance, it may be regarded roughly as a point positive charge ze in a free-electron gas, and the potential is given immediately by (7.81), with $q = ze$.

The calculation also provides a rough indication of the screening effect of all the other electrons on the field of any one of them — in other words, of the way in which Coulomb correlations reduce the effective range of the interaction among electrons. This problem will be dealt with more fully in Chapter 10, and it will be seen that the Thomas-Fermi result exaggerates the screening effect, that is, it gives too small a screening distance.

CHAPTER 8

BLOCH FUNCTIONS AND BRILLOUIN ZONES

8.1. Motion of an Electron in a One-Dimensional Lattice: Bloch's theorem

In the free-electron model the periodic electrostatic field present in an actual metal is neglected. In order to obtain some idea of the effects of the periodic field we will first discuss the idealized problem of the motion of a single electron in a one-dimensional crystal lattice; the potential energy $V(x)$ being a periodic function of x, the distance measured along the lattice, such as that shown in Figure 8.1. We will take the period to be a and the length of the lattice to be $L = Ga$, where G is an integer. Periodic boundary conditions are applied, so that, as in § 7.3, we may imagine the lattice bent round until the two ends coincide, to form a ring.

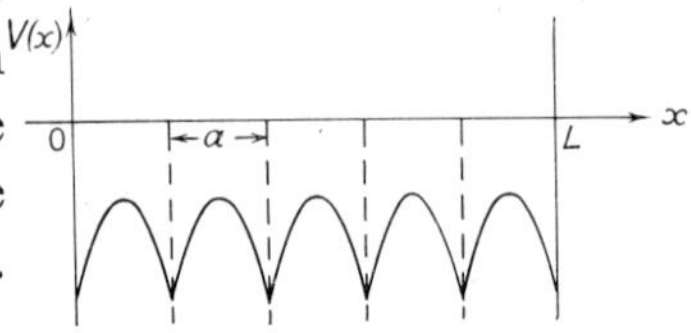

Fig. 8.1. Potential energy of an electron in a one-dimensional lattice.

Now, when the potential energy is constant, we know that the wave function of an electron is of the form

$$\psi_k(x) = e^{ikx}, \tag{8.1}$$

where

$$k = \frac{2\pi g}{L}, \qquad g = 0, \pm 1, \pm 2, \ldots.$$

Taking the periodic field into account, we should expect the wave function to be of similar type, but modulated by the field. Since the assumption of periodic boundary conditions implies that surface effects, or, in this case, end effects, are neglected, we should expect the modulating function to have the period of the lattice — in other words, it is expected that a wave function will have the form

$$\psi_k(x) = e^{ikx} u_k(x), \tag{8.2}$$

where the function $u_k(x)$ has the period of the lattice, that is,

$$u_k(x+a) = u_k(x), \tag{8.3}$$

and in general depends upon k.

The proof that the wave functions of an electron in a periodic field actually are of this type was given by Bloch in 1928, and is known as *Bloch's theorem* in metal theory, although it is mathematically the same as a much earlier theorem due to Floquet. The functions (8.2) are called *Bloch functions.* We will now give an elementary proof of Bloch's theorem.

We wish to find the general form of the acceptable solutions of the Schrödinger equation

$$\frac{d^2\psi}{dx^2} + \frac{2m}{\hbar^2}[\varepsilon - V(x)]\psi = 0, \tag{8.4}$$

where

$$V(x) = V(x+a), \tag{8.5}$$

subject to the periodic boundary condition

$$\psi(x) = \psi(x+Ga). \tag{8.6}$$

If, as described above, we imagine the lattice bent round to form a ring, it is clear from the symmetry of the ring that the probability density must be a periodic function of period a. In other words, we must have

$$|\psi(x)|^2 = |\psi(x+a)|^2,$$

which means that †

---

† This result may be obtained without any reference to the probability density in the following way:

Equation (8.4) may be written

$$H\,\psi(x) = \varepsilon\,\psi(x),$$

where

$$H = -\frac{\hbar^2}{2m}\frac{d^2}{dx^2} + V(x).$$

Now, if Γ is an operator which changes x into $x+a$, so that

$$\Gamma\psi(x) = \psi(x+a),$$

then

$$\Gamma H\,\psi(x) = \left[-\frac{\hbar^2}{2m}\frac{d^2}{d(x+a)^2} + V(x+a)\right]\psi(x+a)$$
$$= H\psi(x+a) = H\Gamma\psi(x),$$

owing to (8.5) and the fact that $d/d(x+a) = d/dx$. Γ thus commutes with H, so that the two operators have simultaneous eigenfunctions (see § 2.6), and we may therefore write

$$\Gamma\psi(x) = \lambda\psi(x) = \psi(x+a).$$

$$\psi(x+a) = \lambda\, \psi(x), \tag{8.7}$$

where λ is a constant. Also,

$$\psi(x+2a) = \lambda\, \psi(x+a) = \lambda^2\, \psi(x),$$

and, if g is any integer,

$$\psi(x+ga) = \lambda^g \psi(x).$$

It follows from this and equation (8.6) that

$$\psi(x+Ga) = \lambda^G \psi(x) = \psi(x).$$

Hence,

$$\lambda^G = 1,$$

or

$$\lambda = \mathrm{e}^{2\pi \mathrm{i} g/G}, \quad \text{where } g = 0, \pm 1, \pm 2, \ldots.$$

The wave functions must therefore satisfy the so-called *Bloch condition*

$$\psi(x+a) = \mathrm{e}^{2\pi \mathrm{i} g/G} \psi(x). \tag{8.8}$$

If k is defined as in equation (8.1),

$$k = \frac{2\pi g}{Ga}, \qquad g = 0, \pm 1, \pm 2, \ldots, \tag{8.9}$$

then the functions

$$\psi_k(x) = \mathrm{e}^{\mathrm{i}kx} u_k(x) \tag{8.10}$$

satisfy (8.8), provided that

$$u_k(x+a) = u_k(x). \tag{8.11}$$

Since we have made no assumption about $u_k(x)$, apart from its periodicity, this result is quite general, and we may assume that the wave functions are of the form (8.10), which is Bloch's theorem.

8.2. Brillouin Zones in One Dimension

It is easily seen that k is not uniquely specified by (8.10) and (8.11), for we may write

$$\mathrm{e}^{\mathrm{i}kx} u_k(x) = \mathrm{e}^{\mathrm{i}(k+2\pi n/a)x} [\mathrm{e}^{-\mathrm{i}2\pi n x/a} u_k(x)], \tag{8.12}$$

where n is any integer, and the function in square brackets still has the period of the lattice. This means that we may replace k by $k+(2\pi n/a)$ without destroying the form of the Bloch function. It is therefore possible to restrict the values of k to an interval of length $2\pi/a$, which for convenience we take to be symmetrical about $k=0$ — that is to say, we choose k to lie in the interval †

$$-\frac{\pi}{a} \leqq k \leqq \frac{\pi}{a}, \tag{8.13}$$

which we will call the *fundamental domain of k*.

The wave functions are then written

$$\psi_{kl}(x) = e^{ikx} u_{kl}(x), \tag{8.14}$$

where

$$u_{kl}(x+a) = u_{kl}(x), \tag{8.15}$$

and there is an infinite number of states, labelled by the quantum number l, corresponding to any value of k in the fundamental domain. Substituting (8.14) in (8.4), and dividing by e^{ikx}, we find that u_{kl} must satisfy the differential equation

$$\frac{d^2 u_{kl}}{dx^2} + 2ik \frac{du_{kl}}{dx} + \frac{2m}{\hbar^2} \left[\varepsilon_l(k) - \frac{\hbar^2 k^2}{2m} - V(x) \right] u_{kl} = 0. \tag{8.16}$$

The complex conjugate of this equation, assuming $V(x)$ to be a real function, is

$$\frac{d^2 u_{kl}^*}{dx^2} - 2ik \frac{du_{kl}^*}{dx} + \frac{2m}{\hbar^2} \left[\varepsilon_l(k) - \frac{\hbar^2 k^2}{2m} - V(x) \right] u_{kl}^* = 0, \tag{8.17}$$

and, changing k to $-k$ in (8.16), the equation for u_{-kl} is found to be

$$\frac{d^2 u_{-kl}}{dx^2} - 2ik \frac{du_{-kl}}{dx} + \frac{2m}{\hbar^2} \left[\varepsilon_l(-k) - \frac{\hbar^2 k^2}{2m} - V(x) \right] u_{-kl} = 0. \tag{8.18}$$

Comparing equations (8.17) and (8.18), we deduce that

$$u_{kl}^*(x) = u_{-kl}(x), \tag{8.19}$$

and

$$\varepsilon_l(k) = \varepsilon_l(-k). \tag{8.20}$$

The functions ψ_{kl} and ψ_{-kl} are therefore degenerate.

A very small change in k in equation (8.16) will result in only a small change in u_{kl} and in $\varepsilon_l(k)$. Hence, if a given label l is properly ascribed, it

† Since $k = 2\pi g/Ga$, where g is an integer, it is evident that the end points of this interval, $\pm\pi/a$, will only be included if G is an *even* integer. Furthermore, since the end points differ by $2\pi/a$, it is only necessary to include one of them in the domain of k, the choice being arbitrary. For a real metal, however, G is a very large number, so that k is almost a continuous variable, and the question of the inclusion or not of the end points is of no practical importance.

will specify a set of states, one for each k value, for which the energy $\varepsilon_l(k)$ is a quasi-continuous function of k. This set of states is called a *Brillouin zone*. The nomenclature in this part of the subject is by no means universal, however, and it should be noted that what we have called the *fundamental domain* of k is more often referred to as the *basic Brillouin zone*, or, for reasons which will appear, the *first Brillouin zone* or the *reduced zone*.

As a simple example, let us consider the free-electron model, even though the introduction of a lattice periodicity is rather artificial in this case. It may be verified directly by substitution in the Schrödinger equation (8.4), with $V(x) = 0$, that the wave functions and corresponding energies may be written

$$\left.\begin{aligned} \psi_{kl}(x) &= \mathrm{e}^{\mathrm{i}kx}\mathrm{e}^{-\mathrm{i}2\pi lx/a}, \\ \varepsilon_l(k) &= \frac{\hbar^2}{2m}\left(k - \frac{2\pi l}{a}\right)^2, \end{aligned}\right\} \quad 0 < k \leqq \frac{\pi}{a}, \tag{8.21}$$

$$\left.\begin{aligned} \psi_{kl}(x) &= \mathrm{e}^{\mathrm{i}kx}\mathrm{e}^{\mathrm{i}2\pi lx/a}, \\ \varepsilon_l(k) &= \frac{\hbar^2}{2m}\left(k + \frac{2\pi l}{a}\right)^2, \end{aligned}\right\} \quad -\frac{\pi}{a} < k \leqq 0. \tag{8.22}$$

These wave functions are of Bloch form, and all possible states are included by letting l have the values 0, 1, 2 . . ., each value specifying a Brillouin zone. The curves of $\varepsilon_l(k)$ against k are shown in Figure 8.2 (a).

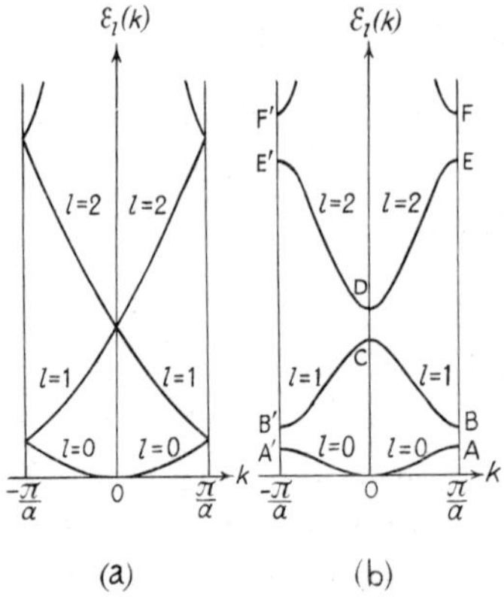

Fig. 8.2. Energy of an electron in a one-dimensional lattice as a function of k: (a) zero potential energy (free electron), (b) small periodic potential energy.

It is seen that, in this case, the energy curves of consecutive zones touch either at $k = 0$ or at $k = \pm\pi/a$. The reason for this is quite obvious from the nature of the free-electron model — we know that the energy distribution is quasi-continuous. However, this is not so when a non-zero periodic field is present. Figure 8.2 (b) shows the general effect of a small field with period a (we shall consider this in detail in the following section). The energy curves for the different zones are now smooth as well as continuous, and those of adjacent zones no longer touch — there are finite *energy gaps*, such as AB, CD, EF, between the zones, and no state has energy lying within these gaps. The energy distribution is thus no longer quasi-continuous, but is broken up into quasi-continuous *bands* of energy levels separated by forbidden energy regions. Although Figure 8.2 (b) shows only small energy gaps, and energy curves which do not differ much from the free-electron curves, this is by no means necessary, but only applies when the periodic field is small. If the periodic field is of large amplitude, the energy curves may deviate considerably from the free-electron curves, but, none the less, their general characteristics will be as shown.

We have mentioned that the introduction of a lattice periodicity is rather artificial in the case of free electrons, and the use of the Bloch functions in equations (8.21) and (8.22), although correct, is unnecessarily tedious. Since the potential energy is constant there is no reason for choosing one period rather than another — in fact, here it is more natural simply to use the wave functions (8.1) without restricting the range of k. The one-electron energies are then given by

$$\varepsilon(k) = \frac{\hbar^2 k^2}{2m}, \tag{8.23}$$

and the energy curve is the simple parabola shown in Figure 8.3 (a). Even when a periodic field is present it is possible to use a similar representation, that is, one in which the range of k is not restricted. Since we know that the form of a Bloch function is unaltered when k is replaced by $k+(2\pi n/a)$, where n is any integer, positive or negative, it follows that any energy curve in Figure 8.2 (b), or segment of such a curve, may be translated through a distance $2\pi n/a$ parallel to the k axis and the result will remain correct. In particular, the right and left halves of the energy curves may be translated separately, so as to give, by analogy with the free-electron parabola, the energy curve shown in Figure 8.3 (b). For example, the segments BC and B′C are translated a distance $2\pi/a$ to the left and to the right respectively. This is called the *extended zone scheme*, the *first* Brillouin zone now corresponding to values of k between $-\pi/a$ and π/a,

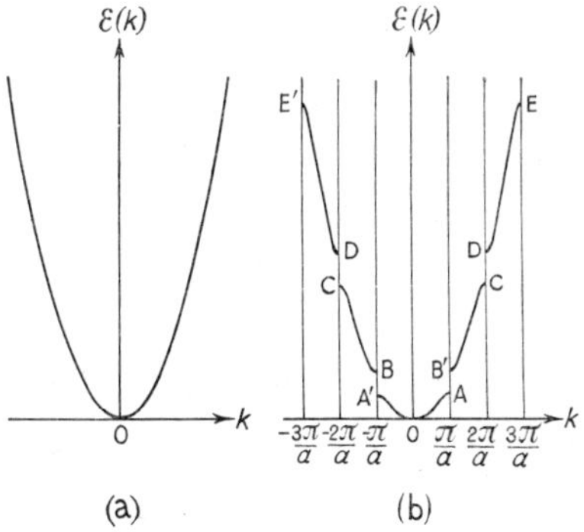

Fig. 8.3. Energy of an electron in a one-dimensional lattice, according to the extended zone scheme: (a) zero potential energy (free electron), (b) small periodic potential energy.

the second Brillouin zone to values of k lying between $-2\pi/a$ and $-\pi/a$ as well as between π/a and $2\pi/a$, and so on. On the other hand, the situation represented in Figure 8.2 is often called the *reduced zone scheme* — clearly, it is possible to start with the extended zone picture and reduce it to that shown in Figure 8.2 by suitable translations through $2\pi n/a$, which is the approach often adopted in elementary treatments. This explains the alternative names given to the fundamental domain of k.

The reduced and extended zone schemes are equally valid, and which one is used in a particular problem is largely a matter of convenience. Although the extended zone scheme appears to be the more natural when one considers free, or nearly free, electrons, we wish to emphasize that this is by no means so in general. In solving the Schrödinger equation for an electron in a periodic field one assumes solutions of the form (8.10), and this leads naturally to $\varepsilon(k)$ being found as a *many-valued* function of k, the different values of which we have distinguished by means of the subscript l. If no restriction is put upon k, therefore, the energy curves which one obtains by straightforward calculation are not immediately those of the extended zone scheme, Figure 8.3 (b), but those shown in Figure 8.4. The essential thing to notice is that the energy is a periodic

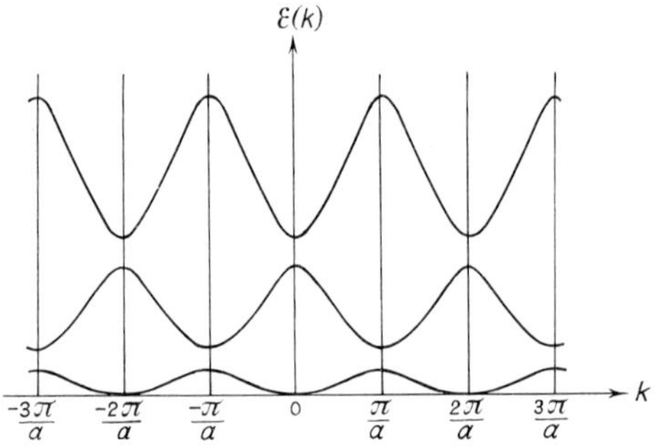

Fig. 8.4. Energy of an electron in a one-dimensional lattice as a many-valued function of k, when k is unrestricted.

function of k, with period $2\pi/a$. All possible states are included in a single period, which is the justification of the reduced zone scheme. The choice of the fundamental domain of k to be from $-\pi/a$ to π/a is purely one of convenience, however, and is due to the fact that the energy curves are symmetrical about the origin — it is important to realize that *any* interval of length $2\pi/a$ would suffice. The extended zone scheme is obtained by choosing one particular energy curve in each half period — in the case of nearly free electrons, we choose the one which lies closest to the free-electron parabola, and, in general, we choose the one which makes ε a monotonic increasing function of $|k|$.

The energy curves are continuous and smooth (the free-electron case excepted), and it follows from their periodicity and symmetry about $k = 0$ that they must all have zero slope at $k = 0$ and $k = \pm\pi/a$. Thus, owing to the periodicity, we have

$$\frac{\mathrm{d}}{\mathrm{d}k}\,\varepsilon_l(k) = \frac{\mathrm{d}}{\mathrm{d}k}\,\varepsilon_l\left(k + \frac{2\pi}{a}\right), \tag{8.24}$$

and, in particular,

$$\left(\frac{\mathrm{d}\varepsilon_l}{\mathrm{d}k}\right)_{-\pi/a} = \left(\frac{\mathrm{d}\varepsilon_l}{\mathrm{d}k}\right)_{\pi/a}, \tag{8.25}$$

while, owing to the symmetry about $k = 0$, we have

$$\varepsilon_l(k) = \varepsilon_l(-k),$$

and

$$\frac{\mathrm{d}}{\mathrm{d}k}\,\varepsilon_l(k) = -\frac{\mathrm{d}}{\mathrm{d}k}\,\varepsilon_l(-k). \tag{8.26}$$

From (8.25) and (8.26), we have, finally,

$$\left(\frac{\mathrm{d}\varepsilon_l}{\mathrm{d}k}\right)_{-\pi/a} = -\left(\frac{\mathrm{d}\varepsilon_l}{\mathrm{d}k}\right)_{\pi/a} = 0. \tag{8.27}$$

It also follows from (8.26) that

$$\left(\frac{\mathrm{d}\varepsilon_l}{\mathrm{d}k}\right)_0 = 0.$$

According to equation (8.9) there is an interval $2\pi/Ga$ between one k value and the next. In the fundamental domain of k, therefore, there are

$$\frac{2\pi}{a}\,\frac{Ga}{2\pi} = G$$

k values, and this is the number of orbital states in each Brillouin zone.

Before going on to a more quantitative discussion of energy gaps it will be useful to prove the following theorem:

if $V(x)$ has period a, then

$$\int_0^L e^{ikx} V(x) dx = 0, \tag{8.28}$$

unless $k = 2\pi n/a$, where n is a positive or negative integer or zero.

Here, as before, $L = Ga$, so that, if q denotes an integer, we may write

$$\int_0^L e^{ikx} V(x) dx = \sum_{q=0}^{G-1} \int_{qa}^{(q+1)a} e^{ikx} V(x) dx, \tag{8.29}$$

which just breaks the range of integration up into G intervals of length a. Also, writing $x = X+qa$, we have

$$\begin{aligned}\int_{qa}^{(q+1)a} e^{ikx} V(x) dx &= \int_0^a e^{ik(X+qa)} V(X+qa) dX \\ &= e^{ikqa} \int_0^a e^{ikX} V(X) dX,\end{aligned} \tag{8.30}$$

owing to the periodicity of $V(x)$. It is immaterial whether we use X or x as the variable of integration in (8.30), since this is a definite integral. Hence, the same integral is a factor of every term in (8.29), which becomes

$$\sum_{q=0}^{G-1} e^{ikqa} \int_0^a e^{ikx} V(x) dx. \tag{8.31}$$

Now,

$$\begin{aligned}\sum_{q=0}^{G-1} e^{ikqa} &= 1+e^{ika}+e^{i2ka}+ \dots +e^{i(G-1)ka} \\ &= \frac{1-e^{iGka}}{1-e^{ika}} = \frac{1-e^{i2\pi g}}{1-e^{i2\pi g/G}} = 0,\end{aligned} \tag{8.32}$$

unless $e^{ika} = 1$, that is, unless $k = 2\pi n/a$, where n is a positive or negative integer or zero. In the latter case, each term of the series is unity, and the sum is G. This completes the required proof and shows, in addition, that

$$\int_0^L e^{i2\pi nx/a} V(x) dx = G \int_0^a e^{i2\pi nx/a} V(x) dx, \tag{8.33}$$

which is otherwise obvious, since the integrand has period a.

It follows immediately, if $\psi_k(x)$ and $\psi_{k'}(x)$ are Bloch functions defined by (8.10), that

$$\int_0^L \psi_k^*(x) V(x) \psi_{k'}(x) dx = 0, \tag{8.34}$$

unless $k' - k = 2\pi n/a$, for this integral is

$$\int_0^L e^{i(k'-k)x} V(x) u_k^*(x) u_{k'}(x) dx,$$

and is of the same form as that in equation (8.28), since $V(x)u_k^*(x)u_{k'}(x)$ has period a.

Also, if $\psi_{kl}(x)$ and $\psi_{k'l'}(x)$ are Bloch functions defined by (8.14) in the reduced zone scheme, then

$$\int_0^L \psi_{kl}^*(x) V(x) \psi_{k'l'}(x) dx = 0, \tag{8.35}$$

unless $k = k'$, since, when k and k' are restricted to the fundamental domain, the only permissible value of n is zero.

8.3. Energy Gaps in One Dimension by Perturbation Theory: Nearly Free Electrons

We will now calculate the energy gaps for a one-dimensional lattice on the assumption that the periodic potential energy $V(x)$ is of very small amplitude. We may then treat $V(x)$ as a small perturbation applied to a free-electron system.

Since we are starting with free-electron functions it is convenient in this case to use the extended zone scheme — in other words, we take the unperturbed wave functions, normalized in the length L of the lattice, to be given by

$$\psi_k(x) = \frac{1}{\sqrt{L}} e^{ikx}, \tag{8.36}$$

where k is not restricted to the fundamental domain.

Now, the unperturbed functions $\psi_k(x)$ and $\psi_{-k}(x)$ are degenerate, both corresponding to the unperturbed energy $\hbar^2k^2/2m$, so let us apply the first-order perturbation theory for a doubly degenerate state described in § 3.7. The functions are orthonormal in the length L, so that, if ε' is the perturbation energy, the secular equation, from (3.85), is

$$\begin{vmatrix} V_{k,k} - \varepsilon' & V_{k,-k} \\ V_{-k,k} & V_{-k,-k} - \varepsilon' \end{vmatrix} = 0. \tag{8.37}$$

Here †

† The quantities $V_{k,k}$, $V_{k,-k}$, etc., are the *matrix elements* of the potential energy with respect to the unperturbed wave functions.

$$V_{k,k} = \int_0^L \psi_k^* V(x)\psi_k \mathrm{d}x$$

$$= \frac{1}{L}\int_0^L V(x)\mathrm{d}x = V_{-k,-k}, \tag{8.38}$$

$$V_{k,-k} = \int_0^L \psi_k^* V(x)\psi_{-k} \mathrm{d}x$$

$$= \frac{1}{L}\int_0^L \mathrm{e}^{-2\mathrm{i}kx} V(x)\mathrm{d}x, \tag{8.39}$$

and

$$V_{-k,k} = \int_0^L \psi_{-k}^* V(x)\psi_k \mathrm{d}x$$

$$= \frac{1}{L}\int_0^L \mathrm{e}^{2\mathrm{i}kx} V(x)\mathrm{d}x = V_{k,-k}^*. \tag{8.40}$$

Equation (8.38) shows that $V_{k,k}$, which is the same as $V_{-k,-k}$, is just the average of $V(x)$ over the lattice, and we may choose our zero of energy so that this average vanishes. The secular equation then becomes

$$\varepsilon'^2 = V_{k,-k}V_{-k,k} = |V_{k,-k}|^2. \tag{8.41}$$

From (8.28) we see that $V_{k,-k}$ is, in fact, zero unless $k = n\pi/a$, where n is a positive or negative integer or zero, and in this case $V_{k,-k}$ becomes

$$V_n = \frac{1}{L}\int_0^L \mathrm{e}^{-\mathrm{i}2\pi nx/a} V(x)\mathrm{d}x = \frac{1}{a}\int_0^a \mathrm{e}^{-\mathrm{i}2\pi nx/a} V(x)\mathrm{d}x, \tag{8.42}$$

by (8.33). First-order perturbation theory thus predicts no splitting of the degenerate energy levels, except when $k = n\pi/a$, and here the unperturbed level splits into the two perturbed levels given by

$$\frac{\hbar^2}{2m}\left(\frac{n\pi}{a}\right)^2 \pm |V_n|.$$

The energy gap at $k = n\pi/a$, that is, between zone $|n|$ and zone $|n|+1$ in the reduced zone scheme, is therefore

$$\Delta\varepsilon(n\pi/a) = 2|V_n|. \tag{8.43}$$

Of course, although energy gaps only occur at $k = n\pi/a$, the energy levels for other values of k must be displaced, so that the final energy curve is like that in Figure 8.3 (b), but this displacement is not given by first-order perturbation theory.

The quantities V_n are just the Fourier coefficients of the potential energy, that is, the coefficients appearing in the complex Fourier series

$$V(x) = \sum_{n=-\infty}^{\infty} V_n e^{i2\pi nx/a}. \tag{8.44}$$

It may be verified by the method described in Appendix 2 that, if a function $V(x)$ with period a is expanded in such a series, the coefficients are given by (8.42).

The perturbed wave functions at $k = n\pi/a$ are linear combinations of the unperturbed functions, and so have the form

$$A_1 e^{in\pi x/a} + A_2 e^{-in\pi x/a}.$$

Considerations of symmetry, or direct calculation by perturbation theory, show that $A_1 = \pm A_2$, and the perturbed functions are proportional to

$$\sin \frac{n\pi x}{a} \quad \text{and} \quad \cos \frac{n\pi x}{a}.$$

Thus, the perturbed functions at the zone boundaries are no longer running waves, but are *standing waves*. It is clear why such standing waves should in general have different energies, for the maxima of their squared moduli do not coincide. If $V(x)$ has troughs at $x = 0, a, 2a, \ldots$, as shown in Figure 8.5, then the cosine function will always have the lower energy, for

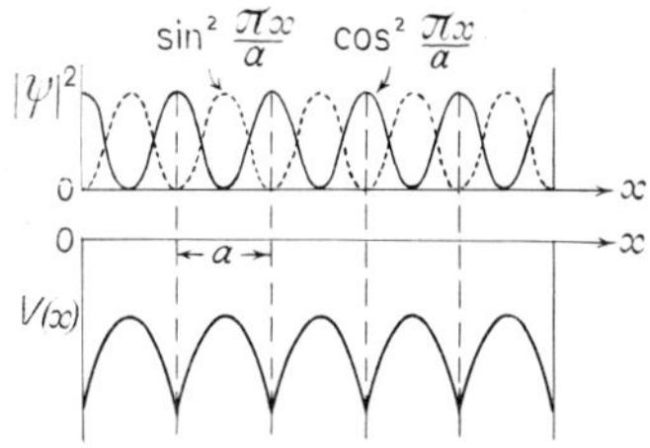

Fig. 8.5. Potential energy function for an electron in a one-dimensional lattice and probability densities for states at the boundaries of the first Brillouin zone.

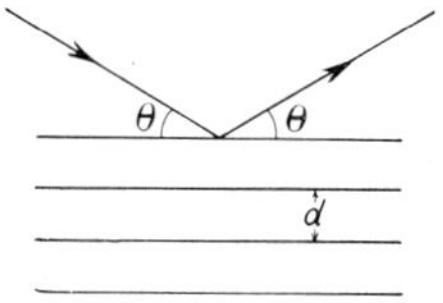

Fig. 8.6. Reflection of a beam of electrons from a crystal.

$\cos^2 (n\pi x/a)$ has maxima at the points of lowest potential energy, whereas $\sin^2 (n\pi x/a)$ has minima. The squares of the two functions with $n = 1$ are also shown in Figure 8.5 — the cosine function corresponds to the point

A (or A′) in Figure 8.2 (b), and the sine function to the point B (or B′).

There is a correspondence between the occurrence of energy gaps and the condition for the Bragg reflection of electrons (or X-rays) from a crystal, which is worth noting. If a beam of electrons (or X-rays) with wavelength λ is incident at an angle θ to a face of a crystal, and d is the distance between planes of atoms parallel to that face, as shown in Figure 8.6 the beam will be reflected provided the Bragg condition

$$n\lambda = 2d \sin \theta \tag{8.45}$$

is satisfied. This is because electron waves reflected from successive planes of atoms will be in phase, and hence reinforce one another, when this condition is satisfied. If we have only a one-dimensional lattice, or, what amounts to the same thing, if a beam of electrons is incident *normally* on a face of a crystal, and the lattice spacing is a, then the condition for reflection is

$$n\lambda = 2a, \tag{8.46}$$

from (8.45), θ being $\pi/2$ in this case. Since $\lambda = 2\pi/k$, this condition becomes

$$k = n\pi/a.$$

This is in agreement with the theory of energy gaps developed above, for no electron can move through the lattice with energy lying in an energy gap, and these occur at $k = n\pi/a$. Hence, if a beam of electrons with such energy is incident on a lattice it must be totally reflected.

8.4. The Tight Binding Approximation in One Dimension

Let us first consider an electron in an isolated potential well $U(x)$, such as that shown in Figure 8.7 (a), which we may regard as the potential energy of the electron due to a one-dimensional 'atom'. We will fix our attention upon a particular bound state of this electron, whose wave function $\chi(x)$ satisfies the Schrödinger equation

$$\frac{d^2\chi}{dx^2} + \frac{2m}{\hbar^2}[\varepsilon_0 - U(x)]\chi = 0, \tag{8.47}$$

and falls exponentially to zero as x tends to $\pm\infty$. If it is the ground state wave function, $\chi(x)$ will have a form similar to that shown in Figure 8.7 (a), but there is no reason why $\chi(x)$ should not be the wave function of an excited state, and hence have nodes. We will assume, however, that $\chi(x)$ is non-degenerate, which is generally the case in one dimension, and also that $U(x)$ is an even function, that is,

$$U(x) = U(-x). \tag{8.48}$$

Now, if a number G of such one-dimensional atoms is arranged on a line, with a distance a between one atom and the next, the result is a lattice of the type discussed above, and the potential energy $V(x)$ of an electron in the lattice is just the sum of the potential functions of all the atoms, namely,

$$V(x) = \sum_l U(x-la), \tag{8.49}$$

where l ranges over G successive integers †.

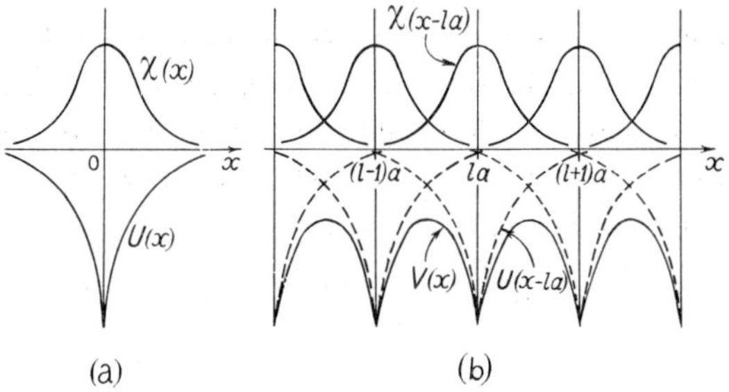

Fig. 8.7. (a) Potential energy $U(x)$ and wave function $\chi(x)$ of an electron in an isolated one-dimensional atom. (b) Potential energy $V(x)$ of an electron in a lattice of such atoms, and the overlapping atomic functions.

The Schrödinger equation for an electron in the lattice is thus

$$\frac{d^2\psi}{dx^2} + \frac{2m}{\hbar^2}[\varepsilon - \sum_l U(x-la)]\psi = 0. \tag{8.50}$$

If the lattice spacing a is so large that there is little overlap between the atomic wave functions of different atoms — more specifically, if the product $U(x-la)\,\chi(x-na)$ is small except when $l = n$ — then it is easily seen that any of the functions $\chi(x-la)$ is approximately a solution of equation (8.50). The equation satisfied by $\chi(x-la)$ is

$$\frac{d^2\chi(x-la)}{dx^2} + \frac{2m}{\hbar^2}[\varepsilon_0 - U(x-la)]\,\chi(x-la) = 0, \tag{8.51}$$

† In fact, if G is a finite number, $V(x)$ as given by (8.49) is not strictly periodic. However, we assume that G is a *very large* number, so that the departure from periodicity is only noticeable at the extreme ends of the lattice, and its effect is completely negligible — this is consistent with the discussion of the field in a real metal given at the beginning of Chapter 7.

which is what equation (8.50) becomes, with $\varepsilon = \varepsilon_0$, when we drop all terms in the potential energy except $U(x-la)$. Since all the functions $\chi(x-la)$ are equally good approximate solutions when overlap is neglected, we expect the proper solution of (8.50), in the case of small but finite overlap, to be very nearly a linear combination of these functions, that is,

$$\psi(x) = \sum_l c_l \chi(x-la), \tag{8.52}$$

approximately, where the constant coefficients c_l are to be determined. This is called the *tight binding* approximation in metal theory, and is just the LCAO (Linear Combinations of Atomic Orbitals) approximation described in connection with the hydrogen molecule in § 5.8.

The coefficients c_l may be obtained by the variational method, but this is not necessary, for they are given immediately by the requirement that the wave function satisfy the Bloch condition. Thus, if we introduce the wave number k, defined as before, and write

$$\psi_k(x) = \sum_l \mathrm{e}^{ikla} \chi(x-la), \tag{8.53}$$

we see that

$$\begin{aligned}\psi_k(x+a) &= \sum_l \mathrm{e}^{ikla} \chi[x-(l-1)a] \\ &= \mathrm{e}^{ika} \sum_l \mathrm{e}^{ik(l-1)a} \chi[x-(l-1)a] \\ &= \mathrm{e}^{ika} \psi_k(x),\end{aligned} \tag{8.54}$$

for a sufficiently long lattice, as required. The function (8.53) is thus a Bloch function and is of the general form (8.52).

If we assume that the atomic orbitals are normalized in the length of the lattice (or, nearly enough, in infinite length), and ignore overlap between those on different atoms, then

$$\int \chi^*(x-na)\chi(x-la)\mathrm{d}x = \delta_{nl}, \tag{8.55}$$

and

$$\begin{aligned}\int \psi_k^* \psi_k \mathrm{d}x &= \sum_n \sum_l \mathrm{e}^{ik(l-n)a} \int \chi^*(x-na)\chi(x-la)\mathrm{d}x \\ &= \sum_n \sum_l \mathrm{e}^{ik(l-n)a} \delta_{nl} = G,\end{aligned}$$

all integrals being over the length of the lattice. The *normalized* approximate wave function of the state k is, therefore,

$$\psi_k(x) = G^{-\frac{1}{2}} \sum_l \mathrm{e}^{ikla} \chi(x-la), \tag{8.56}$$

and the corresponding approximate energy is

$$\varepsilon(k) = \int \psi_k^* H \psi_k \mathrm{d}x, \tag{8.57}$$

where

$$H = -\frac{\hbar^2}{2m}\frac{\mathrm{d}^2}{\mathrm{d}x^2} + V(x). \tag{8.58}$$

Now,

$$\begin{aligned} H\psi_k &= G^{-\frac{1}{2}} \sum_l \mathrm{e}^{ikla} H\chi(x-la) \\ &= G^{-\frac{1}{2}} \sum_l \mathrm{e}^{ikla} \left[-\frac{\hbar^2}{2m}\frac{\mathrm{d}^2}{\mathrm{d}x^2} + U(x-la) \right] \chi(x-la) \\ &\qquad + G^{-\frac{1}{2}} \sum_l \mathrm{e}^{ikla} [V(x) - U(x-la)]\chi(x-la) \\ &= \varepsilon_0 \psi_k + G^{-\frac{1}{2}} \sum_l \mathrm{e}^{ikla} [V(x) - U(x-la)]\chi(x-la), \end{aligned} \tag{8.59}$$

using (8.51), so that

$$\begin{aligned} \varepsilon(k) &= \int \psi_k^* \varepsilon_0 \psi_k \mathrm{d}x \\ &\quad + G^{-1} \sum_n \sum_l \mathrm{e}^{ik(l-n)a} \int \chi^*(x-na)[V(x) - U(x-la)]\chi(x-la)\mathrm{d}x. \end{aligned} \tag{8.60}$$

Writing $X = x - la$, we have

$$\begin{aligned} &\int \chi^*(x-na)\, [V(x) - U(x-la)]\, \chi(x-la)\, \mathrm{d}x \\ &\qquad = \int \chi^*(X+ma)\, [V(X+la) - U(X)]\, \chi(X)\, \mathrm{d}X \\ &\qquad = \int \chi^*(X+ma)\, [V(X) - U(X)]\, \chi(X)\, \mathrm{d}X, \end{aligned}$$

where $m = l - n$. Strictly speaking, the limits of integration with respect to X should be different for each value of l, and hence vary with m and n, but for a very long lattice, and consistent with the use of periodic boundary conditions, this fact may be neglected and all the integrals taken over the same range. We then have

$$\varepsilon(k) = \varepsilon_0 + \sum_m e^{ikma} \int \chi^*(x+ma)[V(x) - U(x)]\chi(x)\mathrm{d}x. \tag{8.61}$$

Our initial assumption was that overlap between different atomic orbitals is small, so we will neglect all the integrals in (8.61) except those for which $m = 0$ or ± 1 — that is to say, we will only take into account overlap between nearest neighbouring atoms. We will also write

$$\alpha = -\int \chi^*(x)\,[V(x) - U(x)]\,\chi(x)\,\mathrm{d}x,$$

$$\gamma = -\int \chi^*(x+a)\,[V(x) - U(x)]\,\chi(x)\,\mathrm{d}x,$$

and it is easily verified that, as $U(x)$ is an even function, and $\chi(x)$ is either even or odd,

$$\gamma = -\int \chi^*(x-a)\,[V(x) - U(x)]\,\chi(x)\,\mathrm{d}x$$

also. This gives, finally,

$$\varepsilon(k) = \varepsilon_0 - \alpha - 2\gamma \cos ka. \tag{8.62}$$

We thus see that the atomic energy level ε_0 splits up into a *band* of energy levels in the lattice, and, as $\cos ka$ lies between -1 and 1, the width of the band is 4γ. It will be noticed that all possible states in this band, or Brillouin zone, are represented by values of k lying between $-\pi/a$ and π/a, ε being a periodic function with period $2\pi/a$ (compare Figure 8.4).

Now, if $U(x)$ is negative, $V(x) - U(x)$ is also negative, so that α is positive. Furthermore, if $\chi(x)$ is an even function of the type shown in Figure 8.7 (a), $\chi(x)$ and $\chi(x+a)$ have the same sign, so that γ is positive. In this case, the energy curve is that shown in Figure 8.8, which resembles the curves for $l = 0$ or $l = 2$ in Figure 8.2 (b). On the other hand, if $\chi(x)$ is an odd function with one node at the origin, as it might be for the first excited state, α is still positive, but γ is negative, so that the energy curve now has a maximum at $k = 0$ and resembles the curve for $l = 1$ in Figure 8.2 (b).

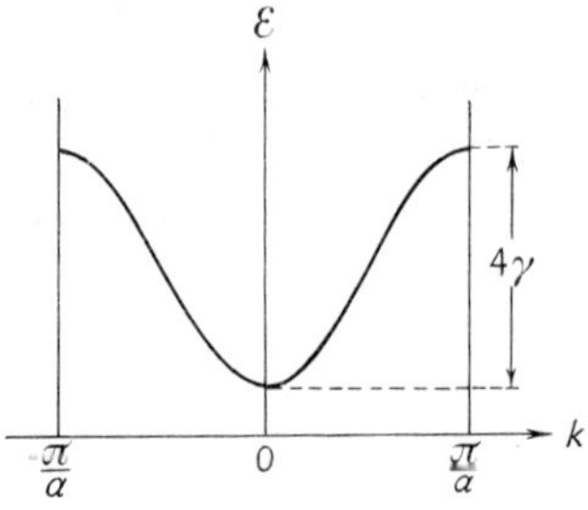

Fig. 8.8. Energy as a function of k for one-dimensional tight binding example.

There is an important difference between the curve of Figure 8.8 and the lowest curve, say, of Figure 8.2 (b), which represents the nearly free electron approximation. In the former, the segment between $k = 0$ and $k = \pi/a$, for example, has a symmetry about $k = \pi/2a$ which is not present in the latter curve, this being almost a parabola except near the zone boundaries.

In principle, every atomic level will broaden into such a band of levels, so that by taking all the atomic levels in turn we would get an infinite set of energy curves, as in Figure 8.2 (b), the equation of each being (8.62), with appropriate values of ε_0, α, and γ. The approximations we have employed must be borne in mind, however. In particular, we have assumed that the atomic wave functions overlap very little, which implies that γ, and hence the energy band width 4γ, must be small. On the other hand, the construction of the Bloch functions from the single atomic function $\chi(x)$ associated with the energy level ε_0 implies, not only that this level is non-degenerate, but that it is isolated from any other atomic energy levels. The simple method we have described is thus appropriate only when it leads to narrow energy bands with wide energy gaps between them. The perturbation method described in the foregoing section, however, is appropriate only when the energy bands are wide and the energy gaps narrow.

The method can easily be extended to degenerate levels. Instead of the single function χ, a linear combination of the degenerate functions associated with a given level is used to construct Bloch functions similar to (8.53), the coefficients being determined by the variational method. Mathematical techniques have also been developed to facilitate the extension of the method to cases where overlap is considerable and involves more than nearest neighbours, but the computational labour involved in obtaining accurate results in such cases generally makes other methods preferable.

We may expand cos ka in equation (8.26) and, when k is very small, retain only the first two terms in the expansion. This gives

$$\varepsilon(k) = \varepsilon_0 - \alpha - 2\gamma + \gamma a^2 k^2, \tag{8.63}$$

which, apart from the position of the zero, is of form similar to that of the free-electron energy (8.23). To point this similarity we sometimes write

$$\gamma a^2 = \hbar^2/2m^*, \tag{8.64}$$

where m^* is known as the *effective mass* of an electron near $k = 0$.

So far, in this chapter, we have been concerned essentially with the pure mathematical problem of the solution of the one-dimensional Schrödinger equation (8.4) for a single electron in a periodic field. This solution can be obtained to any degree of accuracy using numerical methods, but the labour involved is generally considerable, which is why we have confined ourselves to the two important approximations discussed above. Exact solutions have been obtained by simple analysis only when the potential function is either constant (free electrons) or consists of equally spaced delta functions † (Kronig and Penney model). The latter case is rather artificial and tells us little that we have not already established, so we will omit it — accounts of it may be found in many of the works listed in the Bibliography.

In extending these ideas to real metals it must be remembered that many electrons are present, and these contribute substantially to the field acting upon any one of them. It is clear that here again Coulomb correlations are going to play an important part. The effect of these correlations, in fact, is such that Bloch functions do not always provide the best description of the electronic motion. For example, we expect Bloch functions to be appropriate for the valence electrons in a metal, but not for the electrons in the very tightly bound inner shells. The reason for this should be clear from our discussion of the relative merits of the Heitler-London and molecular orbital methods in § 5.8. For the closed inner shells the distinction, in fact, is not important, for it can be shown that in this case the Heitler-London and Bloch methods lead to the same results. It is less easy to decide whether atomic or molecular orbitals are more appropriate for the electrons in, say, the 3d sub-shells of the transition metals.

In discussing the energy bands in metals we shall generally have in mind the electrons which lie outside the closed shells of a free atom, and shall assume that the Bloch method is appropriate.

8.5. The Crystal Structures of Metals

In a metal, as in other solids, the nuclei of the atoms are arranged in a periodic spatial array, or crystal lattice, which may be thought of as constructed from identical *unit cells*, each containing one or more atoms. For the simplest kind of crystal lattice, called a *Bravais lattice*, the unit

† The delta function $\delta(x)$ may be defined as follows:

$$\delta(x) = 0 \text{ for } x \neq 0, \text{ and } \int_{-a}^{b} \delta(x)\, dx = 1,$$

where a and b are any positive numbers. One may usefully think of $\delta(x)$ as the limit, as $c \to 0$, of a function which has value zero outside the interval $(-c, c)$ and value $1/2c$ within this interval.

cell may be taken to be a parallelepiped containing one atom, as shown in Figure 8.9. It is convenient, although not necessary, to take the position of the atom (or more precisely, the nucleus of the atom) to be at a corner of the cell; then, if the edges of the cell are specified by the vectors $\boldsymbol{a}_1$, $\boldsymbol{a}_2$, $\boldsymbol{a}_3$, any atomic position, or *lattice point*, may be obtained from any other by a translation through a *lattice vector* $\boldsymbol{R}_n$, given by

$$\boldsymbol{R}_n = n_1\boldsymbol{a}_1 + n_2\boldsymbol{a}_2 + n_3\boldsymbol{a}_3, \tag{8.65}$$

where n_1, n_2, and n_3 are integers. A more complicated lattice may be described as a Bravais lattice *with a basis;* that is to say, the unit cell contains more than one atom and the *basis* gives the positions of the atoms within the unit cell. In this case only the positions of similarly situated atoms within two unit cells differ by a translational vector of the form (8.65).

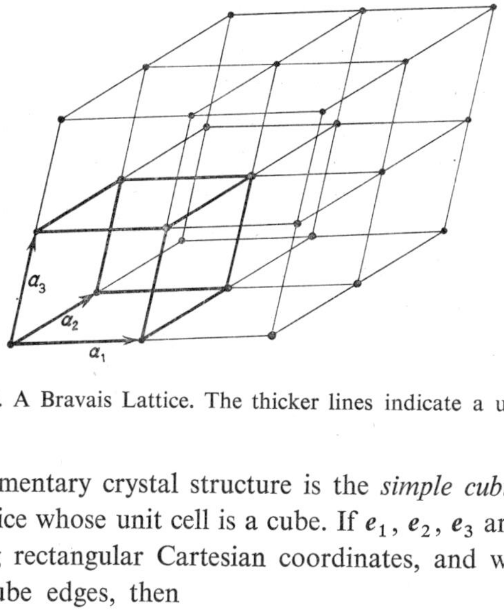

Fig. 8.9. A Bravais Lattice. The thicker lines indicate a unit cell.

The most elementary crystal structure is the *simple cubic lattice*, which is a Bravais lattice whose unit cell is a cube. If $\boldsymbol{e}_1$, $\boldsymbol{e}_2$, $\boldsymbol{e}_3$ are, as usual, unit vectors defining rectangular Cartesian coordinates, and we take these to be along the cube edges, then

$$\boldsymbol{a} = a\boldsymbol{e}_1, \quad \boldsymbol{a}_2 = a\boldsymbol{e}_2, \quad \boldsymbol{a}_3 = a\boldsymbol{e}_3, \tag{8.66}$$

where a is the distance between nearest neighbouring atoms. Although no metal crystallizes in this structure, we shall sometimes use it as a simple model of a three-dimensional lattice.

Most metals have crystal structures of one of the following types: (i) body-centred cubic, (ii) face-centred cubic, (iii) close-packed hexagonal. The first two are simple Bravais lattices, having rhombohedral unit cells, but the last is not — it may be described as a Bravais lattice with a basis, its unit cell containing two atoms. Even in the case of the cubic structures, as the name implies, it is generally more convenient to take the unit cell to be a cube, containing several atoms — two for the body-centred cubic lattice, and four for the face-centred cubic lattice. In other words, we take each of them to be a simple cubic lattice with a basis. Let us consider these important structures in more detail.

(i) *The body-centred cubic lattice.* For this structure the unit cubic cell has atoms at the corners and one at the centre, as shown in Figure 8.10. Seven of the corner atoms are associated with neighbouring cells, however, so that there are only two atoms per unit cell. The lattice may be thought of as two interpenetrating simple cubic lattices, the lattice points of one being at the centres of the unit cells of the other. On the other hand, if $\boldsymbol{e}_1$, $\boldsymbol{e}_2$, $\boldsymbol{e}_3$ again denote unit vectors along the cube edges, and a is the length of an edge, the lattice may be described as a Bravais lattice, with rhombohedral unit cell, having edges

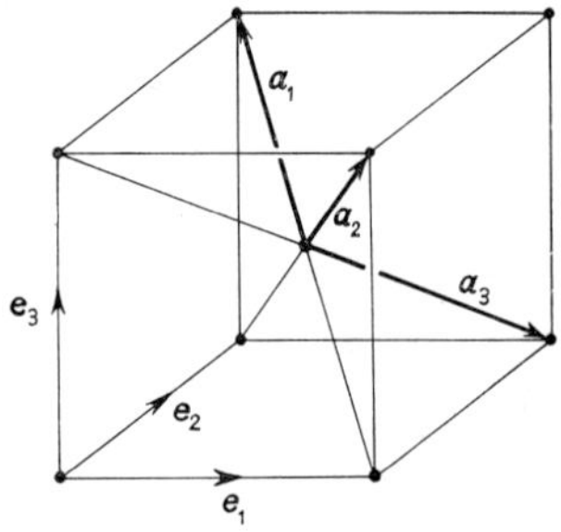

Fig. 8.10. The body-centred cubic structure. The vectors $\boldsymbol{a}_1$, $\boldsymbol{a}_2$, $\boldsymbol{a}_3$ are the edges of the rhombohedral cell of the Bravais lattice.

$$
\begin{aligned}
\boldsymbol{a}_1 &= \tfrac{1}{2}a(-\boldsymbol{e}_1+\boldsymbol{e}_2+\boldsymbol{e}_3),\\
\boldsymbol{a}_2 &= \tfrac{1}{2}a(\boldsymbol{e}_1-\boldsymbol{e}_2+\boldsymbol{e}_3),\\
\boldsymbol{a}_3 &= \tfrac{1}{2}a(\boldsymbol{e}_1+\boldsymbol{e}_2-\boldsymbol{e}_3).
\end{aligned}
\tag{8.67}
$$

It may be verified that all the lattice points are then given by equation (8.65). The volume of this cell is

$$\boldsymbol{a}_1 \cdot \boldsymbol{a}_2 \wedge \boldsymbol{a}_3 = \tfrac{1}{2}a^3,$$

which is one half the volume of the cubic cell — this is expected, since there are two atoms to each cubic cell and only one to each rhombohedral cell.

Each atom has eight nearest neighbours at distance $\sqrt{3}a/2$, and six second nearest neighbours at distance a.

(ii) *The face-centred cubic lattice.*

For this structure the unit cubic cell has atoms at the corners and at the centre of each face, as shown in Figure 8.11. Only four of these atoms belong to the unit cell, the others belonging to neighbouring cells, and the lattice may thus be considered as four interpenetrating simple cubic lattices. Alternatively, it may be described as a Bravais lattice, with rhombohedral unit cell, having edges

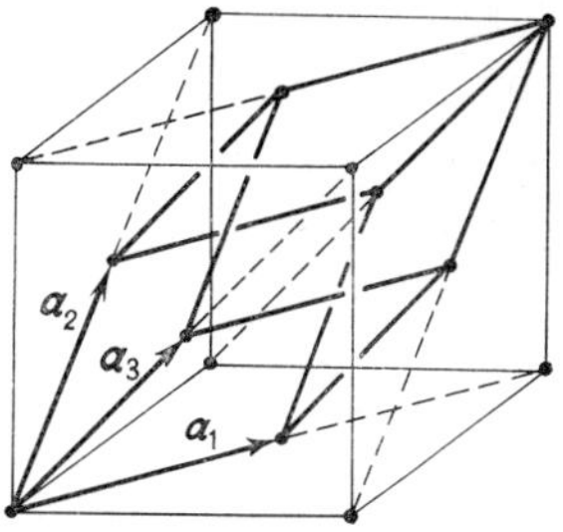

Fig. 8.11. The face-centred cubic structure. The thicker lines are the edges of the rhombohedral cell of the Bravais lattice.

$$\begin{aligned} \boldsymbol{a}_1 &= \tfrac{1}{2}a(\boldsymbol{e}_1+\boldsymbol{e}_2), \\ \boldsymbol{a}_2 &= \tfrac{1}{2}a(\boldsymbol{e}_2+\boldsymbol{e}_3), \\ \boldsymbol{a}_3 &= \tfrac{1}{2}a(\boldsymbol{e}_3+\boldsymbol{e}_1), \end{aligned} \tag{8.68}$$

which is also shown in Figure 8.11. The volume of this cell is

$$\boldsymbol{a}_1 \cdot \boldsymbol{a}_2 \wedge \boldsymbol{a}_3 = \tfrac{1}{4}a^3,$$

which is one quarter of the volume of the cube, as expected.

Each atom has twelve nearest neighbours at distance $a/\sqrt{2}$.

(iii) *The close-packed hexagonal lattice*

In this structure the atoms are arranged in equidistant parallel planes, in each of which every atom has six equidistant neighbours. The atoms of alternate planes are perpendicularly above each other, but the atoms of any one plane are perpendicularly above the centres of the triangles formed by groups of three atoms in the next plane, as shown in Figure 8.12. The lattice obtained by taking alternate planes only is a *simple hexagonal lattice*, so that the close-packed hexagonal structure consists of two interpenetrating simple hexagonal lattices. If c is the distance between alternate planes and a is the distance between nearest neighbouring atoms in any one plane, the lattice may be described as a Bravais lattice (the simple hexagonal lattice) with a basis, the unit cell having edges

$$\boldsymbol{a}_1 = a\boldsymbol{e}_1, \qquad \boldsymbol{a}_2 = \tfrac{1}{2}a\boldsymbol{e}_1+\tfrac{1}{2}\sqrt{3}\,a\boldsymbol{e}_2, \qquad \boldsymbol{a}_3 = c\boldsymbol{e}_3, \tag{8.69}$$

where the axes $\boldsymbol{e}_1$, $\boldsymbol{e}_2$, $\boldsymbol{e}_3$ are as shown in the figure. The cell contains two atoms, one at the origin, and one at

$$\tfrac{1}{2}a\boldsymbol{e}_1+\tfrac{1}{6}\sqrt{3}\,a\boldsymbol{e}_2+\tfrac{1}{2}c\boldsymbol{e}_3\,,$$

or, in terms of the basic lattice vectors, at $\boldsymbol{O}$ and $\frac{1}{3}\boldsymbol{a}_1+\frac{1}{3}\boldsymbol{a}_2+\frac{1}{2}\boldsymbol{a}_3$. The *basis* is generally written (0, 0, 0), ($\frac{1}{3}$, $\frac{1}{3}$, $\frac{1}{2}$), giving the oblique coordinates of the atoms in terms of the edges of the cell. The volume of the cell is $\frac{1}{2}\sqrt{3}\,a^2c$.

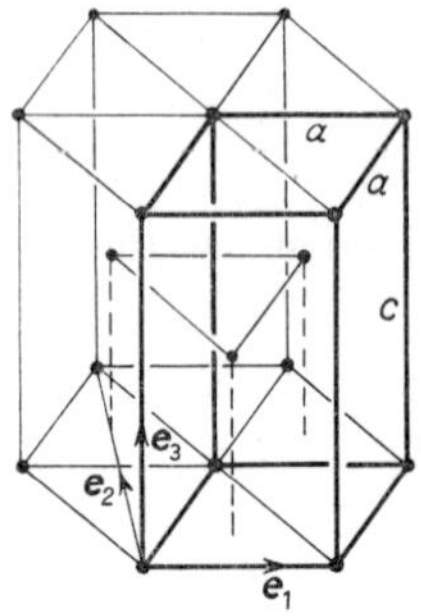

Fig. 8.12. The close-packed hexagonal structure. The thicker lines are the edges of the unit cell.

Now, the close-packed hexagonal structure and the face-centred cubic structure (sometimes called *close-packed cubic*) represent the two ways in which hard spheres may be most densely packed. In the close-packed hexagonal lattice each atom has six neighbours at a distance a in the *basal* plane through the atom. There are three others at distance $\sqrt{(\frac{1}{3}a^2+\frac{1}{4}c^2)}$ in each of the planes on either side of the basal plane. In the case of the ideal close packing of hard spheres the axial ratio c/a has the value $(8/3)^{\frac{1}{2}} = 1.63$, when all twelve neighbours are at the same distance a. We have remarked that in the face-centred cubic structure also each atom has twelve equidistant neighbours. However, in metals having the close-packed hexagonal structure the axial ratio generally differs slightly from the ideal value, the greatest difference being in zinc, for which $c/a = 1.86$. Strictly speaking, therefore, in these metals each atom has only six nearest neighbours.

A few metals have other kinds of lattice structures, but we will not consider these — the vast majority have structures of the foregoing types. Many metals have different structures in different ranges of temperature and pressure, a phenomenon which is known as *polymorphism*.

8.6. Bloch Functions in a Three-Dimensional Lattice

Let us consider a crystal lattice whose unit cell has edges $\boldsymbol{a}_1$, $\boldsymbol{a}_2$, $\boldsymbol{a}_3$, and let the dimensions of the lattice be G_1a_1, G_2a_2, G_3a_3 along $\boldsymbol{a}_1$, $\boldsymbol{a}_2$, and $\boldsymbol{a}_3$ respectively, G_1, G_2, and G_3 being integers. If it is a simple Bravais lattice, then, the total number of atoms is $G_1G_2G_3$. The potential energy $V(\boldsymbol{r})$ of an electron moving in this lattice will have the same periodicity as the lattice (neglecting surface effects), so that we may write

$$V(\boldsymbol{r}+\boldsymbol{R}_n) = V(\boldsymbol{r}), \tag{8.70}$$

where $\boldsymbol{R}_n$ is defined by (8.65). If there are many electrons present, as in an actual metal, we assume that the potential energy is due to the self-consistent field, and satisfies the same condition.

The basic problem is to solve the Schrödinger equation

$$\nabla^2\psi + \frac{2m}{\hbar^2}[\varepsilon - V(\boldsymbol{r})]\psi = 0. \tag{8.71}$$

As in the one-dimensional case, we assume a cyclic system, and apply periodic boundary conditions, which now take the form

$$\psi(\boldsymbol{r}) = \psi(\boldsymbol{r}+G_1\boldsymbol{a}_1) = \psi(\boldsymbol{r}+G_2\boldsymbol{a}_2) = \psi(\boldsymbol{r}+G_3\boldsymbol{a}_3). \tag{8.72}$$

Bloch's theorem in three dimensions, which may be proved by an extension of the method used for a one-dimensional lattice, then shows that the wave functions must satisfy the *Bloch condition*

$$\psi_{\boldsymbol{k}}(\boldsymbol{r}+\boldsymbol{R}_n) = \mathrm{e}^{\mathrm{i}\boldsymbol{k}\cdot\boldsymbol{R}_n}\psi_{\boldsymbol{k}}(\boldsymbol{r}), \tag{8.73}$$

the wave vector $\boldsymbol{k}$ being defined in such a way that the boundary conditions are satisfied. We deduce from this that the wave functions have the form

$$\psi_{\boldsymbol{k}}(\boldsymbol{r}) = \mathrm{e}^{\mathrm{i}\boldsymbol{k}\cdot\boldsymbol{r}}u_{\boldsymbol{k}}(\boldsymbol{r}), \tag{8.74}$$

where $u_{\boldsymbol{k}}(\boldsymbol{r})$ has the periodicity of the lattice, that is to say,

$$u_{\boldsymbol{k}}(\boldsymbol{r}+\boldsymbol{R}_n) = u_{\boldsymbol{k}}(\boldsymbol{r}). \tag{8.75}$$

From the periodic boundary conditions (8.72) and equation (8.75) we have

$$\psi_{\boldsymbol{k}}(\boldsymbol{r}) = \psi_{\boldsymbol{k}}(\boldsymbol{r}+G_1\boldsymbol{a}_1) = \mathrm{e}^{\mathrm{i}G_1\boldsymbol{k}\cdot\boldsymbol{a}_1}\psi_{\boldsymbol{k}}(\boldsymbol{r}),$$

and similarly for the other two conditions. Hence,

$$\mathrm{e}^{\mathrm{i}G_1\boldsymbol{k}\cdot\boldsymbol{a}_1} = \mathrm{e}^{\mathrm{i}G_2\boldsymbol{k}\cdot\boldsymbol{a}_2} = \mathrm{e}^{\mathrm{i}G_3\boldsymbol{k}\cdot\boldsymbol{a}_3} = 1,$$

so that

$$\boldsymbol{k}\cdot\boldsymbol{a}_1 = \frac{2\pi g_1}{G_1}, \qquad \boldsymbol{k}\cdot\boldsymbol{a}_2 = \frac{2\pi g_2}{G_2}, \qquad \boldsymbol{k}\cdot\boldsymbol{a}_3 = \frac{2\pi g_3}{G_3}, \tag{8.76}$$

where g_1, g_2, and g_3 are integers.

It follows immediately *for a simple cubic lattice*, where $\boldsymbol{a}_1$, $\boldsymbol{a}_2$, and $\boldsymbol{a}_3$ are defined by equations (8.66), that the wave vector $\boldsymbol{k}$ is given by

$$\boldsymbol{k} = \frac{2\pi}{a}\left(\frac{g_1}{G_1}\boldsymbol{e}_1 + \frac{g_2}{G_2}\boldsymbol{e}_2 + \frac{g_3}{G_3}\boldsymbol{e}_3\right). \tag{8.77}$$

This is not true in general, however. In order to define $\boldsymbol{k}$ in general we will introduce what is called the *reciprocal lattice.*

8.7. The Reciprocal Lattice: Brillouin Zones

We define a set of vectors $\boldsymbol{b}_1, \boldsymbol{b}_2, \boldsymbol{b}_3$, perpendicular to the coordinate planes of the oblique axes $\boldsymbol{a}_1, \boldsymbol{a}_2, \boldsymbol{a}_3$, by means of the relations

$$\boldsymbol{a}_i \cdot \boldsymbol{b}_j = 2\pi\delta_{ij} \qquad (i, j = 1, 2, 3), \tag{8.78}$$

where δ_{ij} is the Kronecker delta. We will call the vectors $\boldsymbol{b}_j$ the *reciprocal vectors,* and the set of points whose position vectors are given by

$$\boldsymbol{K_m} = m_1\boldsymbol{b}_1 + m_2\boldsymbol{b}_2 + m_3\boldsymbol{b}_3\,, \tag{8.79}$$

where m_1, m_2, m_3 take on all integral values including zero, we will call the *reciprocal lattice.* The reciprocal vectors are, in fact, generally defined by equation (8.78) without the factor 2π on the right hand side, that is, as our vectors $\boldsymbol{b}_j$ divided by 2π, the reciprocal lattice being defined accordingly. Here, however, it is convenient to include the factor 2π, and there is little point in introducing new names for so trivial a difference. It is easily verified that the explicit expressions for the reciprocal vectors are

$$\boldsymbol{b}_1 = \frac{2\pi}{\Omega}\,\boldsymbol{a}_2 \wedge \boldsymbol{a}_3, \quad \boldsymbol{b}_2 = \frac{2\pi}{\Omega}\,\boldsymbol{a}_3 \wedge \boldsymbol{a}_1, \quad \boldsymbol{b}_3 = \frac{2\pi}{\Omega}\,\boldsymbol{a}_1 \wedge \boldsymbol{a}_2, \tag{8.80}$$

where $\Omega = \boldsymbol{a}_1 \cdot \boldsymbol{a}_2 \wedge \boldsymbol{a}_3$, the volume of a unit cell of the crystal lattice.

It now follows from equations (8.76) that, in general, the wave vector $\boldsymbol{k}$ is given by

$$\boldsymbol{k} = \frac{g_1}{G_1}\,\boldsymbol{b}_1 + \frac{g_2}{G_2}\,\boldsymbol{b}_2 + \frac{g_3}{G_3}\,\boldsymbol{b}_3, \tag{8.81}$$

so that what we have called '$\boldsymbol{k}$-space' is the space of the reciprocal lattice, and it is consequently referred to as the *reciprocal space* of the crystal.

From equations (8.65) and (8.79) we have

$$\boldsymbol{K_m} \cdot \boldsymbol{R_n} = 2\pi(m_1n_1 + m_2n_2 + m_3n_3),$$

and the number in brackets is an integer, so that

$$e^{i\boldsymbol{K_m} \cdot \boldsymbol{R_n}} = 1.$$

The function $\exp(\mathrm{i}\boldsymbol{K}_m \cdot \boldsymbol{r})$ thus has the periodicity of the lattice, since

$$\mathrm{e}^{\mathrm{i}\boldsymbol{K}_m \cdot (\boldsymbol{r}+\boldsymbol{R}_n)} = \mathrm{e}^{\mathrm{i}\boldsymbol{K}_m \cdot \boldsymbol{r}}. \tag{8.82}$$

It may now be seen immediately that the wave vector $\boldsymbol{k}$ is undetermined to the extent of an added reciprocal lattice vector $\boldsymbol{K}_m$, for we may write equation (8.74) as

$$\psi_{\boldsymbol{k}}(\boldsymbol{r}) = \mathrm{e}^{\mathrm{i}(\boldsymbol{k}+\boldsymbol{K}_m)\cdot \boldsymbol{r}}\left[\mathrm{e}^{-\mathrm{i}\boldsymbol{K}_m \cdot \boldsymbol{r}}\, u_{\boldsymbol{k}}(\boldsymbol{r})\right], \tag{8.83}$$

and the function in square brackets still has the periodicity of the lattice, so that the form of the Bloch function is unchanged.

Just as in the one-dimensional case, therefore, we may restrict the $\boldsymbol{k}$ vectors to a single cell of the reciprocal lattice, which we will call the *fundamental domain of* $\boldsymbol{k}$. Solution of the Schrödinger equation will give an infinite number of states for each $\boldsymbol{k}$ vector in the fundamental domain, and we may label these by a quantum number l; thus, the wave function

$$\psi_{\boldsymbol{k}l}(\boldsymbol{r}) = \mathrm{e}^{\mathrm{i}\boldsymbol{k}\cdot \boldsymbol{r}}\, u_{\boldsymbol{k}l}(\boldsymbol{r}) \tag{8.84}$$

corresponds to the energy level $\varepsilon_l(\boldsymbol{k})$. Again, if a given label l is properly ascribed, it will specify a set of states, one for each $\boldsymbol{k}$ vector, for which the energy $\varepsilon_l(\boldsymbol{k})$ is a quasi-continuous function of $\boldsymbol{k}$, and this set of states is called a *Brillouin zone.*

The fundamental domain of $\boldsymbol{k}$, or basic cell of the reciprocal lattice, may be chosen in any number of ways, but it is most convenient to choose it to be a polyhedron with as much symmetry as possible about the origin. We therefore draw the reciprocal lattice vectors joining the origin, $\boldsymbol{k} = \boldsymbol{0}$, to the other lattice points, and construct the planes which perpendicularly bisect these vectors. We then take the fundamental domain of $\boldsymbol{k}$ to be the smallest region † surrounding the origin and bounded by these planes. As a rule, only the planes bisecting the position vectors of lattice points which are nearest and, perhaps, next nearest neighbours of the origin form the surface of the cell.

The equation of any face of the fundamental domain is easily seen to be

$$2\boldsymbol{k} \cdot \boldsymbol{K}_m = |\boldsymbol{K}_m|^2, \tag{8.85}$$

where $\boldsymbol{K}_m$ is the vector bisected by that face. Thus, from Figure 8.13, if

† It will be seen in the following chapter that the region defined in this way is just the *Wigner-Seitz* cell of the reciprocal lattice.

P is the mid-point of $\boldsymbol{K}_m$, and $\boldsymbol{k}$ is the position vector of any point in the plane through P, we have

$$\mathrm{OP} = \tfrac{1}{2}|\boldsymbol{K}_m| = k\cos\theta = \frac{\boldsymbol{k}\cdot\boldsymbol{K}_m}{|\boldsymbol{K}_m|},$$

and (8.85) follows. To each face there is a parallel face, whose equation is

$$2\boldsymbol{k}\cdot\boldsymbol{K}_m + |\boldsymbol{K}_m|^2 = 0, \tag{8.86}$$

the perpendicular distance between the two planes being $\boldsymbol{K}_m$.

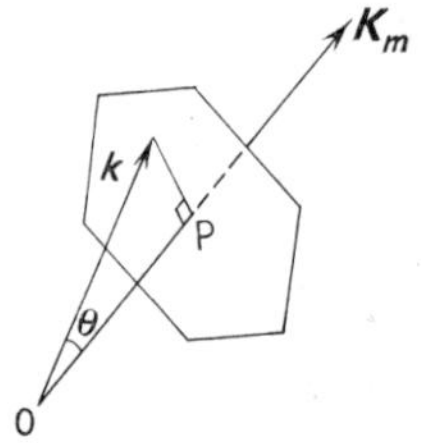

Fig. 8.13. $\boldsymbol{k}$ is the position vector of a point on the plane which perpendicularly bisects $\boldsymbol{K}_m$, P being the mid-point of $\boldsymbol{K}_m$.

As an example, let us consider the *simple cubic lattice*. We obtain, directly from (8.80), or from (8.77) and (8.81),

$$\boldsymbol{b}_1 = \frac{2\pi}{a}\boldsymbol{e}_1, \quad \boldsymbol{b}_2 = \frac{2\pi}{a}\boldsymbol{e}_2, \quad \boldsymbol{b}_3 = \frac{2\pi}{a}\boldsymbol{e}_3, \tag{8.87}$$

the reciprocal vectors being parallel to the lattice vectors. The fundamental domain of $\boldsymbol{k}$ is thus a cube of side $2\pi/a$. The vectors $\boldsymbol{K}_m$ bisected by the faces are $\pm\boldsymbol{b}_1$, $\pm\boldsymbol{b}_2$, $\pm\boldsymbol{b}_3$. If k_1, k_2, k_3 are the components of $\boldsymbol{k}$ along $\boldsymbol{e}_1, \boldsymbol{e}_2, \boldsymbol{e}_3$, respectively, the equations of the six faces are

$$k_1 = \pm\frac{\pi}{a}, \qquad k_2 = \pm\frac{\pi}{a}, \qquad k_3 = \pm\frac{\pi}{a}, \tag{8.88}$$

which also follow from equation (8.85).

Whatever the shape chosen for the basic cell of the reciprocal lattice, its volume is always given by

$$\boldsymbol{b}_1\cdot\boldsymbol{b}_2\wedge\boldsymbol{b}_3 = \frac{8\pi^3}{\Omega^3}(\boldsymbol{a}_2\wedge\boldsymbol{a}_3)\cdot(\boldsymbol{a}_3\wedge\boldsymbol{a}_1)\wedge(\boldsymbol{a}_1\wedge\boldsymbol{a}_2).$$

It may be verified that

$$(\boldsymbol{a}_3\wedge\boldsymbol{a}_1)\wedge(\boldsymbol{a}_1\wedge\boldsymbol{a}_2) = [\boldsymbol{a}_1\cdot(\boldsymbol{a}_2\wedge\boldsymbol{a}_3)]\boldsymbol{a}_1 = \Omega\boldsymbol{a}_1.$$

Hence

$$\boldsymbol{b}_1\cdot\boldsymbol{b}_2\wedge\boldsymbol{b}_3 = \frac{8\pi^3}{\Omega^2}\boldsymbol{a}_1\cdot\boldsymbol{a}_2\wedge\boldsymbol{a}_3 = \frac{8\pi^3}{\Omega}. \tag{8.89}$$

The volume of the fundamental domain of $\boldsymbol{k}$ is thus $8\pi^3$ times the reciprocal of the volume of a unit cell of the crystal lattice. Also, we see directly from equation (8.81) that the number of $\boldsymbol{k}$ vectors in this domain is $G_1G_2G_3$, and their end points are uniformly distributed (the $\boldsymbol{k}$ vectors describe a lattice whose unit cell has edges $\boldsymbol{b}_1/G_1$, $\boldsymbol{b}_2/G_2$, $\boldsymbol{b}_3/G_3$). The number of $\boldsymbol{k}$ vectors with end points in a volume $\mathrm{d}\boldsymbol{k}$ of $\boldsymbol{k}$-space is, therefore

$$G_1G_2G_3\Omega\,\mathrm{d}\boldsymbol{k}/8\pi^3 = v\,\mathrm{d}\boldsymbol{k}/8\pi^3, \tag{8.90}$$

where v is the volume of the crystal. This result is the same as we obtained for free electrons — which might have been expected, for the distribution of $\boldsymbol{k}$ vectors is independent of the potential energy, and must be the same when this is zero.

The number $G_1G_2G_3$ of $\boldsymbol{k}$ vectors in the fundamental domain is also the number of orbital states in a Brillouin zone, which is thus equal to the number of unit cells in the crystal. Since each orbital state can accommodate two electrons, with opposite spins, a Brillouin zone can accommodate a number of electrons equal to twice the number of unit cells in the crystal. *If the crystal is a simple Bravais lattice*, so that each unit cell contains only one atom, *a Brillouin zone can accommodate two electrons per atom of the crystal.* If the number of electrons per atom is greater than two, the electrons must be spread over several Brillouin zones.

It must be pointed out that what we have called the *fundamental domain of* $\boldsymbol{k}$ is itself generally called the *first Brillouin zone* or the *reduced zone*, for reasons similar to those given in the case of the one-dimensional lattice. Regions of the first Brillouin zone, in this terminology, may be translated through reciprocal lattice vectors to form polyhedra symmetrically surrounding the first zone. The bounding planes of these polyhedra still bisect the position vectors of reciprocal lattice points, so that they are given by equation (8.85). The region between the first zone and the second smallest polyhedron is then called the *second* Brillouin zone, and so on, each zone having the same volume (see Figure 8.14). This is called the *extended zone scheme*, and it permits the energy $\varepsilon(\boldsymbol{k})$ to be described as a single-valued function of $\boldsymbol{k}$, which now ranges over the whole of $\boldsymbol{k}$-space. On the

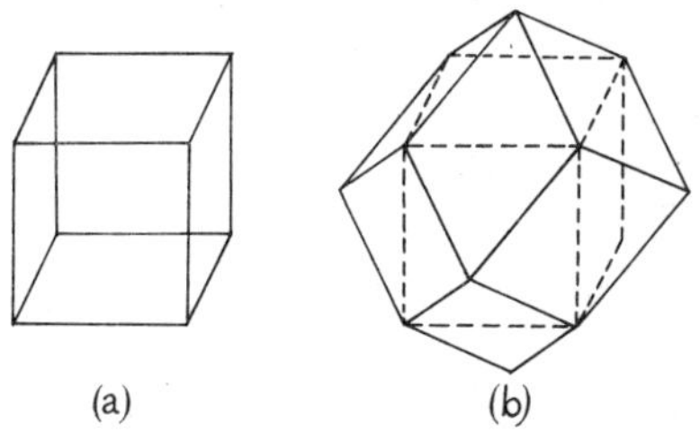

Fig. 8.14. The first and second Brillouin zones for a simple cubic lattice, according to the extended zone scheme.

other hand, the first method we described, in which $\boldsymbol{k}$ is restricted to the fundamental domain, and the energy is an infinitely many-valued function of $\boldsymbol{k}$, is often called the *reduced zone scheme*. Both schemes are equally valid, and, if the sets of states described as the first, second, third, . . . Brillouin zones in the reduced zone scheme are those allotted to the first, second, third, . . . Brillouin zones, respectively, in the extended zone scheme, the correspondence between the two schemes is exact — we shall always assume this to be the case. It should be remarked, however, that the allotment of states to the various zones in the extended zone scheme is not unique, so that the reduced zone scheme must be regarded as the more fundamental — this argument has been elaborated in the one-dimensional case (§ 8.2).

8.8. Energy Bands and Energy Gaps

Within any Brillouin zone the energy is a quasi-continuous function of $\boldsymbol{k}$, but energy gaps generally occur at the zone boundaries, that is, on the planes whose equations are (8.85) or (8.86). This may be shown by an extension to three dimensions of the perturbation method described in § 8.3.

The unperturbed wave functions are now the free-electron functions

$$\psi_{\boldsymbol{k}}(\boldsymbol{r}) = \frac{1}{\sqrt{v}} \mathrm{e}^{\mathrm{i}\boldsymbol{k}\cdot\boldsymbol{r}}, \tag{8.91}$$

which are normalized in the volume v of the crystal. In one dimension we found that energy gaps occurred when the matrix element $V_{k,-k}$ of the potential energy did not vanish. Here the degeneracy is much greater than in the one-dimensional case, for all the unperturbed states which lie on a sphere of radius k in $\boldsymbol{k}$-space have the same energy, $\hbar^2k^2/2m$. None the less, energy gaps can only occur when some of the off-diagonal elements of the secular determinant are different from zero, that is to say, when the $\boldsymbol{k}$ vector is such that the matrix element $V_{\boldsymbol{k},\boldsymbol{k}'}$, where $|\boldsymbol{k}| = |\boldsymbol{k}'|$, does not vanish.

The matrix element is

$$\begin{aligned} V_{\boldsymbol{k},\boldsymbol{k}'} &= \int \psi_{\boldsymbol{k}}^* V(\boldsymbol{r}) \psi_{\boldsymbol{k}'} \mathrm{d}\boldsymbol{r} \\ &= \frac{1}{v} \int \mathrm{e}^{\mathrm{i}(\boldsymbol{k}'-\boldsymbol{k})\cdot\boldsymbol{r}} V(\boldsymbol{r}) \mathrm{d}\boldsymbol{r}, \end{aligned} \tag{8.92}$$

the integral being over the volume of the crystal. We will evaluate this by means of a device which has already been used in the one-dimensional case (at the end of § 8.2). The integral may be reduced to an integration over a unit cell of the lattice by making use of the periodicity of $V(\boldsymbol{r})$, expressed in equation (8.70). Letting $\boldsymbol{r} = \boldsymbol{r}' + \boldsymbol{R}_n$, we find

$$V_{\boldsymbol{k},\boldsymbol{k}'} = \frac{1}{v}\sum_{\boldsymbol{n}}\int_{\text{cell } \boldsymbol{n}} e^{i(\boldsymbol{k}'-\boldsymbol{k})\cdot(\boldsymbol{r}'+\boldsymbol{R}_n)}V(\boldsymbol{r}')d\boldsymbol{r}'$$

$$= \frac{1}{v}\sum_{\boldsymbol{n}} e^{i(\boldsymbol{k}'-\boldsymbol{k})\cdot\boldsymbol{R}_n}\int_{\text{cell}} e^{i(\boldsymbol{k}'-\boldsymbol{k})\cdot\boldsymbol{r}}V(\boldsymbol{r})d\boldsymbol{r}, \tag{8.93}$$

the summation being over all the cells of the lattice. Now, from equation (8.65) and (8.76), we obtain

$$(\boldsymbol{k}'-\boldsymbol{k})\cdot\boldsymbol{R}_n = 2\pi\left[\frac{(g_1'-g_1)n_1}{G_1}+\frac{(g_2'-g_2)n_2}{G_2}+\frac{(g_3'-g_3)n_3}{G_3}\right],$$

so that $V_{\boldsymbol{k},\boldsymbol{k}'}$ contains the factor

$$\sum_{n_1=0}^{G_1-1} e^{i2\pi(g_1'-g_1)n_1/G_1}\sum_{n_2=0}^{G_2-1} e^{i2\pi(g_2'-g_2)n_2/G_2}\sum_{n_3=0}^{G_3-1} e^{i2\pi(g_3'-g_3)n_3/G_3},$$

and this is zero, unless

$$g_1' = g_1-m_1G_1, \qquad g_2' = g_2-m_2G_2, \qquad g_3' = g_3-m_3G_3,$$

where m_1, m_2, and m_3 are positive or negative integers or zero. Thus, using equations (8.79) and (8.81), we see that $V_{\boldsymbol{k},\boldsymbol{k}'}$ is zero unless

$$\boldsymbol{k}' = \boldsymbol{k}-\boldsymbol{K}_m. \tag{8.94}$$

But $|\boldsymbol{k}'| = |\boldsymbol{k}|$, so that $V_{\boldsymbol{k},\boldsymbol{k}'}$ is zero unless

$$|\boldsymbol{k}|^2 = |\boldsymbol{k}-\boldsymbol{K}_m|^2,$$

or

$$2\boldsymbol{k}\cdot\boldsymbol{K}_m = |\boldsymbol{K}_m|^2,$$

which is equation (8.85), defining the bounding planes of the Brillouin zones. Equation (8.86) could be obtained equally well by changing the sign of $\boldsymbol{K}_m$ in (8.94).

We have seen [equation (8.82)] that functions of the form $\exp(i\boldsymbol{K}_m\cdot\boldsymbol{r})$ have the periodicity of the lattice, and it follows that

$$\int_v e^{i(\boldsymbol{K}_m-\boldsymbol{K}_l)\cdot\boldsymbol{r}}d\boldsymbol{r} = 0, \quad \text{if } \boldsymbol{K}_m \neq \boldsymbol{K}_l,$$
$$= v, \quad \text{if } \boldsymbol{K}_m = \boldsymbol{K}_l. \tag{8.95}$$

The potential energy may therefore be expanded in a triple Fourier series of the form

$$V(\boldsymbol{r}) = \sum_{\boldsymbol{m}} V_{\boldsymbol{m}} \mathrm{e}^{\mathrm{i}\boldsymbol{K}_{\boldsymbol{m}} \cdot \boldsymbol{r}}, \tag{8.96}$$

the sum being over all the positive and negative integral values (including zero) of m_1, m_2, and m_3. Application of the method described in Appendix 2 shows that the Fourier coefficient $V_{\boldsymbol{m}}$ is given by

$$V_{\boldsymbol{m}} = \frac{1}{v} \int \mathrm{e}^{-\mathrm{i}\boldsymbol{K}_{\boldsymbol{m}} \cdot \boldsymbol{r}}\, V(\boldsymbol{r}) \mathrm{d}\boldsymbol{r}, \tag{8.97}$$

which is just what (8.92) becomes when condition (8.94) is satisfied. Hence, there is a finite energy gap on the plane defined by $\boldsymbol{K}_{\boldsymbol{m}}$, provided the corresponding Fourier coefficient of the potential energy is not zero †. It is possible, however, if the lattice is not a simple Bravais lattice, that some of the Fourier coefficients may be zero — in other words, that some of the terms may be missing from the Fourier series (8.96), as we shall now see.

Let us suppose that the crystal lattice is a composite lattice, that is, a Bravais lattice with a basis. The lattice may then be described as a number of interpenetrating Bravais lattices, the number being that of the atoms in a unit cell of the composite lattice. As an idealization of the physical situation we may assume that the total potential energy $V(\boldsymbol{r})$ is simply the sum of the potential energies due to these Bravais lattices separately. Let the unit cell of the composite lattice contain q atoms, whose position vectors relative to a corner of the cell are $\boldsymbol{s}_1, \boldsymbol{s}_2, \ldots \boldsymbol{s}_q$ (one of these is normally chosen to be zero), and let the potential energy of an electron due to one of the constituent Bravais lattices only be $V'(\boldsymbol{r})$. Then

$$V(\boldsymbol{r}) = \sum_{j=1}^{q} V'(\boldsymbol{r} - \boldsymbol{s}_j). \tag{8.98}$$

The Fourier expansion of $V'(\boldsymbol{r})$ is

$$V'(\boldsymbol{r}) = \sum_{\boldsymbol{m}} V'_{\boldsymbol{m}} \mathrm{e}^{\mathrm{i}\boldsymbol{K}_{\boldsymbol{m}} \cdot \boldsymbol{r}},$$

and that of $V(\boldsymbol{r})$ can therefore be written

$$V(\boldsymbol{r}) = \sum_{j=1}^{q} \sum_{\boldsymbol{m}} V'_{\boldsymbol{m}} \mathrm{e}^{\mathrm{i}\boldsymbol{K}_{\boldsymbol{m}} \cdot (\boldsymbol{r} - \boldsymbol{s}_j)} = \sum_{\boldsymbol{m}} V'_{\boldsymbol{m}} S_{\boldsymbol{m}} \mathrm{e}^{\mathrm{i}\boldsymbol{K}_{\boldsymbol{m}} \cdot \boldsymbol{r}}, \tag{8.99}$$

† It must be remembered that *first-order* perturbation theory has been used here. Even when the Fourier coefficient of the potential energy is zero, second-order perturbation theory *may* give an energy gap, but this will probably be small.

where

$$S_{\boldsymbol{m}} = \sum_{j=1}^{q} \mathrm{e}^{-\mathrm{i}\boldsymbol{K}_{\boldsymbol{m}} \cdot \boldsymbol{s}_j}. \tag{8.100}$$

$S_{\boldsymbol{m}}$ is called the *structure factor*, and the Fourier coefficients of $V(\boldsymbol{r})$ are given by

$$V_{\boldsymbol{m}} = V'_{\boldsymbol{m}} S_{\boldsymbol{m}}.$$

Clearly, $V_{\boldsymbol{m}}$ and the corresponding energy gap vanish when the structure factor is zero, and this is generally so for some $\boldsymbol{K}_{\boldsymbol{m}}$.

As an example, let us consider the body-centred cubic lattice as a simple cubic lattice with a basis. The first Brillouin zone is then a cube whose faces are given by equations (8.88), but it is easily seen that there are no energy gaps on these planes. The basis is (0, 0, 0), $(\frac{1}{2}, \frac{1}{2}, \frac{1}{2})$, the position vectors of the two atoms in the unit cell being $\boldsymbol{s}_1 = \boldsymbol{0}$ and $\boldsymbol{s}_2 = \frac{1}{2}a(\boldsymbol{e}_1 + \boldsymbol{e}_2 + \boldsymbol{e}_3)$. Also, from equations (8.87),

$$\boldsymbol{K}_{\boldsymbol{m}} = \frac{2\pi}{a}(m_1\boldsymbol{e}_1 + m_2\boldsymbol{e}_2 + m_3\boldsymbol{e}_3),$$

and the structure factor is, therefore,

$$S_{\boldsymbol{m}} = 1 + \mathrm{e}^{-\mathrm{i}\pi(m_1 + m_2 + m_3)}.$$

At the surface of the first Brillouin zone the values of (m_1, m_2, m_3) are $(\pm 1, 0, 0)$, $(0, \pm 1, 0)$, or $(0, 0, \pm 1)$, for all of which the structure factor vanishes, together with the energy gap. The first planes at which there is a non-vanishing energy gap are those which bound the second Brillouin zone for the simple cubic lattice, as shown in Figure 8.14 (b) — it will be seen in the following section that, not unexpectedly, this constitutes the *first* Brillouin zone of the body-centred cubic lattice, when it is constructed from the proper Bravais lattice, with rhombohedral unit cell defined by equations (8.67).

The foregoing work shows that along any $\boldsymbol{k}$ direction the energy as a function of k is represented by curves like those in Figure 8.2 (b) (reduced zone scheme) or those in Figure 8.3 (b) (extended zone scheme). There is an important difference between the three-dimensional and the one-dimensional cases, however. In the latter we saw that the energy spectrum was broken up into allowed energy bands with forbidden energy gaps between them. In the three-dimensional case this need no longer be true, in spite of the occurrence of energy gaps in every $\boldsymbol{k}$ direction. This is because an energy which falls in an energy gap in one direction may not do so in another direction, so that there may be no energy forbidden to an electron, and no gaps in the energy spectrum. We shall see in § 8.12 that this phenomenon, which is known as the *overlapping of energy bands*, or the *overlapping of zones*, is of great importance in the theory of metals. Whether or not the bands overlap depends upon the size of the energy gaps, as illustrated in Figure 8.15, which shows schematically curves of energy as a function of k for two different $\boldsymbol{k}$ directions, according to the extended zone scheme. In Figure 8.15 (a) the energy gaps are small and the energy bands overlap. In Figure 8.15 (b) the energy gaps are large, and the bands do not overlap, so that there is a gap in the energy spectrum.

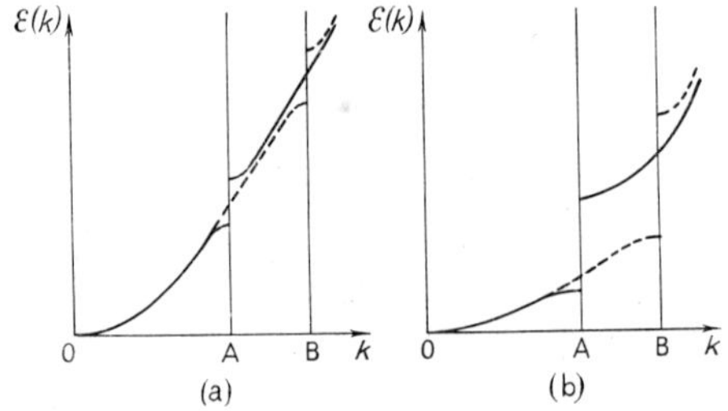

Fig. 8.15. A and B are on the first planes of energy discontinuity along two lines through the origin of $\boldsymbol{k}$-space, for which the energy curves are the full and broken curves respectively. In (a) the energy gaps are small, and the bands overlap; while in (b) the energy gaps are large, and the bands do not overlap. Only one half of each energy curve is shown, since these are symmetrical about $k = 0$.

8.9. Brillouin Zones for Some Metallic Structures

We will now obtain the fundamental domain of $\boldsymbol{k}$, or first Brillouin zone, for each of the important metallic structures described in § 8.5.

(i) *The body-centred cubic lattice*

Substituting $\boldsymbol{a}_1$, $\boldsymbol{a}_2$, and $\boldsymbol{a}_3$ from equations (8.67) in equations (8.80), we obtain the reciprocal lattice vectors

$$\begin{aligned} \boldsymbol{b}_1 &= \frac{2\pi}{a}(\boldsymbol{e}_2+\boldsymbol{e}_3), \\ \boldsymbol{b}_2 &= \frac{2\pi}{a}(\boldsymbol{e}_1+\boldsymbol{e}_3), \\ \boldsymbol{b}_3 &= \frac{2\pi}{a}(\boldsymbol{e}_1+\boldsymbol{e}_2). \end{aligned} \tag{8.101}$$

Comparing these with equations (8.68), we see that the reciprocal lattice is face-centred cubic.

A vector $\boldsymbol{K}_{\boldsymbol{m}}$ is given by

$$\boldsymbol{K}_{\boldsymbol{m}} = m_1\boldsymbol{b}_1+m_2\boldsymbol{b}_2+m_3\boldsymbol{b}_3$$
$$= \frac{2\pi}{a}[(m_2+m_3)\boldsymbol{e}_1+(m_1+m_3)\boldsymbol{e}_2+(m_1+m_2)\boldsymbol{e}_3],$$

and the bounding planes of the first Brillouin zone bisect the twelve shortest vectors $\boldsymbol{K}_{\boldsymbol{m}}$, for which (m_1, m_2, m_3) are permutations of the sets of values (1, 0, 0,), (−1, 0, 0), (1, −1, 0). These vectors are

$$\frac{2\pi}{a}(\pm\boldsymbol{e}_1\pm\boldsymbol{e}_2), \quad \frac{2\pi}{a}(\pm\boldsymbol{e}_2\pm\boldsymbol{e}_3), \quad \frac{2\pi}{a}(\pm\boldsymbol{e}_1\pm\boldsymbol{e}_3), \tag{8.102}$$

and equation (8.85) gives, for the equations of the bounding planes,

$$\pm k_1\pm k_2 = \frac{2\pi}{a}, \quad \pm k_2\pm k_3 = \frac{2\pi}{a}, \quad \pm k_1\pm k_3 = \frac{2\pi}{a}. \tag{8.103}$$

The first Brillouin zone is thus the rhombododecahedron shown in Figure 8.16 (a) — as we have mentioned previously, it contains both the first and second zones for the simple cubic lattice [see Figure 8.14 (b)]. As there is one atom per unit cell of the Bravais lattice, the zone can accommodate two electrons per atom of the crystal.

(ii) *The face-centred cubic lattice*

From equations (8.68) and (8.80), we obtain

$$\boldsymbol{b}_1 = \frac{2\pi}{a}(\boldsymbol{e}_1+\boldsymbol{e}_2-\boldsymbol{e}_3),$$
$$\boldsymbol{b}_2 = \frac{2\pi}{a}(-\boldsymbol{e}_1+\boldsymbol{e}_2+\boldsymbol{e}_3), \tag{8.104}$$
$$\boldsymbol{b}_3 = \frac{2\pi}{a}(\boldsymbol{e}_1-\boldsymbol{e}_2+\boldsymbol{e}_3),$$

Comparing these with equations (8.67), we see that the reciprocal lattice is body-centred cubic.

Using the same method as above we find the shortest $\boldsymbol{K}_{\boldsymbol{m}}$ to be the eight vectors

$$\frac{2\pi}{a}(\pm\boldsymbol{e}_1\pm\boldsymbol{e}_2\pm\boldsymbol{e}_3),$$

and the next shortest to be the six vectors

$$\pm \frac{4\pi}{a} \boldsymbol{e}_1, \qquad \pm \frac{4\pi}{a} \boldsymbol{e}_2, \qquad \pm \frac{4\pi}{a} \boldsymbol{e}_3,$$

The first Brillouin zone is the truncated octohedron shown in Figure 8.16 (b). The equations of the hexagonal faces, which bisect the shortest $\boldsymbol{K}_m$ vectors, are

$$\pm k_1 \pm k_2 \pm k_3 = \frac{3\pi}{a}, \tag{8.105}$$

and the equations of the square faces, which bisect the next shortest $\boldsymbol{K}_m$ vectors, are

$$k_1 = \pm \frac{2\pi}{a}, \qquad k_2 = \pm \frac{2\pi}{a}, \qquad k_3 = \pm \frac{2\pi}{a}. \tag{8.106}$$

This zone again can accommodate two electrons per atom of the crystal.

(iii) *The close-packed hexagonal lattice*

From equations (8.69) and (8.80), we obtain

$$\begin{aligned} \boldsymbol{b}_1 &= \frac{2\pi}{a}\left(\boldsymbol{e}_1 - \frac{1}{\sqrt{3}} \boldsymbol{e}_2\right), \\ \boldsymbol{b}_2 &= \frac{4\pi}{\sqrt{3}a} \boldsymbol{e}_2, \\ \boldsymbol{b}_3 &= \frac{2\pi}{c} \boldsymbol{e}_3. \end{aligned} \tag{8.107}$$

These are the reciprocal vectors of the simple hexagonal lattice and they also define a simple hexagonal lattice. The first Brillouin zone is thus the hexagonal prism shown in Figure 8.16 (c). The bounding planes bisect the vectors $\pm \boldsymbol{b}_1$, $\pm(\boldsymbol{b}_1+\boldsymbol{b}_2)$, $\pm \boldsymbol{b}_2$, $\pm \boldsymbol{b}_3$, and their equations are, therefore,

$$\pm k_1 \pm \frac{1}{\sqrt{3}} k_2 = \frac{4\pi}{3a}, \qquad k_2 = \pm \frac{2\pi}{\sqrt{3}a}, \qquad k_3 = \pm \frac{\pi}{c}. \tag{8.108}$$

The position vectors of the two atoms in the unit cell of the close-packed hexagonal lattice are $\boldsymbol{s}_1 = \boldsymbol{0}$ and $\boldsymbol{s}_2 = \frac{1}{3}\boldsymbol{a}_1 + \frac{1}{3}\boldsymbol{a}_2 + \frac{1}{2}\boldsymbol{a}_3$. The structure factor is, thus,

$$S_m = 1 + \mathrm{e}^{-\mathrm{i}\pi(\frac{2}{3}m_1 + \frac{2}{3}m_2 + m_3)}, \tag{8.109}$$

and this is zero when $\boldsymbol{K}_m = \pm \boldsymbol{b}_3$. Hence, there is no energy gap at the hexagonal faces, $k_3 = \pm\pi/c$. The zone can accommodate two electrons per unit cell of the crystal, which is only *one* electron per atom. The region containing the first and second Brillouin zones, which we will not consider in detail, can accommodate two electrons per atom, but it also contains planes of energy discontinuity within it (the rectangular faces of the first

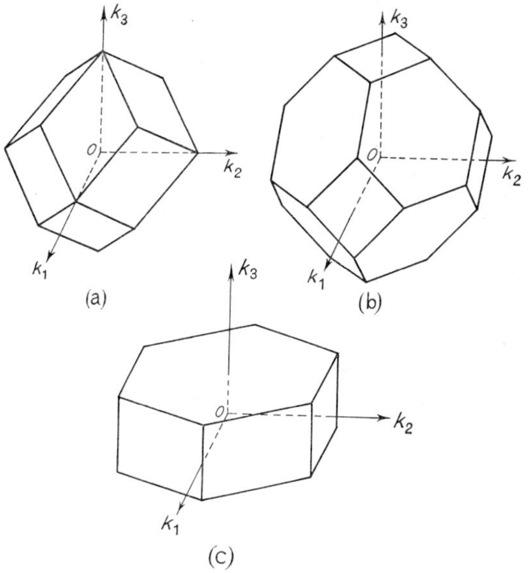

Fig. 8.16. The fundamental domain of $\boldsymbol{k}$, or first Brillouin zone, for (a) the body-centred cubic lattice, (b) the face-centred cubic lattice, and (c) the close-packed hexagonal lattice.

zone). It may be shown that the smallest region bounded on all sides by planes of energy discontinuity can accommodate

$$2 - \frac{3}{4}\left(\frac{a}{c}\right)^2 + \frac{3}{16}\left(\frac{a}{c}\right)^4$$

electrons per atom.

8.10. Energy Surfaces by the Tight Binding Method

When discussing the energy bands in actual metals it will be useful to have before us a definite model, even if a somewhat idealized one. The essential problem is to find the eigenvalues of the Schrödinger equation (8.71), but this cannot be done analytically for any real metal, and accurate results using numerical methods have only been obtained at isolated points in $\boldsymbol{k}$-space (see the following chapter). We therefore turn to the tight binding method to provide a simple semi-quantitative example. Also, we will only consider its application to simple Bravais lattices and to energy bands derived from non-degenerate atomic s states.

The method is a direct extension to three dimensions of that described in § 8.4, so we need give no more than an outline here. We assume that the potential energy of an electron in a free atom is $U(r)$, and that ε_0 is the energy of an s state with wave function $\chi(r)$. Thus, $\chi(r)$ satisfies the Schrödinger equation

$$\nabla^2\chi + \frac{2m}{\hbar^2}[\varepsilon_0 - U(r)]\chi = 0. \tag{8.110}$$

We now consider an electron in a lattice of ions, its potential energy due to the ion at $\boldsymbol{R}_n$ being $U(\boldsymbol{r}-\boldsymbol{R}_n)$, so that its total potential energy is

$$V(\boldsymbol{r}) = \sum_n U(\boldsymbol{r}-\boldsymbol{R}_n),$$

the sum being over all the lattice points, and the Schrödinger equation (8.71) becomes

$$\nabla^2\psi + \frac{2m}{\hbar^2}[\varepsilon - \sum_n U(\boldsymbol{r}-\boldsymbol{R}_n)]\psi = 0. \tag{8.111}$$

On the assumption that the functions $\chi(\boldsymbol{r}-\boldsymbol{R}_n)$ centred on different lattice points do not overlap very much, we construct approximate solutions of (8.111) of the LCAO type,

$$\psi_{\boldsymbol{k}}(\boldsymbol{r}) = \sum_l e^{i\boldsymbol{k}\cdot\boldsymbol{R}_l}\chi(\boldsymbol{r}-\boldsymbol{R}_l), \tag{8.112}$$

the coefficients having been chosen so that the functions satisfy the Bloch condition (8.73); thus,

$$\begin{aligned}\psi_{\boldsymbol{k}}(\boldsymbol{r}+\boldsymbol{R}_n) &= \sum_l e^{i\boldsymbol{k}\cdot\boldsymbol{R}_l}\chi(\boldsymbol{r}-\boldsymbol{R}_l+\boldsymbol{R}_n)\\ &= e^{i\boldsymbol{k}\cdot\boldsymbol{R}_n}\sum_l e^{i\boldsymbol{k}\cdot(\boldsymbol{R}_l-\boldsymbol{R}_n)}\chi[\boldsymbol{r}-(\boldsymbol{R}_l-\boldsymbol{R}_n)]\\ &= e^{i\boldsymbol{k}\cdot\boldsymbol{R}_n}\psi_{\boldsymbol{k}}(\boldsymbol{r}).\end{aligned} \tag{8.113}$$

If, for purposes of normalization, we ignore overlap between atomic functions centred on different lattice points, and assume that these functions are normalized in the volume of the crystal (or, nearly enough, in all space), the normalizing factor for $\psi_{\boldsymbol{k}}$ is easily found to be $N^{-\frac{1}{2}}$, where N is the number of atoms in the crystal.

Following the same procedure as in the one-dimensional case [see equation (8.61)], we find the approximate energy to be

$$\varepsilon(\boldsymbol{k}) = \varepsilon_0 + \sum_n \mathrm{e}^{\mathrm{i}\boldsymbol{k}\cdot\boldsymbol{R}_n} \int \chi^*(\boldsymbol{r}+\boldsymbol{R}_n)[V(\boldsymbol{r})-U(\boldsymbol{r})]\chi(\boldsymbol{r})\mathrm{d}\boldsymbol{r}, \qquad (8.114)$$

the integral being throughout the volume of the crystal. If we now neglect overlap except between nearest neighbouring atoms, this equation reduces to

$$\varepsilon(\boldsymbol{k}) = \varepsilon_0 - \alpha - \gamma \sum_n \mathrm{e}^{\mathrm{i}\boldsymbol{k}\cdot\boldsymbol{R}_n}, \qquad (8.115)$$

where

$$\alpha = -\int \chi^*(\boldsymbol{r})[V(\boldsymbol{r})-U(\boldsymbol{r})]\chi(\boldsymbol{r})\mathrm{d}\boldsymbol{r},$$

$$\gamma = -\int \chi^*(\boldsymbol{r}+\boldsymbol{R}_n)[V(\boldsymbol{r})-U(\boldsymbol{r})]\chi(\boldsymbol{r})\mathrm{d}\boldsymbol{r},$$

and the sum is over the position vectors of nearest neighbours of the atom at the origin only — since $\chi(\boldsymbol{r})$ is a spherically symmetrical function, γ is the same for all nearest neighbours. We may take $U(\boldsymbol{r})$ to be negative, so that $V(\boldsymbol{r})-U(\boldsymbol{r})$ is negative, and, for s states with small overlap, α and γ are *positive*.

For the *simple cubic lattice* the required $\boldsymbol{R}_n$ are $\pm a\boldsymbol{e}_1$, $\pm a\boldsymbol{e}_2$, $\pm a\boldsymbol{e}_3$, so that

$$\varepsilon(\boldsymbol{k}) = \varepsilon_0 - \alpha - 2\gamma(\cos k_1 a + \cos k_2 a + \cos k_3 a). \qquad (8.116)$$

The energy levels are thus spread over a band of width 12γ. It is immediately obvious that the energy is a triply periodic function of $\boldsymbol{k}$, and that all states are accounted for if $\boldsymbol{k}$ is restricted to lie within a cube bounded by the planes

$$k_1 = \pm\frac{\pi}{a}, \qquad k_2 = \pm\frac{\pi}{a}, \qquad k_3 = \pm\frac{\pi}{a},$$

which is what we have already found to be the fundamental domain of $\boldsymbol{k}$. The normal derivative of $\varepsilon(\boldsymbol{k})$ vanishes on the bounding planes, as may be verified by differentiating (8.116); thus,

$$\frac{\partial\varepsilon}{\partial k_1} = 2\gamma a \sin k_1 a = 0 \quad \text{when } k_1 = \pm\frac{\pi}{a}.$$

When k is small we may write, approximately,

$$\varepsilon(\boldsymbol{k}) = \varepsilon_0 - \alpha - 6\gamma + \gamma a^2 k^2, \tag{8.117}$$

and, as in the one-dimensional case, we define the *effective mass* near $k = 0$ as

$$m^* = \frac{\hbar^2}{2\gamma a^2}. \tag{8.118}$$

Along the k_1, k_2, and k_3 axes the energy is given as a function of k by curves like that shown in Figure 8.8. The state of lowest energy is at the centre of the zone and the states of highest energy are at the corners. Every state of the free atom will give rise to an energy band, but some of them will have energy curves with maxima at the centre, similar to that marked $l = 1$ in Figure 8.2 (b), or at other points in the zone. The simple procedure described above applies, of course, only when the atomic state is non-degenerate and tightly bound. A degenerate atomic state will give rise to a number of energy bands or zones equal to the degree of degeneracy.

Surfaces may be drawn through all points in **k**-space representing states with the same energy, and these are called *energy surfaces*. Figure 8.17 shows three typical energy surfaces for the simple cubic lattice, as given by equation (8.116). It follows from equation (8.117) that, near $\boldsymbol{k} = \boldsymbol{0}$, the surfaces are approximately spheres, as for free electrons, but as they get larger they bulge more and more towards the centres of the zone faces, until eventually they touch, and then intersect, the zone boundary. The energy surfaces which intersect the zone boundary do so orthogonally, since the normal derivative of $\varepsilon(\boldsymbol{k})$ vanishes on the bounding planes. A cross-section through energy surfaces at equal energy intervals in any one of the coordinate planes is shown in Figure 8.18.

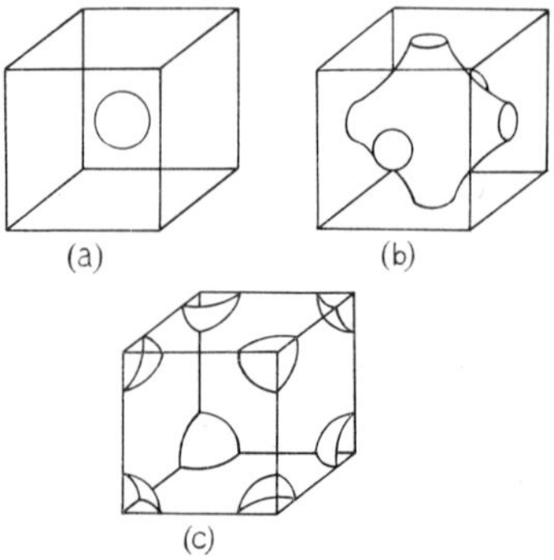

Fig. 8.17. Energy surfaces for the simple cubic lattice (tight binding approximation), corresponding to energy (a) near the bottom of the band, (b) about half way up the band, (c) near the top of the band. The origin of **k**-space is at the centre of the cube, and the k_1, k_2, k_3 axes are parallel to cube edges.

It would appear, at first sight, that the energy surfaces (a) and (c) in Figure 8.17 are of completely different forms, but this is not really so, and is due entirely to our choice of the fundamental domain of $\boldsymbol{k}$. Owing to the periodicity of $\varepsilon(\boldsymbol{k})$ in $\boldsymbol{k}$-space, we could equally well have chosen our basic cell to be a cube centred at one of the corner points of our present cell. The energy surface (c) would then have been approximately spherical, and (a) would have consisted of eight separate octants at the corners of the cube. If $\boldsymbol{k}'$ is one of the eight vectors defined by

$$k_1' = k_1 \pm \frac{\pi}{a}, \qquad k_2' = k_2 \pm \frac{\pi}{a}, \qquad k_3' = k_3 \pm \frac{\pi}{a}, \tag{8.119}$$

equation (8.116) becomes

$$\varepsilon(\boldsymbol{k}') = \varepsilon_0 - \alpha + 2\gamma(\cos k_1' a + \cos k_2' a + \cos k_3' a). \tag{8.120}$$

Thus, if k' is small, that is, in the neighbourhood of any of the corner points in Figure 8.17, we have, approximately,

$$\varepsilon(\boldsymbol{k}') = \varepsilon_0 - \alpha + 6\gamma - \gamma a^2 k'^2. \tag{8.121}$$

In other words, the energy surfaces are again approximately spheres, as for free electrons, and we may define the effective mass near a corner point as

$$m_1^* = -\frac{\hbar^2}{2\gamma a^2}, \tag{8.122}$$

which is equal to $-m^*$, where m^* is the effective mass near $k = 0$.

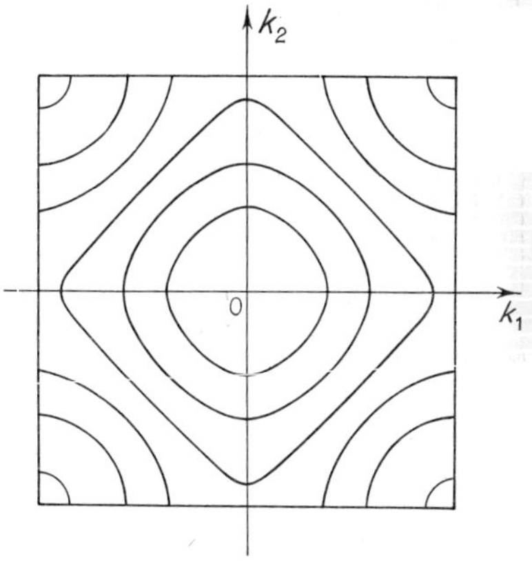

Fig. 8.18. Cross-section through energy surfaces at equal energy intervals in any one of the coordinate planes of $\boldsymbol{k}$-space, for tightly bound electrons in a simple cubic lattice.

The simple tight binding method we have described is certainly not applicable to the valence or conduction electrons in a metal, which are of most interest to us, although it is a reasonable approximation for the inner shells. Also, we have considered in detail only the simple cubic lattice. None the less, the qualitative features of the energy surfaces we have obtained are believed to hold for the zones containing the valence electrons of a real metal. That is to say, the energy surfaces near the centre of the first Brillouin zone (taking this to represent the state of lowest energy of a valence electron in the metal) are very nearly spheres, but they bulge towards the nearest points of the zone boundary as they get larger. Since the surfaces are always spheres for free electrons, the amount of bulging clearly depends upon the potential energy function, and it must therefore differ even among metals with the same crystal structure — this point is not brought out in our tight binding example. Owing to the periodicity of $\varepsilon_l(k)$ we have

$$\varepsilon_l(\boldsymbol{k}_1) = \varepsilon_l(\boldsymbol{k}_2). \tag{8.123}$$

where $\boldsymbol{k}_1$ and $\boldsymbol{k}_2$ are corresponding points on opposite faces of the zone, and the inward normal derivative at $\boldsymbol{k}_1$ equals the outward normal derivative at $\boldsymbol{k}_2$. It follows from this and the symmetry of the energy surfaces that generally (but not invariably) the normal derivative of $\varepsilon_l(\boldsymbol{k})$ is zero over the zone boundary — in other words, energy surfaces which intersect the zone boundary generally do so orthogonally.

8.11. The Density of States in Energy

We may define a density of states in energy $\mathcal{N}(\varepsilon)$ in the same way as for free electrons. That is to say, $\mathcal{N}(\varepsilon)\mathrm{d}\varepsilon$ is defined as the number of orbital states with energies lying between ε and $\varepsilon+\mathrm{d}\varepsilon$, where $\mathrm{d}\varepsilon$ is a very small interval which still contains a large number of energy levels. Thus,

$$\mathcal{N}(\varepsilon)\mathrm{d}\varepsilon = \frac{v}{8\pi^3}\int \mathrm{d}\boldsymbol{k}, \tag{8.124}$$

the integral being over the volume of $\boldsymbol{k}$-space lying between the surfaces of energy ε and $\varepsilon+\mathrm{d}\varepsilon$. Now, $\mathrm{grad}_{\boldsymbol{k}}\, \varepsilon(\boldsymbol{k})$, that is,

$$\boldsymbol{e}_1 \frac{\partial\varepsilon}{\partial k_1} + \boldsymbol{e}_2 \frac{\partial\varepsilon}{\partial k_2} + \boldsymbol{e}_3 \frac{\partial\varepsilon}{\partial k_3},$$

is the derivative of $\varepsilon(\boldsymbol{k})$ in a direction normal to the energy surface through the point $\boldsymbol{k}$, and hence the distance between the surfaces of energy ε and $\varepsilon+\mathrm{d}\varepsilon$ at this point is $\mathrm{d}\varepsilon/|\mathrm{grad}_{\boldsymbol{k}}\, \varepsilon(\boldsymbol{k})|$. Therefore,

$$\mathcal{N}(\varepsilon) = \frac{v}{8\pi^3}\int \frac{\mathrm{d}S}{|\mathrm{grad}_{\boldsymbol{k}}\, \varepsilon(\boldsymbol{k})|}, \tag{8.125}$$

this being a surface integral over the energy surface $\varepsilon(\boldsymbol{k}) = \varepsilon$.

The calculation of the density of states using this formula requires a knowledge of the energy surfaces, and, since these are not known accurately for any real metal, an exact determination of $\mathcal{N}(\varepsilon)$ is not yet possible. The difficulties are enhanced by the fact that the potential energy $V(\boldsymbol{r})$

to be used in the Schrödinger equation is itself a source of much speculation. None the less, approximate calculations of $\mathcal{N}(\varepsilon)$ have been made, which suffice for many purposes. Also, some idea of the shapes of $\mathcal{N}(\varepsilon)$ curves may be obtained from experimental data, such as X-ray spectra and electronic specific heats, as discussed in Chapter 7.

In the tight binding example considered above, the energy near $\boldsymbol{k} = \boldsymbol{0}$ may be written in the form

$$\varepsilon(\boldsymbol{k}) = \frac{\hbar^2}{2m^*} k^2, \tag{8.126}$$

if the zero of energy is taken to be the lowest energy in the zone. It follows, therefore, that the density of states in this neighbourhood is given by the same expression as that for free electrons, equation (7.5), with the effective mass m^* replacing m; thus.

$$\mathcal{N}(\varepsilon) = \frac{v}{4\pi^2}\left(\frac{2m^*}{\hbar^2}\right)^{\frac{3}{2}} \varepsilon^{\frac{1}{2}}. \tag{8.127}$$

Near the corner points of the cube the energy surfaces are again almost spherical, and equation (8.121) shows that here we may write

$$\varepsilon_{\mathrm{H}} - \varepsilon(\boldsymbol{k}) = \frac{\hbar^2}{2m^*} k'^2, \tag{8.128}$$

where $\boldsymbol{k}'$ is the vector defined relative to the appropriate corner point by equations (8.119), ε_{H} is the *highest* energy in the zone, and m^* is the same *positive* effective mass as used in equation (8.127). It follows that, for energies near ε_{H}

$$\mathcal{N}(\varepsilon) = \frac{v}{4\pi^2}\left(\frac{2m^*}{\hbar^2}\right)^{\frac{3}{2}} (\varepsilon_{\mathrm{H}} - \varepsilon)^{\frac{1}{2}}. \tag{8.129}$$

The $\mathcal{N}(\varepsilon)$ curve in this example is therefore parabolic at both ends, and, if the whole curve is computed from equations (8.116) and (8.125), it is found to have the shape shown in Figure 8.19 (a). The curve is symmetrical about the mean value of the energy, but this is a result of the tight binding approximation and is not expected to hold in general. In the case of free electrons, for example, if we restrict ourselves to a single zone, the energy surfaces are spherical and the $\mathcal{N}(\varepsilon)$ curve is parabolic until the zone boundary is reached, after which the energy surfaces consist only of portions of spheres lying within the zone and the $\mathcal{N}(\varepsilon)$ curve descends, as shown in Figure 8.19 (b). For the zones containing the valence electrons of a metal the $\mathcal{N}(\varepsilon)$ curve will lie between (a) and (b), and hence will have a shape something like that shown in Figure 8.19 (c). The curve is parabolic at both ends, although not with the same magnitude of the effective mass, and is not symmetrical about the mean energy. The maximum occurs roughly where the energy surfaces first touch the zone boundary, and the increased slope of the curve just before the maximum is due to the bulging

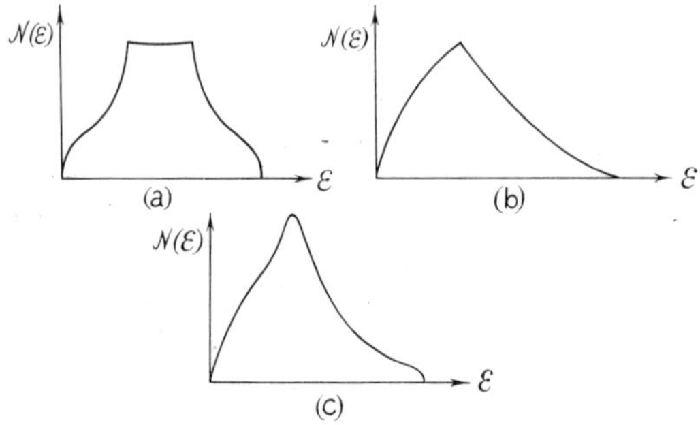

Fig. 8.19. Density of states for a single zone of an electron in a simple cubic lattice: (a) tight binding approximation, (b) free-electron approximation, (c) a compromise between the two, which is probably the approximate shape of the curve for a zone containing the valence electrons of a real metal.

of the energy surfaces, which increases the volume enclosed between two surfaces separated by energy $d\varepsilon$. Although we have only considered the simple cubic lattice, the $\mathcal{N}(\varepsilon)$ curves for actual metallic structures must be of similar form — there may, however, be a subsidiary maximum if the zone is bounded by two sets of planes at different distances from the origin. It follows from the discussion of § 8.7 that the area enclosed by the $\mathcal{N}(\varepsilon)$ curve and the ε axis must equal the number of unit cells in the lattice.

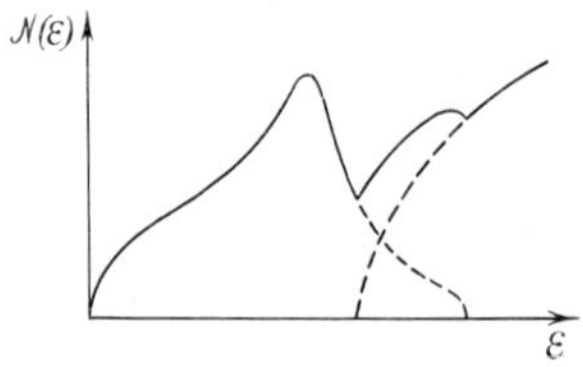

Fig. 8.20. The full curve is the total density of states for two overlapping zones.

So far we have been discussing a single Brillouin zone. There will, of course, be a density of states curve for every zone. In the case of tightly bound electrons, when the energy gaps at the zone boundaries are large, as shown in Figure 8.15 (b), the energy bands and corresponding $\mathcal{N}(\varepsilon)$ curves of adjacent zones will be completely separated. In the case of electrons which are nearly free, however, so that the energy gaps are small, as shown in Figure 8.15 (a), the energy bands and $\mathcal{N}(\varepsilon)$ curves will overlap. The total density of states is then obtained by summing the contributions from the overlapping zones, and the $\mathcal{N}(\varepsilon)$ curve will not fall to zero (see Figure 8.20).

8.12. Metals, Insulators and Semiconductors

In the foregoing sections we have been principally concerned with the calculation of the energy levels of a single electron moving in a crystal lattice. In a solid, of course, there is a large number of electrons, and the interaction of the electrons among themselves has an important effect upon the motion. As an approximation, however, we may regard each electron as moving in the same self-consistent field, so that the same energy band system applies to all of them. Now, an orbital state can accommodate two electrons, with opposite spins, and hence, at the absolute zero of temperature, all the orbital states of lowest energy will be occupied by two electrons each. We will denote by ε_F the highest occupied energy level at this temperature, and the surface drawn through all points of $\boldsymbol{k}$-space representing states with this energy is called the *Fermi surface* †.

Let us for the moment consider only simple Bravais lattices, such as the cubic structures. We have seen in § 8.7 that, in this case, a Brillouin zone can accommodate two electrons per atom of the crystal. In general there are more than two electrons per atom, and therefore the occupied states must extend over several zones. If there is an *even* number of electrons per atom, and the highest occupied zone does not overlap the succeeding one, then the electrons must completely fill the occupied zones. On the other hand, if there is an *odd* number of electrons per atom, whether or not the zones overlap, the highest occupied zone, at least, must be only partially filled. If the two highest occupied zones overlap, of course, then, whatever the number of electrons per atom, the highest zone, at least, must remain only partially filled. These facts have an important bearing upon the nature of solids, as we shall now see.

Metals are distinguished from other solids principally by the fact that they are good conductors of electricity. The application of an electric field, however small, to a metal must result in an electric current, that is, an overall drift of electrons in one direction. Now, a free electron in the

† ε_F is sometimes referred to as the *Fermi energy*, but we prefer to use this term in another connection (see § 7.2), and so will refer to ε_F as the *energy at the Fermi surface*.

state $\boldsymbol{k}$ has momentum $\hbar\boldsymbol{k}$, and its velocity is therefore $\hbar\boldsymbol{k}/m$. This is not true in general for an electron in a periodic field, but we will show in Chapter 11 that the *average* velocity $\langle \boldsymbol{v}_{\boldsymbol{k}} \rangle$ of an electron in the state $\boldsymbol{k}$ is always given by

$$\hbar\langle \boldsymbol{v}_{\boldsymbol{k}} \rangle = \text{grad}_{\boldsymbol{k}}\, \varepsilon(\boldsymbol{k}). \tag{8.130}$$

Owing to the symmetry of $\varepsilon(\boldsymbol{k})$, therefore, the average velocity of an electron in the state $\boldsymbol{k}$ is equal in magnitude and opposite in direction to that of an electron in the state $-\boldsymbol{k}$. At the absolute zero of temperature, when there is no applied field, all those states are fully occupied which lie within the Fermi surface, and, since this is symmetrical about the origin, to every electron with a given average velocity there is one with equal and opposite average velocity. The total current is therefore zero.

If a solid is to be a conductor, then, it must be possible for an applied field to excite electrons to states of slightly higher energy, in such a way that the velocity distribution becomes asymmetrical. This clearly is not possible if the occupied region of $\boldsymbol{k}$-space is bounded on every side by planes of energy discontinuity, that is, if all the occupied zones are completely filled; for the nearest energy level into which an electron could be excited is then separated from the highest occupied level by a finite energy gap, and only a very large field could excite an electron over this gap (electrons cannot be excited within the filled region of $\boldsymbol{k}$-space, of course, because all the states there are occupied). Such a solid must therefore be an insulator. If the highest occupied zone of a solid is only partially filled, however, a very small applied field can excite some of those electrons at the Fermi surface into slightly higher energy levels, and such a solid is a metallic conductor. The essential difference between an insulator and a metal is, therefore, that in the former all the occupied zones are completely filled, and in the latter at least one zone is only partially filled.

The tightly bound inner shells of an atom contain an even number of electrons. The tight binding method shows that, in a solid, these shells will give rise to a number of very narrow energy bands which are completely filled and separated from the energy bands of the outer shells by a large energy gap. These inner shells cannot contribute to the conductivity, therefore, and in discussing conduction properties we may ignore them and concentrate upon the more loosely bound outer shells, and, in particular, the valence electrons. Without loss of generality we may take the origin of $\boldsymbol{k}$-space, in either the extended or the reduced zone schemes, to correspond to the state of lowest energy of a valence electron in the solid. Also, in drawing $\mathcal{N}(\varepsilon)$ curves, we will take the zero of energy to be the lowest energy of a valence electron — in such diagrams the energy bands of the tightly bound inner shells would appear almost as delta functions far to the left of the origin. In a metal the band of energy levels occupied by valence electrons is generally referred to as the *conduction band*, although it may extend over several zones.

It follows from the previous discussion that a solid with an odd number of valence electrons per atom must be a metal. The fact that there are many metals with an even number of valence electrons per atom is due solely to the overlapping of the zones containing these electrons. Figure 8.21(a) shows the distribution of occupied states, at the absolute zero of temperature, in the conduction band of a monovalent metal, such as sodium. The first zone is only half filled, and the distribution is very nearly parabolic, as for free electrons — the effective mass will generally be different from m, however. Figure 8.21 (b) shows the distribution for a divalent metal, such as magnesium †. Here, owing to the overlapping of zones, electrons have begun to fill up the second zone before the first zone has been completely filled. There are thus two unfilled zones, both of which contribute to the conductivity. Figure 8.21 (c) shows the $\mathcal{N}(\varepsilon)$ curve for the highest filled zone of an insulator, such as diamond — it is separated by a large energy gap from the next zone, which is empty.

It may be observed in Figure 8.21 (b) that the density of *unoccupied* states is very nearly parabolic. In this case it is generally more convenient to describe the conduction properties of this zone in terms of these unoccupied states. Now, we have seen that the current due to a completely filled zone is zero. Hence, the current due to a zone with a single unoccupied state (including spin) must be the negative of the current due to a zone which is empty except for a single electron in this state. This means that, in describing conduction processes for a nearly filled zone, the electrons

† It should be noted that metallic magnesium, and indeed most of the divalent metals, have the close-packed hexagonal structure, which is not a simple Bravais lattice. The first Brillouin zone can accomodate only one electron per atom, and we have seen in § 8.9 that it is not bounded on all sides by planes of energy discontinuity. However, there *is* a zone (consisting of the first and second Brillouin zones) which can accommodate two electrons per atom and is bounded on all sides by planes of energy discontinuity, and the first $\mathcal{N}(\varepsilon)$ curve in Fig. 8.21 (b) may be taken to represent this larger zone, which we will refer to as the *first zone* in the present context. The situation is complicated by the fact that planes of energy discontinuity occur within this larger zone, so the diagram must be regarded as only schematic.

may be ignored and each unoccupied state (including spin) may be treated as if it were occupied by a *positively charged* particle, known as a *positive hole*, the magnitude of the charge being the same as that of an electron. Needless to say, this is only a convenient way of viewing the situation, the current always being due to the motion of electrons.

So far we have only considered solids at the absolute zero of temperature. In a metal, at higher temperatures, the distribution of occupied states will not fall abruptly to zero, as in Figures 8.21 (a) and (b), but, according to the Fermi-Dirac statistics, will tail off smoothly, as shown for free electrons in Figure 7.4. The effective width of the thermally disturbed region is only of the order of kT, however, which has the value 0.026 eV at 300°K, so that except at very high temperatures the distribution is little different from that at absolute zero. In the case of insulators, an increase in the temperature will result in the excitation of some electrons from the highest

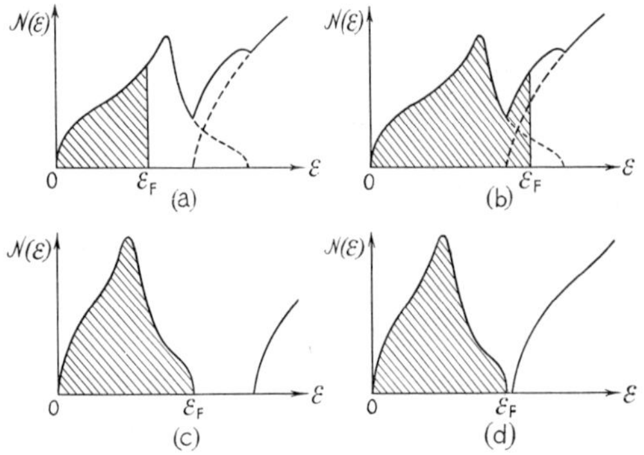

Fig. 8.21. The shaded regions show the distribution of occupied states, at the absolute zero of temperature, for (a) a monovalent metal, (b) a divalent metal, (c) an insulator, and (d) an intrinsic semiconductor.

filled zone to the first empty zone, so that electronic conduction is possible in principle. If the energy gap is large, however, as in Figure 8.21 (c), the number of excited electrons will be too small to give rise to an appreciable conductivity. On the other hand, in the solid whose $\mathcal{N}(\varepsilon)$ curve is shown in Figure 8.21 (d), which is an insulator at absolute zero, the energy gap is so small that at normal temperatures a sufficient number of electrons will be excited to give rise to a measurable conductivity. Such solids, examples of which are silicon and germanium, are called *intrinsic semiconductors*. The energy gaps in silicon and germanium are 1.2 and 0.8 eV respectively, while that in diamond, for example, is about 6 eV. It should be noted that, in the case of semiconductors, the filled energy band containing the valence electrons is called the *valence band*, and the empty band into which electrons are thermally excited is called the *conduction band*, although the holes left in the valence band also affect the conductivity.

A more important source of conduction electrons and holes in semiconductors is the presence of impurities. These may give rise to energy levels lying *inside* the energy gap between the valence and conduction bands. It is then very much easier for electrons to be excited from these levels, if occupied, into the conduction band, or from the valence band into these levels, if unoccupied, than for electrons to be excited from the valence band into the conduction band. The conductivity at normal temperatures is thus much greater than for purely intrinsic semiconductivity. Impurity energy levels from which electrons are thermally excited into the conduction band are called *donor levels*, and they may arise when the dissolved impurity atoms have a higher valency than the solvent — for example, phosphorus (valency 5) in silicon (valency 4). A semiconductor which contains such impurities is called an n-*type semiconductor*, the n standing for the *negative* charge of the excited electrons which are the current carriers. On the other hand, impurity energy levels to which electrons are thermally excited from the valence band are called *acceptor levels*, and may arise when the dissolved impurity atoms have a lower valency than the solvent — for example, boron (valency 3) in silicon. A semiconductor which contains such impurities is called a p-*type semiconductor*, the p standing for the *positive* charge of the holes in the valence band which are here the current carriers.

Finally, we must briefly mention a class of metals whose energy band structures are slightly more complicated than those we have considered above, owing to the presence, in the free atoms, of electrons in d states whose energies do not differ greatly from those of the valence electrons. These are the *transition metals* and those which immediately follow them in the Periodic Table. As a specific example, we will consider the technologically important *iron group* of transition elements, *scandium*, *titanium*, *vanadium*, *chromium*, *manganese*, *iron*, *cobalt*, and *nickel*, all of which have incomplete 3d sub-shells (see § 4.3) in addition to 4s electrons, and at the same time we may consider *copper*, in which the 3d sub-shell is complete and there is one 4s electron. The numbers of 3d and 4s electrons in each of these elements are shown in the following table:

	Sc	Ti	V	Cr	Mn	Fe	Co	Ni	Cu
Number of 3d electrons	1	2	3	5	5	6	7	8	10
Number of 4s electrons	2	2	2	1	2	2	2	2	1

Further groups of transition elements are obtained when the 4d and 5d sub-shells are filling up, but we will not consider these in detail.

Now, we have mentioned in connection with the tight binding method that for every state in a free atom there is a Brillouin zone in the metal. It is important to realize, however, that a particular zone can only be regarded rigorously as deriving from a particular atomic state (in the sense of the tight binding method) if its energy band is narrow and separated from those of neighbouring zones by large energy gaps. If several zones overlap, they must all be regarded as deriving from the same *group* of atomic states. None the less, it is possible in principle to establish a correspondence between the states of a free atom and the zones in a metal, which is conceptually useful. If we consider, not the solid metal under normal conditions of temperature and pressure, but a dispersed gas of free atoms, it is clear that all the occupied states of the free atoms will be tightly bound, according to our definition, for these atoms will be so far apart that not even the wave functions of the valence electrons will overlap appreciably. We may, for convenience, imagine these atoms to be arranged on a crystal lattice of the same structure as that of the solid metal, but very much larger, and apply the Bloch method to this expanded lattice. It is clear that the tight binding method (with provision made for degeneracy) will apply to all the occupied zones, and their energy bands will be extremely narrow — in fact, hardly to be distinguished from the energy levels of a single free atom. If this lattice is now contracted, the atomic wave functions will begin to overlap and the energy bands corresponding to the various atomic levels will begin to widen. They will not all widen at the same rate, however — the bands corresponding to the valence electron states will widen most rapidly, because the valence electron wave functions are most widespread and hence overlap more at large interatomic distances. The bands corresponding to the tightly bound inner shells, however, will hardly widen at all until the interatomic distance is reduced *below* that of the normal solid metal. In the case of the transition metals considered above the wave functions of the 3d atomic states are neither as widespread as those of the valence electrons nor as constricted as those of the inner shells, and the corresponding band will have an appreciable width at the interatomic distance of the normal metal, but this width will be considerably less than that of the valence electron band.

The way in which the various bands are thought to widen in the case of copper is shown schematically in Figure 8.22, and, apart from the relative positions of the 3d and 4s atomic levels, the picture is believed to be very similar for the transition metals. We may call the band corresponding to the atomic valence electron level the *4s band* and that corresponding to the 3d atomic level the *3d band*, although again we must emphasize that the electronic states in these bands are *not* obtained simply by linear combination of atomic 4s and 3d states respectively. As shown in the diagram, the band corresponding to the normally unoccupied 4p atomic level overlaps the 4s band at the interatomic distance of the solid metal, so that the 4p states must strongly affect the wave functions of the valence electrons in the metal.

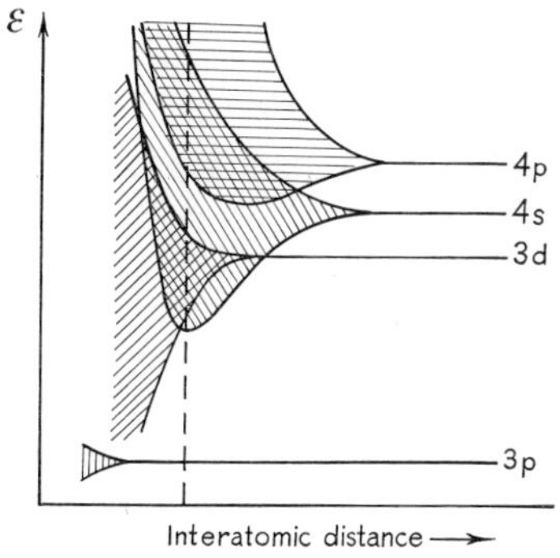

Fig. 8.22. The dependence of energy band withs upon interatomic distance in copper (schematic). The vertical broken line is drawn at roughly the interatomic distance of the normal solid metal.

Many of the properties of the transition metals may be explained on the assumption, borne out by some detailed calculation, that the 3d band in the normal metal is very narrow and overlaps the 4s band. Since the 3d atomic state is five-fold degenerate, the 3d band, in spite of its narrow width, must cover *five* Brillouin zones, so that the density of states in the 3d band must be very great compared with that in the 4s band. Thus, the $\mathcal{N}(\varepsilon)$ curve for the 3d band is very tall and narrow, while that of the 4s band is flat and wide, as shown schematically in Figure 8.23. Now, ten electrons per atom are required to fill the 3d band completely, and nickel is the only transition metal with ten 3d and 4s electrons per atom. However, even in nickel, owing to the overlapping of the 3d and 4s bands, some electrons must go into the 4s band, and the 3d band is not completely filled, as shown in Figure 8.23 (a). Hence, all the transition metals of the iron group have incompletely filled 3d bands. In copper, on the other hand, which has eleven 3d and 4s electrons per atom, there is evidence that the 3d band is completely filled, and the 4s band therefore contains one electron per atom, as shown in Figure 8.23 (b) — detailed calculations indicate that the width of the 3d band is about half the width of the occupied part of the 4s band, and that the energy at the Fermi surface is 3 or 4 eV above the highest energy in the 3d band.

The density of states at the Fermi surface is very high in the transition metals, owing to the incompletely filled 3d band, and this explains the high electronic specific heats of these metals — the low temperature electronic specific heat of nickel, for example, is ten times that of copper. The incomplete filling of the 3d band also provides an explanation of the ferromagnetism of iron, cobalt, and nickel. The ferromagnetic state occurs when, in the absence of an external magnetic field, there are more electrons with one kind of spin than there are with the other. Hence, if the ferromagnetism is due to the 3d electrons, as is believed, it can only occur when the 3d band is incompletely filled — if the 3d band is completely filled, as in copper, there must be equal numbers of 3d electrons with both kinds of spin. Although this explains how iron, cobalt, and nickel can be ferromagnetic, while copper is not, it does not explain why ferromagnetism occurs in these three metals only and not in the other transition metals. The explanation of this depends upon an analysis of the terms contributing to the cohesive energy of a metal (in particular, the 'exchange' term) which is still largely speculative, and so we will omit it.

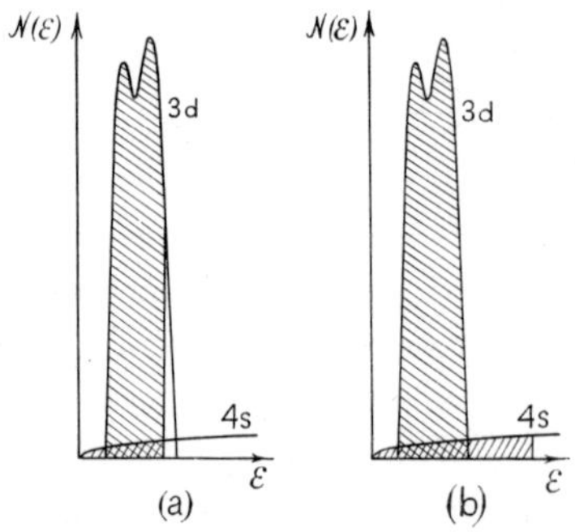

Fig. 8.23. Density of states (schematic) in the 3d and 4s bands of (a) nickel and (b) copper. The shaded regions show the distribution of occupied states at the absolute zero of temperature.

CHAPTER 9

THE METHOD OF WIGNER AND SEITZ

9.1. The Cellular Method

We will now consider a more direct method of calculating the wave functions of the electrons in a metal, which has had much success. This was first applied by WIGNER and SEITZ [1933, 1934] to metallic sodium, and, in its more general application, is known as the *cellular method.*

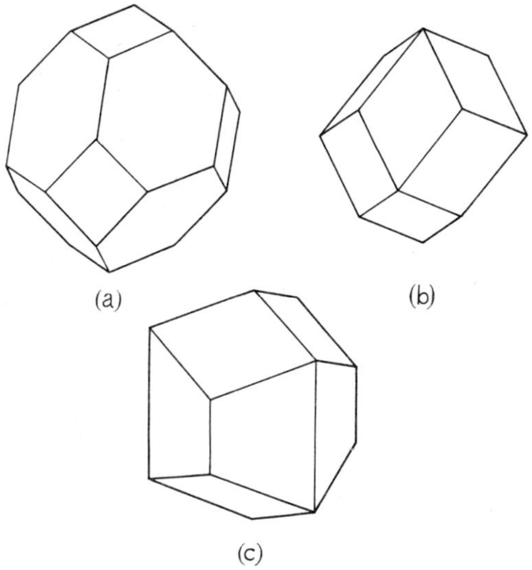

Fig. 9.1. Atomic polyhedra for (a) the body-centred cubic lattice, (b) the face-centred cubic lattice, and (c) the close-packed hexagonal lattice.

Owing to the periodicity of the function $u_k(r)$ appearing in the Bloch function (8.74), it is only necessary to solve the Schrödinger equation (8.71) within a single unit cell of the crystal lattice. In order to obtain the simplest boundary conditions, we choose the unit cell to be a polyhedron with the greatest possible symmetry about an atomic position. Thus, we draw lines connecting an atom to its nearest and next nearest neighbours and construct the planes which bisect these lines perpendicularly. We then choose the unit cell to be the smallest polyhedron surrounding the central atom and bounded by these planes. It is variously called the *Wigner-Seitz cell*, *atomic polyhedron*, *cellular polyhedron*, or, in older works, the *s-polyhedron*. The atomic polyhedra for the body-centred cubic, face-centred cubic, and close-packed hexagonal lattices are shown in Figure 9.1.

It is apparent that the method of constructing the atomic polyhedron is the same as that employed in § 8.7 to construct the fundamental domain of $\boldsymbol{k}$, so that the latter is just the Wigner-Seitz cell of the reciprocal lattice. Since we have seen that the body-centred cubic lattice has a face-centred cubic reciprocal lattice, and *vice versa*, it follows that the atomic polyhedron for either of these lattices must have the same shape as the fundamental domain of $\boldsymbol{k}$ for the other (compare Figures 8.16 and 9.1). The atomic polyhedra completely fill the space of the lattice, and, in the case of the cubic structures (or other simple Bravais lattices), any one may be brought into coincidence with any other by a translation through a lattice vector $\boldsymbol{R}_n$, given by equation (8.65). This is not true in the case of the close-packed hexagonal lattice, for which a rotation as well as a translation through a lattice vector may be necessary to bring two atomic polyhedra into coincidence — this causes a slight complication in the application of the cellular method to the close-packed hexagonal lattice, and in the following work we will consider only the cubic structures.

Let us, then, determine the boundary conditions which a Bloch function must satisfy at the surface of an atomic polyhedron in one of the cubic lattices. We note first that to each face of the cell there is a parallel face, and the vector going perpendicularly from one to the other is a translational vector of the lattice. Suppose that O is the centre of the cell (Figure 9.2), and A and B are the centre points of a pair of opposite faces. The vector **AB** is thus a lattice vector, which we will denote by $\boldsymbol{R}$. Also, let P and Q be corresponding points on the A and B faces, respectively, so that **AP** = **BQ**, and, if **OP** = $\boldsymbol{r}$, then **OQ** = $\boldsymbol{r}+\boldsymbol{R}$.

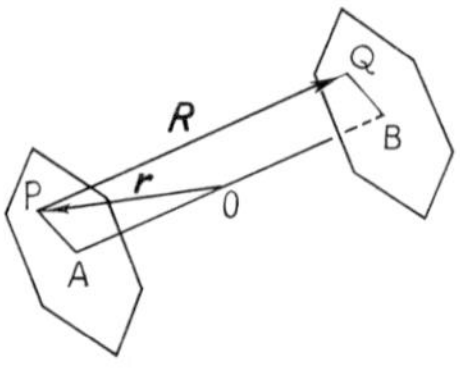

Fig. 9.2.

Now, any Bloch function must satisfy the condition

$$\psi_{\boldsymbol{k}}(\boldsymbol{r}+\boldsymbol{R}) = e^{i\boldsymbol{k}\cdot\boldsymbol{R}}\psi_{\boldsymbol{k}}(\boldsymbol{r}). \tag{9.1}$$

Hence, if $\varepsilon\boldsymbol{R}$ is a small displacement in the direction of $\boldsymbol{R}$, we have

$$\psi_{\boldsymbol{k}}(\boldsymbol{r}+\boldsymbol{R}+\varepsilon\boldsymbol{R}) = \mathrm{e}^{\mathrm{i}\boldsymbol{k}\cdot\boldsymbol{R}}\psi_{\boldsymbol{k}}(\boldsymbol{r}+\varepsilon\boldsymbol{R}).$$

Expanding both sides of this equation in Taylor's series (see Appendix 1), we obtain

$$\psi_{\boldsymbol{k}}(\boldsymbol{r}+\boldsymbol{R})+\varepsilon\boldsymbol{R}\cdot\nabla\psi_{\boldsymbol{k}}(\boldsymbol{r}+\boldsymbol{R})+\ \ldots = \mathrm{e}^{\mathrm{i}\boldsymbol{k}\cdot\boldsymbol{R}}[\psi_{\boldsymbol{k}}(\boldsymbol{r})+\varepsilon\boldsymbol{R}\cdot\nabla\psi_{\boldsymbol{k}}(\boldsymbol{r})+\ \ldots], \quad (9.2)$$

in which all the terms not explicitly given contain, as factors, powers of ε higher than the first. Owing to (9.1) the first term can be dropped on each side of (9.2). Dividing through by ε, and then taking the limit as ε tends to zero, gives, finally,

$$\boldsymbol{R}\cdot\nabla\psi_{\boldsymbol{k}}(\boldsymbol{r}+\boldsymbol{R}) = \mathrm{e}^{\mathrm{i}\boldsymbol{k}\cdot\boldsymbol{R}}\boldsymbol{R}\cdot\nabla\psi_{\boldsymbol{k}}(\boldsymbol{r}). \quad (9.3)$$

Every wave function must satisfy conditions (9.1) and (9.3) for each pair of faces of the atomic polyhedron.

The boundary conditions may be further modified according to the symmetry of $\psi_{\boldsymbol{k}}$. It is possible to determine the latter in general using the theory of groups, but as this lies outside the scope of the present work we will confine ourselves to simple cases where the symmetry is obvious. We shall be particularly concerned with the state of lowest energy of a valence electron in the alkali metals (Li, Na, K, Rb, Cs), which are monovalent and have the body-centred cubic structure. Since the valence electrons (that is, electrons whose energies lie in the conduction band) are nearly free, we may assume that the state of lowest energy is at $\boldsymbol{k} = \boldsymbol{0}$, and we denote the wave function by $\psi_0(\boldsymbol{r})$ [or $u_0(\boldsymbol{r})$ — it has the periodicity of the lattice, for the factor exp $(\mathrm{i}\boldsymbol{k}\cdot\boldsymbol{r})$ is unity when $\boldsymbol{k} = \boldsymbol{0}$]. Now, the valence electron in a free atom of one of these metals is in an s state, and we expect ψ_0 to resemble an s function within an atomic polyhedron — in particular, we do not expect it to have any nodal planes. This symmetry type is sometimes denoted by the symbol Γ_{s} — the Γ referring to the centre of the zone, and the subscript s to the fact that the function has no nodal planes. Of course, ψ_0 will not be exactly spherically symmetrical within an atomic polyhedron, but at least it will have the full symmetry of the lattice, which is quite high, as Figure 9.1 (a) shows. From the symmetry of the function, then, it follows that ψ_0 and its *outward* normal derivative must have the same values at similarly situated points on opposite faces of the cell. That is to say, using the notation of Figure 9.2,

$$\psi_0(\boldsymbol{r}+\boldsymbol{R}) = \psi_0(\boldsymbol{r}), \tag{9.4}$$

$$\boldsymbol{R}\cdot\nabla\psi_0(\boldsymbol{r}+\boldsymbol{R}) = -\boldsymbol{R}\cdot\nabla\psi_0(\boldsymbol{r}). \tag{9.5}$$

The boundary condition (9.1), with $\boldsymbol{k} = \boldsymbol{0}$ simply repeats (9.4), but the boundary condition (9.3) tells us that

$$\boldsymbol{R}\cdot\nabla\psi_0(\boldsymbol{r}+\boldsymbol{R}) = \boldsymbol{R}\cdot\nabla\psi_0(\boldsymbol{r}). \tag{9.6}$$

Comparing (9.5) and (9.6), we see that $\boldsymbol{R}\cdot\nabla\psi_0(\boldsymbol{r})$ must be zero everywhere on the surface of the cell. In other words, *the normal derivative* of $\psi_0(\boldsymbol{r})$ *must vanish at the surface of the atomic polyhedron.*

The foregoing result may have been obtained more simply. Since $\psi_0(\boldsymbol{r})$ has the period of the lattice, and is also symmetrical about any nucleus, it is necessary for the normal derivative to vanish at the surface of a cell, for otherwise the gradient would be discontinuous there. However, this applies only to the state of lowest energy, whereas the boundary conditions (9.1) and (9.3) apply to *all* wave functions.

9.2. The State of Lowest Energy of a Valence Electron in a Metal: The Atomic Sphere Approximation

To be specific, we will now consider metallic sodium, which was the first metal to be treated by the Wigner-Seitz method, and remains the metal most ideally suited to this treatment. It should be noted, however, that the method has been applied, with great success, to all the alkali metals, and, with reasonable success, to other metals.

Owing to the high symmetry of the atomic polyhedron [Figure 9.1 (a)], Wigner and Seitz, for the purpose of calculating $\psi_0(\boldsymbol{r})$, replace the cell by a sphere of equal volume. The radius of this *atomic sphere* is r_s, the *atomic radius*, which we have previously defined by

$$\frac{4\pi}{3} r_s^3 = \frac{v}{N}, \tag{9.7}$$

where v is the volume of the metal and N the number of atoms.

We may assume as a good approximation that the wave function ψ_0 is spherically symmetrical within the atomic sphere, and that its normal derivative vanishes at the surface of the sphere, that is,

$$\left(\frac{d\psi_0}{dr}\right)_{r=r_s} = 0. \tag{9.8}$$

It is found, in fact, that ψ_0 is almost constant over a large interval about $r = r_s$, so that the function which satisfies the above boundary condition very nearly satisfies the true boundary condition (the vanishing of the normal derivative at the surface of the cell).

In order to calculate ψ_0 we must first know the potential energy $V(\boldsymbol{r})$ of a valence electron in the crystal, which is sometimes called the *crystal potential*, and this requires further approximations. First, as we have noted in § 6.1.1, the dimensions of the ion-core of a sodium atom are small compared with those of the atomic sphere, so that there is practically no overlapping of the core electron wave functions of different ions in the metal. Consequently, we may assume that the field of an ion-core in the metal is the same spherically-symmetrical field as in a free atom. However, the field of the ion-cores is not the only field we must take into account: there is also that of the other valence electrons.

The total valence electron charge density is periodic with the period of the lattice, since

$$|\psi_{\boldsymbol{k}}(\boldsymbol{r})|^2 = |u_{\boldsymbol{k}}(\boldsymbol{r})|^2, \tag{9.9}$$

so that each cell is electrically neutral, and, as the cells are very nearly spherical, it is a good approximation to take the electrostatic field of each cell to be zero at points outside the cell. Thus, the field acting on any electron † is essentially that of the ion-core *in the cell in which the electron is located* plus the self-consistent field of the other electrons in that cell. However, we have seen in Chapters 6 and 7 that, as a result of the Pauli principle, an electron is always surrounded by a hole of approximate radius r_s in the charge distribution of electrons with parallel spins — this is known as the *Fermi hole*. We have suggested that, as a result of Coulomb correlations, a similar hole must also exist in the distribution of electrons with antiparallel spins. The effects of Coulomb correlations will be investigated in the following chapter, but meanwhile we will accept the existence of a region, roughly of radius r_s, surrounding an electron during its motion, in which it is unlikely that *any* other electron, regardless of spin, will be found. Hence, the presence of any electron in a cell virtually excludes all the other electrons from the cell, and we may assume that the field acting on the electron is that of the ion-core in the cell only. This cannot

† In future, when we refer simply to an *electron*, we shall mean a *valence electron*, unless otherwise stated.

be strictly correct, of course, since the hole follows the electron during its motion, and does not remain centrally placed in the cell, but in view of other approximations which have to be made this is of no importance — it can be shown, in fact, that if the hole is ignored, and the Hartree field of the valence electrons included in $V(\boldsymbol{r})$, the wave function ψ_0 is not significantly changed.

The wave function ψ_0 and energy ε_0 of the lowest state may therefore be found by integrating the Schrödinger equation

$$\frac{\mathrm{d}^2\psi_0}{\mathrm{d}r^2} + \frac{2}{r}\frac{\mathrm{d}\psi_0}{\mathrm{d}r} + \frac{2m}{\hbar^2}[\varepsilon_0 - V(r)]\psi_0 = 0, \tag{9.10}$$

within an atomic sphere, subject to the boundary condition (9.8). $V(r)$ is the same spherically symmetrical ion-core potential function as in a free atom, and might be obtained, for example, by a Hartree-Fock calculation for a free atom. However, the function $V(r)$ used by Wigner and Seitz for sodium was a semi-empirical function constructed by Prokofiev, which was designed to reproduce with reasonable accuracy the spectrum arising from transitions of the valence electron in a free atom. In recent years several methods, based upon that of Wigner and Seitz, have been developed for finding ε_0 directly from the observed atomic energy levels (obtained from spectral data) without explicitly calculating $V(r)$ and $\psi_0(r)$. We will briefly describe the most accurate of these, called the Quantum Defect Method, in a later section.

In practical calculation it is convenient to use the atomic units defined in § 3.3, and also to let $f(r) = r\psi_0(r)$, when equation (9.10) reduces to the simple form

$$\frac{\mathrm{d}^2 f}{\mathrm{d}r^2} + [\varepsilon_0 - V(r)]f = 0, \tag{9.11}$$

and the boundary condition (9.8) becomes

$$\frac{\mathrm{d}f}{\mathrm{d}r} = \frac{f}{r} \quad \text{when } r = r_s . \tag{9.12}$$

There is another condition, which we have not mentioned explicitly. Since the valence electron in a free atom of sodium is in a 3s state, its wave function has two spherical nodes, and calculation shows that these have radii very much less than r_s — in fact, they lie within the effective radius of the ion-core. We therefore require ψ_0 and f to have two spherical nodes within the atomic sphere. This condition is not of great practical importance, for, although equation (9.11) has solutions with any number of nodes, these correspond to energies lying far from the range in which we are interested, and so would not normally be encountered.

We wish to use ε_0 in calculating the cohesive energy and equilibrium atomic radius of the metal, and, for this purpose, we are not so much concerned with calculating ψ_0 and ε_0 for one particular value of r_s as with obtaining ε_0 as a function of r_s. The potential energy $V(r)$ is, of course, a tabulated function and the integration of the Schrödinger equation must be carried out numerically, but we will not give details of the numerical methods used. The procedure is to choose a reasonable value for ε_0 (that is, one which lies an electron-volt or so below the energy of the valence electron in a free atom), integrate equation (9.11) outwards from the origin, where f is zero, and then find the points *lying beyond the second node* of ψ_0 at which the boundary condition (9.12) is satisfied. The result for $f(r)$ and $\psi_0(r)$ will, if ε_0 has not been chosen too low, be as shown schematically in Figure 9.3. The boundary condition is satisfied for two values a and b of r after the second node of ψ_0. Hence, there are two possible values of r_s corresponding to the chosen ε_0.

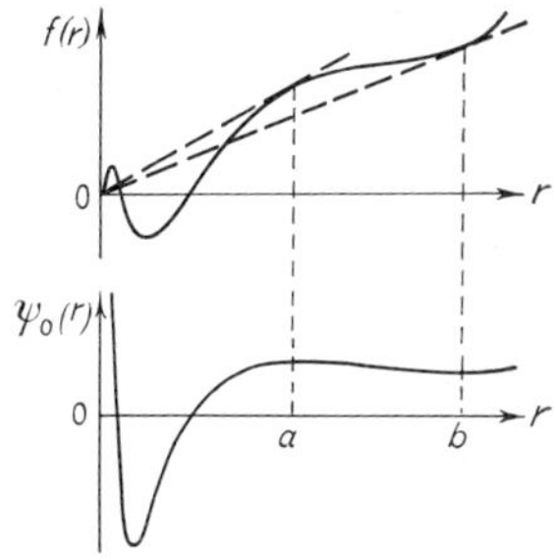

Fig. 9.3. Graphs of $f(r)$ and $\psi_0(r)$ obtained by integrating equation (9.11) with a chosen value of ε_0. The boundary condition (9.8) or (9.12) is satisfied at $r = a$ and $r = b$.

If the value of ε_0 is now lowered slightly (ε_0 is negative so that this means a slight *increase* in its magnitude), and the procedure repeated, the two possible values of r_s will be found to lie closer together. Further repetition will finally result in the boundary condition being satisfied at a single inflection point of ψ_0 only, and for a still lower value of ε_0 the boundary condition will not be satisfied at all beyond the second node of ψ_0. On the other hand, if ε_0 is *raised* from its original chosen value, the two possible values of r_s will diverge, until one of them becomes infinite for an ε_0 equal to the negative of the ionization energy of a free atom — this result is easily comprehended, for $V(r)$ is the ion-core potential function in a free atom and the valence electron wave function in a free atom tends to zero as r tends to infinity. In this way we obtain ε_0 as a function of r_s, and its graph is shown in Figure 9.4.

The wave function ψ_0, corresponding to the observed value of r_s (3.96

B.u.), for metallic sodium is shown in Figure 9.5 (a). The function is almost constant in the region of the atomic sphere lying outside the ion-core, and the volume of this region is roughly 90 per cent of the total volume.

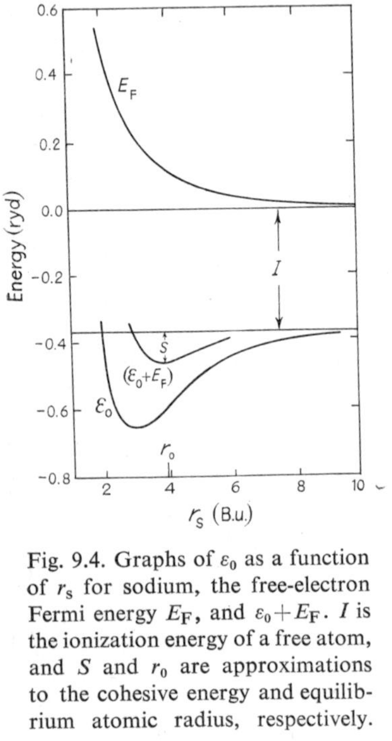

Fig. 9.4. Graphs of ε_0 as a function of r_s for sodium, the free-electron Fermi energy E_F, and ε_0+E_F. I is the ionization energy of a free atom, and S and r_0 are approximations to the cohesive energy and equilibrium atomic radius, respectively.

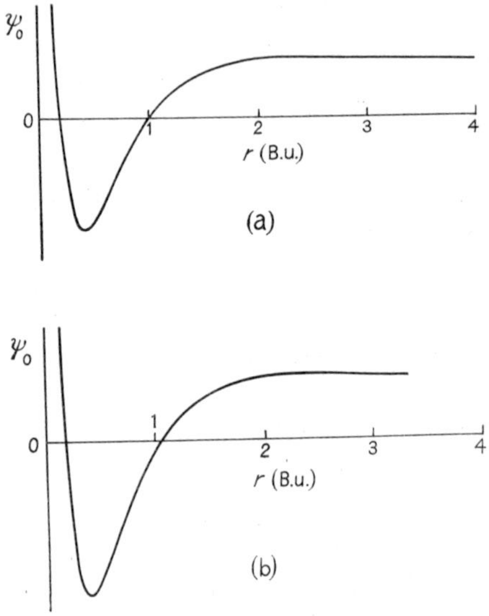

Fig. 9.5. Wave function ψ_0 of the lowest state of a valence electron in (a) metallic sodium ($r_s = 3.96$ B.u.), (b) metallic magnesium ($r_s = 3.33$ B.u.).

If ψ_0 were absolutely constant throughout the whole volume, the electrons would be free, so we may deduce that the valence electrons in metallic sodium are, in fact, very nearly free. This does not apply only to sodium, however. In all metals to which the Wigner-Seitz method has been applied, ψ_0 is found to be almost constant in that part of the atomic sphere lying outside the ion-core. For example, Figure 9.5 (b) shows ψ_0 for the divalent metal magnesium, obtained in the same way as for sodium.

9.3. Occupied States of Higher Energy: The Effective Mass

It must be remembered that ε_0 is just the energy of the lowest state of a valence electron in the metal (or, more precisely, the lowest eigenvalue of the Schrödinger equation for a valence electron in the metal). According to the Pauli principle, only two electrons, with opposite spins, may occupy any orbital state, so that all but two electrons must be in higher energy levels. In order to calculate the cohesive energy we shall need to know the energies of all the occupied states.

The Schrödinger equation for any state $\psi_{\boldsymbol{k}}(\boldsymbol{r})$ is

$$\nabla^2\psi_{\boldsymbol{k}}(\boldsymbol{r})+\frac{2m}{\hbar^2}[\varepsilon(\boldsymbol{k})-V(\boldsymbol{r})]\psi_{\boldsymbol{k}}(\boldsymbol{r})=0, \tag{9.13}$$

where, for the reasons given in the previous section, $V(\boldsymbol{r})$ is assumed to be the potential energy of an electron due to the ion-core in the cell where the electron is located *only*. This equation holds throughout the crystal, but it is only necessary to solve it within a single cell, the boundary conditions to be satisfied at the surface of the cell being (9.1) and (9.3). These boundary conditions cannot be simplified for a state $\boldsymbol{k}$ in general as they can for $\boldsymbol{k} = \boldsymbol{0}$, so that the atomic sphere approximation is of no immediate help. The mathematical difficulties are such that a direct solution of the equation is not practicable and approximate solutions must be sought.

WIGNER and SEITZ [1933], in their first paper on metallic sodium, made the approximation

$$\psi_{\boldsymbol{k}}(\boldsymbol{r})=\mathrm{e}^{\mathrm{i}\boldsymbol{k}\cdot\boldsymbol{r}}u_0(\boldsymbol{r}), \tag{9.14}$$

where $u_0(\boldsymbol{r})$ $[=\psi_0(\boldsymbol{r})]$ is the function calculated in the previous section continued periodically throughout the crystal. The function (9.14) is of the Bloch type, since $u_0(\boldsymbol{r})$ has the period of the lattice, but the approximation lies in the use of $u_0(\boldsymbol{r})$ instead of a function $u_{\boldsymbol{k}}(\boldsymbol{r})$ which varies with $\boldsymbol{k}$. However, there are several reasons for believing that the approximation is a reasonable one. First, if $u_0(\boldsymbol{r})$ were constant, the electrons would be free, so that (9.14) would be perfectly correct; and we have seen that $u_0(\boldsymbol{r})$ *is*, in fact, nearly constant throughout most of the volume of the crystal. Second, the expression (9.14) reduces correctly to $u_0(\boldsymbol{r})$ when $\boldsymbol{k}=\boldsymbol{0}$. Finally, since only the lower half of the first Brillouin zone is occupied in the alkali metals, we might expect that for the occupied states the true $u_{\boldsymbol{k}}(\boldsymbol{r})$ will not differ much from $u_0(\boldsymbol{r})$.

If we assume that $u_0(\boldsymbol{r})$ is normalized in the volume of the crystal, and remembering that it is a real function, we obtain, from equations (9.13) and (9.14), the approximate energy of the state $\psi_{\boldsymbol{k}}(\boldsymbol{r})$ as

$$\varepsilon(\boldsymbol{k})=\int u_0(\boldsymbol{r})\mathrm{e}^{-\mathrm{i}\boldsymbol{k}\cdot\boldsymbol{r}}\left[-\frac{\hbar^2}{2m}\nabla^2+V(\boldsymbol{r})\right]\mathrm{e}^{\mathrm{i}\boldsymbol{k}\cdot\boldsymbol{r}}u_0(\boldsymbol{r})\mathrm{d}\boldsymbol{r}, \tag{9.15}$$

the integral being over the volume of the crystal. Now,

$$e^{i\boldsymbol{k}\cdot\boldsymbol{r}}u_0(\boldsymbol{r}) = e^{i(k_1x+k_2y+k_3z)}\,u_0(x, y, z),$$

so that

$$\frac{\partial}{\partial x}[e^{i\boldsymbol{k}\cdot\boldsymbol{r}}u_0(\boldsymbol{r})] = e^{i\boldsymbol{k}\cdot\boldsymbol{r}}\frac{\partial u_0}{\partial x} + ik_1 e^{i\boldsymbol{k}\cdot\boldsymbol{r}}u_0,$$

and

$$\frac{\partial^2}{\partial x^2}[e^{i\boldsymbol{k}\cdot\boldsymbol{r}}u_0(\boldsymbol{r})] = e^{i\boldsymbol{k}\cdot\boldsymbol{r}}\frac{\partial^2 u_0}{\partial x^2} + 2ik_1 e^{i\boldsymbol{k}\cdot\boldsymbol{r}}\frac{\partial u_0}{\partial x} - k_1^2 e^{i\boldsymbol{k}\cdot\boldsymbol{r}}u_0.$$

Differentiating with respect to y and z in the same way, we have, finally,

$$\nabla^2[e^{i\boldsymbol{k}\cdot\boldsymbol{r}}u_0(\boldsymbol{r})] = e^{i\boldsymbol{k}\cdot\boldsymbol{r}}(\nabla^2 + 2i\boldsymbol{k}\cdot\nabla - k^2)u_0(\boldsymbol{r}). \tag{9.16}$$

Hence

$$\varepsilon(\boldsymbol{k}) = \int u_0(\boldsymbol{r})\left[-\frac{\hbar^2}{2m}\nabla^2 + V(\boldsymbol{r})\right]u_0(\boldsymbol{r})\mathrm{d}\boldsymbol{r} + \frac{\hbar^2k^2}{2m} - \frac{\hbar^2 i}{m}\boldsymbol{k}\cdot\left[\int u_0(\boldsymbol{r})\nabla u_0(\boldsymbol{r})\mathrm{d}\boldsymbol{r}\right]. \tag{9.17}$$

Since $u_0(\boldsymbol{r})$ is an *even* function, that is, $u_0(\boldsymbol{r}) = u_0(-\boldsymbol{r})$, and $\nabla u_0(\boldsymbol{r}) = -\nabla u_0(-\boldsymbol{r})$, the integral in the last term is zero. Also, the equation for $u_0(\boldsymbol{r})$ may be written

$$\left[-\frac{\hbar^2}{2m}\nabla^2 + V(\boldsymbol{r})\right]u_0(\boldsymbol{r}) = \varepsilon_0 u_0(\boldsymbol{r}). \tag{9.18}$$

We therefore have

$$\varepsilon(\boldsymbol{k}) = \varepsilon_0 + \frac{\hbar^2k^2}{2m}, \tag{9.19}$$

which is the energy of the lowest state plus the kinetic energy of a free electron in the state $\boldsymbol{k}$.

For the true wave function of the state $\boldsymbol{k}$,

$$\psi_{\boldsymbol{k}}(\boldsymbol{r}) = e^{i\boldsymbol{k}\cdot\boldsymbol{r}}u_{\boldsymbol{k}}(\boldsymbol{r}), \tag{9.20}$$

we have, by the same method as used in obtaining equation (9.16),

$$\nabla^2\psi_{\boldsymbol{k}}(\boldsymbol{r}) = e^{i\boldsymbol{k}\cdot\boldsymbol{r}}(\nabla^2 + 2i\boldsymbol{k}\cdot\nabla - k^2)u_{\boldsymbol{k}}(\boldsymbol{r}). \tag{9.21}$$

Substituting (9.20) in (9.13), therefore, gives the equation

$$\nabla^2 u_{\boldsymbol{k}} + 2i\boldsymbol{k} \cdot \nabla u_{\boldsymbol{k}} + \frac{2m}{\hbar^2}\left[\varepsilon(\boldsymbol{k}) - \frac{\hbar^2 k^2}{2m} - V(\boldsymbol{r})\right] u_{\boldsymbol{k}} = 0 \qquad (9.22)$$

for $u_{\boldsymbol{k}}(\boldsymbol{r})$. Now, this equation reduces to that of u_0, equation (9.18), when $\varepsilon(\boldsymbol{k})$ is given by (9.19) and the term $2i\boldsymbol{k} \cdot \nabla u_{\boldsymbol{k}}$ is neglected, so that the approximation (9.14) is a reasonable one so long as this term is very small. Whatever the magnitude of $\nabla u_{\boldsymbol{k}}$, this term will certainly be small for states near $\boldsymbol{k} = \boldsymbol{0}$. Hence, for such states, at least, we may obtain a better approximation to the energy than (9.19) by treating $2i\boldsymbol{k} \cdot \nabla u_{\boldsymbol{k}}$ as a small perturbation. This was done by Wigner and Seitz [1934] in their second paper on sodium, but we will describe a rather more elegant method due originally to Bardeen [1938], which gives the final result in a compact analytical form. We wish to remark, however, that the derivation of the result is not essential to an understanding of the remainder of the book, and may be omitted at a first reading.

Let us, on the assumption that k is small, expand $u_{\boldsymbol{k}}$ in powers of k as far as the first, thus

$$u_{\boldsymbol{k}}(\boldsymbol{r}) = u_0(\boldsymbol{r}) + k u_1(\boldsymbol{r}), \qquad (9.23)$$

where $u_0(\boldsymbol{r})$ and $u_1(\boldsymbol{r})$ both have the period of the lattice. In the remainder of this section it will be convenient to use the atomic units defined in § 3.3, so that equation (9.22) becomes

$$\nabla^2 u_{\boldsymbol{k}} + 2i\boldsymbol{k} \cdot \nabla u_{\boldsymbol{k}} + [\varepsilon(\boldsymbol{k}) - k^2 - V(\boldsymbol{r})] u_{\boldsymbol{k}} = 0, \qquad (9.24)$$

and

$$\varepsilon(\boldsymbol{k}) = \frac{\int u_{\boldsymbol{k}}^* [-\nabla^2 - 2i\boldsymbol{k} \cdot \nabla + k^2 + V(\boldsymbol{r})] u_{\boldsymbol{k}} \, \mathrm{d}\boldsymbol{r}}{\int |u_{\boldsymbol{k}}|^2 \, \mathrm{d}\boldsymbol{r}}, \qquad (9.25)$$

where, owing to the periodicity of $u_{\boldsymbol{k}}$, the integrals may be taken over the whole volume of the crystal or over a single cell. Substitution of (9.23) in (9.25), which we will do in detail later, shows that it gives $\varepsilon(\boldsymbol{k})$ correct to terms of the second order in k as

$$\varepsilon(\boldsymbol{k}) = \varepsilon_0 + \alpha k^2, \qquad (9.26)$$

since the first order term,

$$-2i\boldsymbol{k} \cdot \left[\int u_0 \nabla u_0 \, \mathrm{d}\boldsymbol{r}\right],$$

vanishes owing to the symmetry of u_0. The constant α is to be determined.

From equations (9.23), (9.24), and (9.26) we obtain, correct to the *first* order in k,

$$\nabla^2(u_0+ku_1)+2\mathrm{i}\boldsymbol{k}\cdot\nabla(u_0+ku_1)$$
$$+[\varepsilon_0+\alpha k^2-k^2-V(\boldsymbol{r})](u_0+ku_1) = 0. \qquad (9.27)$$

Since we are neglecting any dependence of $\varepsilon(\boldsymbol{k})$ on the *direction* of $\boldsymbol{k}$, we can, without loss of generality, choose $\boldsymbol{k}$ to be in the z-direction, so that

$$\boldsymbol{k}\cdot\nabla(u_0+ku_1) = k\frac{\partial}{\partial z}(u_0+ku_1). \qquad (9.28)$$

Then, equating to zero separately the terms of (9.27) not containing k and those containing the first power of k only (this is possible, because, when a solution in the form of a series is substituted in a differential equation, the result is an *identity*), we obtain

$$[\nabla^2+\varepsilon_0-V(\boldsymbol{r})]u_0 = 0, \qquad (9.28)$$

$$[\nabla^2+\varepsilon_0-V(\boldsymbol{r})]u_1 = -2\mathrm{i}\frac{\partial u_0}{\partial z}. \qquad (9.29)$$

The first equation merely confirms that $u_0 = \psi_0$, as previously defined, and the second must be solved subject to appropriate boundary conditions for u_1.

A particular solution of equation (9.29) is $-\mathrm{i}zu_0$, as we will verify; thus,

$$\nabla^2(-\mathrm{i}zu_0) = -\mathrm{i}u_0\nabla^2 z-2\mathrm{i}\nabla z\cdot\nabla u_0-\mathrm{i}z\nabla^2 u_0$$
$$= 0-2\mathrm{i}\frac{\partial u_0}{\partial z}-\mathrm{i}z\nabla^2 u_0,$$

so that

$$[\nabla^2+\varepsilon_0-V(\boldsymbol{r})](-\mathrm{i}zu_0) = -2\mathrm{i}\frac{\partial u_0}{\partial z}-\mathrm{i}z[\nabla^2+\varepsilon_0-V(\boldsymbol{r})]u_0$$
$$= -2\mathrm{i}\frac{\partial u_0}{\partial z},$$

using equation (9.28). The general solution of equation (9.29) is obtained by adding to this particular solution the *complementary function*, which is the general solution of the homogeneous equation obtained by neglecting the right hand side of (9.29). However, we do not require the general solution, but a solution which satisfies certain boundary conditions, which we will now discuss.

We know that u_0 is an even function, so that $\partial u_0/\partial z$ is an odd function, and hence, in order to satisfy equation (9.29), u_1 must be an odd function; that is to say, $u_1(\boldsymbol{r}) = -u_1(-\boldsymbol{r})$. It is clear that an odd function which has the period of the lattice must change sign at the surface of an atomic polyhedron, and so, if it is to be continuous, its value must be zero there. Thus, the boundary condition on u_1 is that it must vanish at the surface of an atomic polyhedron, or, *using the atomic sphere approximation*,

$$u_1(r_s) = 0. \tag{9.30}$$

To the particular solution $-\mathrm{i}zu_0$ of equation (9.29) already found we must therefore add a solution of the homogeneous equation

$$[\nabla^2 + \varepsilon_0 - V(\boldsymbol{r})]\, u = 0 \tag{9.31}$$

which will ensure that boundary condition (9.30) is satisfied — in other words, we require

$$u = \mathrm{i}zu_0 \quad \text{at} \quad r = r_s. \tag{9.32}$$

It follows that u must have p symmetry (see § 2.4) within an atomic sphere, that is, it must be z times a spherically symmetrical function. Let us write

$$u(r) = \mathrm{i}z\,\frac{P(r)}{r^2}, \tag{9.33}$$

then

$$\begin{aligned} \nabla^2 u &= 2\mathrm{i}\,\frac{\partial}{\partial z}\left(\frac{P}{r^2}\right) + \mathrm{i}z\nabla^2\left(\frac{P}{r^2}\right) \\ &= 2\mathrm{i}\,\frac{z}{r}\frac{\mathrm{d}}{\mathrm{d}r}\left(\frac{P}{r^2}\right) + \mathrm{i}z\left(\frac{\mathrm{d}^2}{\mathrm{d}r^2} + \frac{2}{r}\frac{\mathrm{d}}{\mathrm{d}r}\right)\left(\frac{P}{r^2}\right) \\ &= \frac{\mathrm{i}z}{r^2}\left(\frac{\mathrm{d}^2 P}{\mathrm{d}r^2} - \frac{2P}{r^2}\right), \end{aligned} \tag{9.34}$$

and equation (9.31) becomes

$$\frac{\mathrm{d}^2 P}{\mathrm{d}r^2} + \left[\varepsilon_0 - V(r) - \frac{2}{r^2}\right] P = 0. \tag{9.35}$$

The conditions on $P(r)$ are that it be zero at the origin and scaled so that

$$P(r_s) = r_s^2 u_0(r_s). \tag{9.36}$$

It should be noted that we are not required to find the eigenvalue of equation (9.35), since ε_0 is known. Having found $P(r)$ by integrating (9.35) outwards from the origin, and multiplying it by a suitable constant to satisfy (9.36), we then have

$$u_1(r) = \mathrm{i}z\left(\frac{P}{r^2} - u_0\right), \tag{9.37}$$

which satisfies (9.30). This expression is only valid, of course, within an atomic sphere [where, incidentally, $V(\boldsymbol{r})$ is spherically symmetrical, and might be written $V(r)$] or cell — the function must be continued periodically through the crystal. We note that u_0 is a real function while u_1 is pure imaginary.

From equations (9.23) and (9.25), we have

$$\varepsilon(\boldsymbol{k}) = \frac{\displaystyle\int_\Omega (u_0 + ku_1)^* \left[-\nabla^2 + V(r) + k^2 - 2\mathrm{i}k\frac{\partial}{\partial z}\right](u_0 + ku_1)\mathrm{d}\boldsymbol{r}}{\displaystyle\int_\Omega |u_0 + ku_1|^2 \mathrm{d}\boldsymbol{r}} \tag{9.38}$$

where the integrals are taken, as a good approximation, throughout an *atomic sphere* Ω. Using equations (9.28) and (9.29), this becomes

$$\varepsilon(\boldsymbol{k}) = \varepsilon_0 + k^2 - \frac{2\mathrm{i}k^2 \displaystyle\int_\Omega (u_0 + ku_1)^* \frac{\partial u_1}{\partial z}\mathrm{d}\boldsymbol{r}}{\displaystyle\int_\Omega u_0^2 \mathrm{d}\boldsymbol{r} + k^2 \int_\Omega |u_1|^2 \mathrm{d}\boldsymbol{r}}$$

$$= \varepsilon_0 + k^2 + k^2\left(-2\mathrm{i}\int_\Omega u_0 \frac{\partial u_1}{\partial z}\mathrm{d}\boldsymbol{r}\right)\left(\int_\Omega u_0^2 \mathrm{d}\boldsymbol{r}\right)^{-1}, \tag{9.39}$$

as far as terms in k^2.

Let us assume that u_0 is normalized to unity within an atomic sphere, so that

$$\int_\Omega u_0^2 \mathrm{d}\boldsymbol{r} = 4\pi \int_0^{r_s} r^2 u_0^2 \mathrm{d}r = 1. \tag{9.40}$$

Then, as we have previously remarked,

$$\varepsilon(\boldsymbol{k}) = \varepsilon_0 + \alpha k^2,$$

where

$$\alpha = 1 - 2\mathrm{i} \int_{\Omega} u_0 \frac{\partial u_1}{\partial z} \, \mathrm{d}\boldsymbol{r}. \tag{9.41}$$

Writing $u_1 = \mathrm{i} z g(r)$, where

$$g(r) = \frac{P}{r^2} - u_0,$$

we obtain

$$\begin{aligned}
\alpha &= 1 + 2 \int_{\Omega} u_0 \left(g + \frac{z^2}{r} g' \right) \mathrm{d}\boldsymbol{r} \\
&= 1 + 2 \int_0^{r_s} 4\pi r^2 u_0 g \, \mathrm{d}r + 4\pi \int_0^{r_s} r^3 \, \mathrm{d}r \int_0^{\pi} u_0 g' \cos^2\theta \sin\theta \, \mathrm{d}\theta \\
&= 1 + 8\pi \int_0^{r_s} r^2 u_0 g \, \mathrm{d}r + \frac{8\pi}{3} \int_0^{r_s} r^3 u_0 g' \, \mathrm{d}r \\
&= 1 + 8\pi \int_0^{r_s} r^2 u_0 g \, \mathrm{d}r - \frac{8\pi}{3} \int_0^{r_s} g \frac{\mathrm{d}}{\mathrm{d}r} (r^3 u_0) \mathrm{d}r \\
&= 1 - \frac{8\pi}{3} \int_0^{r_s} r^3 g \, u_0' \, \mathrm{d}r \\
&= 1 - \frac{8\pi}{3} \int_0^{r_s} r(P - r^2 u_0) u_0' \, \mathrm{d}r.
\end{aligned} \tag{9.42}$$

We have performed an integration by parts in the fourth line and used the fact that $g(r_s) = 0$.

In terms of the function $f(r) = r u_0$, (9.42) becomes

$$\alpha = 1 - \frac{8\pi}{3} \int_0^{r_s} (P - rf) \left(\frac{\mathrm{d}f}{\mathrm{d}r} - \frac{f}{r} \right) \mathrm{d}r. \tag{9.43}$$

Now,

$$\int_0^{r_s} r f f' \, \mathrm{d}r = [r f^2]_0^{r_s} - \int_0^{r_s} (f^2 + r f f') \mathrm{d}r,$$

and, from (9.40),

$$4\pi \int_0^{r_s} f^2 \, \mathrm{d}r = 4\pi \int_0^{r_s} r^2 u_0^2 \, \mathrm{d}r = 1,$$

so that

$$\frac{8\pi}{3} \int_0^{r_s} rff' \, \mathrm{d}r = \frac{4\pi}{3} [rf^2]_0^{r_s} - \frac{4\pi}{3} \int_0^{r_s} f^2 \, \mathrm{d}r$$

$$= \frac{4\pi}{3} r_s^3 [u_0(r_s)]^2 - \frac{1}{3}, \tag{9.44}$$

and

$$\alpha = \frac{4\pi}{3} r_s^3 [u_0(r_s)]^2 - \frac{8\pi}{3} \int_0^{r_s} P \left(f' - \frac{f}{r} \right) \mathrm{d}r. \tag{9.45}$$

Also,

$$\int_0^{r_s} P \left(f' - \frac{f}{r} \right) \mathrm{d}r = \int_0^{r_s} Pr \frac{\mathrm{d}}{\mathrm{d}r} \left(\frac{f}{r} \right) \mathrm{d}r$$

$$= [Pf]_0^{r_s} - \int_0^{r_s} \frac{f}{r} (rP' + P) \mathrm{d}r,$$

and, hence,

$$2 \int_0^{r_s} P \left(f' - \frac{f}{r} \right) \mathrm{d}r = [Pf]_0^{r_s} - \int_0^{r_s} \left(fP' - Pf' + \frac{2Pf}{r} \right) \mathrm{d}r. \tag{9.46}$$

From equations (9.11) and (9.35), for f and P, respectively, we have

$$fP'' - Pf'' = \frac{2Pf}{r^2},$$

which gives

$$\frac{\mathrm{d}}{\mathrm{d}r} [r(fP' - Pf')] = fP' - Pf' + \frac{2Pf}{r}. \tag{9.47}$$

From (9.45), (9.46), and (9.47), we obtain

$$\alpha = \frac{4\pi}{3} r_s^3 [u_0(r_s)]^2 - \frac{4\pi}{3} P(r_s) f(r_s) + \frac{4\pi}{3} r_s [f(r_s) P'(r_s) - P(r_s) f'(r_s)]. \tag{9.48}$$

However, boundary condition (9.12) for f tells us that

$$f'(r_s) = \frac{f(r_s)}{r_s} = u_0(r_s),$$

and equation (9.36) gives

$$P(r_s) = r_s^2 u_0(r_s) = r_s f(r_s).$$

Hence,

$$r_s P(r_s) f'(r_s) = P(r_s) f(r_s) = r_s^3 [u_0(r_s)]^2, \tag{9.49}$$

and

$$r_s f(r_s) P'(r_s) = r_s^4 [u_0(r_s)]^2 \frac{P'(r_s)}{P(r_s)}. \tag{9.50}$$

Finally, substituting (9.49) and (9.50) in (9.48), we find

$$\alpha = \gamma \left[\frac{r}{P}\frac{\mathrm{d}P}{\mathrm{d}r} - 1\right]_{r=r_s}, \tag{9.51}$$

where

$$\gamma = \frac{4\pi}{3} r_s^3 [u_0(r_s)]^2. \tag{9.52}$$

Remembering that u_0 is normalized to unity within the atomic sphere, we see that γ is the ratio of the value of u_0^2 at the surface of the sphere to its mean value $(3/4\pi r_s^3)$.

Once u_0 and ε_0 have been found for a given value of r_s, all that is required to determine α for this r_s is a single integration of equation (9.35). The values of α obtained by Bardeen for sodium and lithium were 1.07 and 0.65, respectively, for the observed atomic radii. More recently, Brooks [1953] has used formula (9.51) in conjunction with the Quantum Defect Method (see § 9.7) to calculate α for all the alkali metals, with the following results:

	Li	Na	K	Rb	Cs
α	0.69	1.02	1.08	1.12	1.20

Reverting to ordinary units (α is, of course, a dimensionless constant), the energy $\varepsilon(\boldsymbol{k})$, for small k, becomes

$$\varepsilon(\boldsymbol{k}) = \varepsilon_0 + \alpha \frac{\hbar^2 k^2}{2m}, \tag{9.53}$$

and we may write

$$\alpha = m/m^*, \tag{9.54}$$

where m^* is the *effective mass* near $\boldsymbol{k} = \boldsymbol{0}$. We see that for sodium, in particular, the effective mass is little different from m, again indicating that the valence electrons are very nearly free. Since the first Brillouin zone is only half filled in the alkali metals, it is probable that the energy surfaces in the occupied region do not differ greatly from spheres. Hence, although α has been calculated for small values of k only, we might expect equation (9.53) to hold approximately for all the occupied states. This will be used in the following section.

9.4. The Cohesive Energy of Metallic Sodium

In their first paper on metallic sodium, WIGNER and SEITZ [1933] made use of the approximate formula (9.19) for $\varepsilon(\boldsymbol{k})$. Assuming that the effects of electronic interactions are adequately taken care of by the exclusion of all but one electron from an atomic polyhedron, they then postulated that the *average* energy of a valence electron in the metal is simply $\varepsilon_0 + E_F$, where E_F is the free-electron Fermi energy, given in atomic units by

$$E_F = \frac{2.21}{r_s^2} \text{ ryd} \tag{9.55}$$

[see equation (7.52)]. The graph of $\varepsilon_0 + E_F$ as a function of r_s is shown in Figure 9.4. According to this theory the value of r_s corresponding to the minimum of $\varepsilon_0 + E_F$ is the equilibrium atomic radius, which we will denote by r_0, and the depth of the minimum below the value of ε_0 for infinite r_s is the theoretical cohesive energy (per atom), which we will denote by S. Thus, if I is the (positive) ionization energy of a free atom, we have

$$S = -I - \varepsilon_0(r_0) - \frac{2.21}{r_0^2} \text{ ryd.} \tag{9.56}$$

This procedure is undoubtedly crude, but none the less it cannot be far from the truth, for it yields a calculated cohesive energy and equilibrium atomic radius for sodium which are within a few per cent of the experimental values. A more correct procedure, which we will go on to describe, is to calculate the total energy using a wave function consisting of a single determinant of one-electron functions and then to make a correction for the effect of Coulomb correlations. This is essentially what Wigner and Seitz did in their second paper on metallic sodium [1934].

The energy of a monovalent metal containing N atoms has been found, using a single determinantal wave function, in § 6.1.3, and is given in equation (6.18). In that expression the one-electron functions are denoted by ψ_i, where i ranges from 1 to N. Translating this into the '$\boldsymbol{k}$ notation', and remembering that at the absolute zero of temperature there are two electrons with opposite spins in each occupied orbital state $\psi_{\boldsymbol{k}}$, we obtain

$$\begin{aligned} NE_0 = {} & 2\sum_{\boldsymbol{k}} \int \psi_{\boldsymbol{k}}^*(\boldsymbol{r}) \left[-\frac{\hbar^2}{2m} \nabla^2 + \sum_a^N V_a(\boldsymbol{r}) \right] \psi_{\boldsymbol{k}}(\boldsymbol{r}) \mathrm{d}\boldsymbol{r} \\ & + 2 \sum_{\boldsymbol{k}} \sum_{\boldsymbol{k}'} \iint \frac{e^2}{r_{12}} |\psi_{\boldsymbol{k}}(\boldsymbol{r}_1)|^2 |\psi_{\boldsymbol{k}}(\boldsymbol{r}_2)|^2 \mathrm{d}\boldsymbol{r}_1 \mathrm{d}\boldsymbol{r}_2 \\ & - \sum_{\boldsymbol{k}} \sum_{\boldsymbol{k}'} \iint \frac{e^2}{r_{12}} \psi_{\boldsymbol{k}}^*(\boldsymbol{r}_1) \psi_{\boldsymbol{k}'}^*(\boldsymbol{r}_2) \psi_{\boldsymbol{k}}(\boldsymbol{r}_2) \psi_{\boldsymbol{k}'}(\boldsymbol{r}_1) \mathrm{d}\boldsymbol{r}_1 \mathrm{d}\boldsymbol{r}_2 \\ & + \tfrac{1}{2} \sum_{a \neq b}^N \sum^N \frac{e^2}{R_{ab}}, \end{aligned} \tag{9.57}$$

where we have denoted by E_0 the average energy per electron in this approximation. Here and in the following work, if there is no indication to the contrary, the integrals are throughout the volume of the metal.

The functions $\psi_{\boldsymbol{k}}$ are assumed to be eigenfunctions of the equation

$$\nabla^2 \psi_{\boldsymbol{k}} + \frac{2m}{\hbar^2} [\varepsilon(\boldsymbol{k}) - V(\boldsymbol{r})] \psi_{\boldsymbol{k}} = 0 \tag{9.58}$$

[that is, equation (9.13)], and we will use this equation in order to simplify the terms of (9.57). First, it will be useful to define the potential function $V(\boldsymbol{r})$ more precisely. It will be recalled that this is the potential energy of an electron due to the ion-core in the cell where the electron is located only. Also, in Chapter 6 we defined $V_a(\boldsymbol{r})$ as the potential energy of an electron in the field of the ion-core whose nucleus has position vector $\boldsymbol{R}_a$, and we will refer to the cell containing this ion-core as 'cell (a)'. We may then write

$$V(\boldsymbol{r}) = \sum_a^N U_a(\boldsymbol{r}), \tag{9.59}$$

where

$$U_a(\boldsymbol{r}) = V_a(\boldsymbol{r}) \quad \text{within cell } (a), \qquad = 0 \quad \text{outside cell } (a). \tag{9.60}$$

$V_a(\boldsymbol{r})$ is, of course, spherically symmetrical about the lattice point $\boldsymbol{R}_a$, and may be written $V(|\boldsymbol{r}-\boldsymbol{R}_a|)$.

We will denote by $\rho(\boldsymbol{r})$ the number density of electrons with both kinds of spin at position $\boldsymbol{r}$, that is,

$$\rho(\boldsymbol{r}) = 2\sum_{\boldsymbol{k}} |\psi_{\boldsymbol{k}}(\boldsymbol{r})|^2, \tag{9.61}$$

assuming that the functions $\psi_{\boldsymbol{k}}$ are normalized to unity in the volume of the metal.

Now, using equation (9.58) and the above definitions, the first term in expression (9.57) for NE_0 becomes

$$\begin{aligned}
2\sum_{\boldsymbol{k}}\int \psi_{\boldsymbol{k}}^*(\boldsymbol{r})\left[-\frac{\hbar^2}{2m}\nabla^2+\sum_a^N V_a(\boldsymbol{r})\right]\psi_{\boldsymbol{k}}(\boldsymbol{r})\mathrm{d}\boldsymbol{r} \\
&= 2\sum_{\boldsymbol{k}}\int \psi_{\boldsymbol{k}}^*(\boldsymbol{r})\left[\varepsilon(\boldsymbol{k})-V(\boldsymbol{r})+\sum_a^N V_a(\boldsymbol{r})\right]\psi_{\boldsymbol{k}}(\boldsymbol{r})\mathrm{d}\boldsymbol{r} \\
&= 2\sum_{\boldsymbol{k}}\varepsilon(\boldsymbol{k})+\int \rho(\boldsymbol{r})\left[\sum_a^N V_a(\boldsymbol{r})-V(\boldsymbol{r})\right]\mathrm{d}\boldsymbol{r} \\
&= 2\sum_{\boldsymbol{k}}\varepsilon(\boldsymbol{k})+\sum_a^N\int \rho(\boldsymbol{r})[V_a(\boldsymbol{r})-U_a(\boldsymbol{r})]\mathrm{d}\boldsymbol{r} \\
&= 2\sum_{\boldsymbol{k}}\varepsilon(\boldsymbol{k})+\sum_a^N\left[\int_{(a)}\rho(\boldsymbol{r})\{V_a(\boldsymbol{r})-U_a(\boldsymbol{r})\}\mathrm{d}\boldsymbol{r}\right. \\
&\qquad\left.+\sum_{b\neq a}^N\int_{(b)}\rho(\boldsymbol{r})\{V_a(\boldsymbol{r})-U_a(\boldsymbol{r})\}\mathrm{d}\boldsymbol{r}\right],
\end{aligned}$$

where in the final line the two integrals are throughout cell (a) and cell (b), respectively. However, from the definition of $U_a(\boldsymbol{r})$, we see that $\{V_a(\boldsymbol{r})-U_a(\boldsymbol{r})\}$ is zero within cell (a) and $U_a(\boldsymbol{r})$ is zero within any other cell (b). Hence, the above expression becomes

$$2\sum_{\boldsymbol{k}}\varepsilon(\boldsymbol{k})+\sum^N\sum_{a\neq b}^N\int_{(b)}\rho(\boldsymbol{r})V_a(\boldsymbol{r})\mathrm{d}\boldsymbol{r}. \tag{9.62}$$

We will now make the following additional assumptions:

(i) At all points *outside cell* (a) we assume that

$$V_a(\boldsymbol{r}) = -\frac{e^2}{|\boldsymbol{r}-\boldsymbol{R}_a|}. \tag{9.63}$$

In other words, we assume that the potential energy $V_a(\boldsymbol{r})$ is hydrogenic outside cell (a). This is a very good approximation, since the effective radius of the ion-core is small compared with the atomic radius. Indeed, this approximation is valid well into the atomic cell — a fact which we shall see to be the basis of the Quantum Defect Method.

(ii) We assume that the valence electron charge distribution within any cell (a) is spherically symmetrical, so that, as far as points outside cell (a) are concerned, the charge can be regarded as concentrated at the centre of the cell. This is simply the atomic sphere approximation.

Using these assumptions, the potential energy of the interaction between the ion-core in cell (a) and the valence electron charge distribution in cell (b) is found to be

$$\int_{(b)} \rho(\boldsymbol{r})\, V_a(\boldsymbol{r})\,\mathrm{d}\boldsymbol{r} = -\int_{(b)} \frac{e^2}{|\boldsymbol{r}-\boldsymbol{R}_a|}\,\rho(\boldsymbol{r})\,\mathrm{d}\boldsymbol{r} = -\frac{e^2}{R_{ab}}. \tag{9.64}$$

The expression (9.62) for the first term in NE_0 thus becomes

$$2\sum_{\boldsymbol{k}} \varepsilon(\boldsymbol{k}) - \sum_{a\neq b}^{N}\sum^{N} \frac{e^2}{R_{ab}}. \tag{9.65}$$

The second term on the right hand side of equation (9.57), the *Coulomb term*, becomes

$$\begin{aligned}
\tfrac{1}{2}\iint \frac{e^2}{r_{12}}\,\rho(\boldsymbol{r}_1)\rho(\boldsymbol{r}_2)\,\mathrm{d}\boldsymbol{r}_1\,\mathrm{d}\boldsymbol{r}_2
&= \tfrac{1}{2}\sum_a^N\sum_b^N \int_{(a)}\int_{(b)} \frac{e^2}{r_{12}}\,\rho(\boldsymbol{r}_1)\rho(\boldsymbol{r}_2)\,\mathrm{d}\boldsymbol{r}_1\,\mathrm{d}\boldsymbol{r}_2 \\
&= \tfrac{1}{2}\sum_{a\neq b}^N\sum^N \int_{(a)}\int_{(b)} \frac{e^2}{r_{12}}\,\rho(\boldsymbol{r}_1)\rho(\boldsymbol{r}_2)\,\mathrm{d}\boldsymbol{r}_1\,\mathrm{d}\boldsymbol{r}_2 \\
&\qquad + \frac{N}{2}\int_{(a)}\int_{(a)} \frac{e^2}{r_{12}}\,\rho(\boldsymbol{r}_1)\rho(\boldsymbol{r}_2)\,\mathrm{d}\boldsymbol{r}_1\,\mathrm{d}\boldsymbol{r}_2 \\
&= \tfrac{1}{2}\sum_{a\neq b}^N\sum^N \frac{e^2}{R_{ab}} + \frac{N}{2}\int_{(a)}\int_{(a)} \frac{e^2}{r_{12}}\,\rho(\boldsymbol{r}_1)\rho(\boldsymbol{r}_2)\,\mathrm{d}\boldsymbol{r}_1\,\mathrm{d}\boldsymbol{r}_2.
\end{aligned} \tag{9.66}$$

The last two terms in equation (9.57) cannot be reduced. Adding (9.65) and (9.66) to these, we find

$$NE_0 = 2\sum_{\boldsymbol{k}} \varepsilon(\boldsymbol{k}) + \frac{N}{2}\int_{(a)}\int_{(a)} \frac{e^2}{r_{12}}\, \rho(\boldsymbol{r}_1)\rho(\boldsymbol{r}_2)\mathrm{d}\boldsymbol{r}_1\, \mathrm{d}\boldsymbol{r}_2$$

$$-\sum_{\boldsymbol{k}}\sum_{\boldsymbol{k}'}\iint \frac{e^2}{r_{12}}\, \psi_{\boldsymbol{k}}^*(\boldsymbol{r}_1)\psi_{\boldsymbol{k}'}^*(\boldsymbol{r}_2)\psi_{\boldsymbol{k}}(\boldsymbol{r}_2)\psi_{\boldsymbol{k}'}(\boldsymbol{r}_1)\mathrm{d}\boldsymbol{r}_1\, \mathrm{d}\boldsymbol{r}_2. \qquad (9.67)$$

It remains to evaluate the terms in this expression, which can only be done approximately for a real metal. If we use the formula (9.53) for $\varepsilon(\boldsymbol{k})$, which is a very good approximation for the alkali metals, we obtain

$$2\sum_{\boldsymbol{k}} \varepsilon(\boldsymbol{k}) = N(\varepsilon_0 + \alpha E_{\mathrm{F}}), \qquad (9.68)$$

where E_{F} is again the free-electron Fermi energy, given in equation (9.55).

We have seen that the wave functions of the occupied states in sodium, and, to a lesser extent, in the other alkali metals, are very nearly free-electron functions. Let us therefore use the free-electron approximation to evaluate the remaining two terms of (9.67). Since these terms have opposite signs, it is probable that the errors introduced in this way will partially cancel each other. Now,

$$\tfrac{1}{2}\int_{(a)}\int_{(a)} \frac{e^2}{r_{12}}\, \rho(\boldsymbol{r}_1)\rho(\boldsymbol{r}_2)\mathrm{d}\boldsymbol{r}_1\, \mathrm{d}\boldsymbol{r}_2 \qquad (9.69)$$

is just the self-potential energy of a charge distribution of density $e\rho(\boldsymbol{r})$ within an atomic polyhedron. In the free-electron approximation,

$$\rho(\boldsymbol{r}) = \frac{N}{v} = \frac{3}{4\pi r_{\mathrm{s}}^3}, \qquad (9.70)$$

so that (9.69) becomes

$$\frac{9e^2}{2(4\pi r_{\mathrm{s}}^3)^2}\int_{(a)}\int_{(a)} \frac{\mathrm{d}\boldsymbol{r}_1\, \mathrm{d}\boldsymbol{r}_2}{r_{12}}. \qquad (9.71)$$

If we use the atomic sphere approximation the integral can be evaluated immediately by the method described in Appendix 4. When the region of integration is a sphere of radius r_{s}, we have

$$\iint \frac{\mathrm{d}\boldsymbol{r}_1\, \mathrm{d}\boldsymbol{r}_2}{r_{12}} = 32\pi^2 \int_0^{r_{\mathrm{s}}} r\,\mathrm{d}r \int_0^{r} r^2\,\mathrm{d}r$$

$$= 32\pi^2\, \frac{r_{\mathrm{s}}^5}{15}. \qquad (9.72)$$

The Coulomb term in (9.67) is, therefore,

$$\frac{9e^2N}{2(4\pi r_s^3)^2}\,\frac{32\pi^2}{15}\,r_s^5 = \frac{3e^2N}{5r_s}, \tag{9.73}$$

which, in atomic units, becomes

$$\frac{1.2}{r_s}\,N \text{ ryd.} \tag{9.74}$$

The last term in (9.67), the *exchange energy*, has already been evaluated in the free-electron approximation: it is NE_x [see equation (7.53)], which is, in atomic units,

$$-\frac{0.916}{r_s}\,N \text{ ryd.} \tag{9.75}$$

Adding (9.68), (9.74), and (9.75), and dividing right through by N, we finally obtain the average energy E_0 per electron, as a function of r_s, in the form

$$\begin{aligned} E_0(r_s) &= \varepsilon_0(r_s)+\alpha E_F(r_s)+\frac{1.2}{r_s}-\frac{0.916}{r_s} \text{ ryd} \\ &= \varepsilon_0(r_s)+\alpha\frac{2.21}{r_s^2}+\frac{0.284}{r_s} \text{ ryd,} \end{aligned} \tag{9.76}$$

where r_s is measured in Bohr units. Apart from the use of the free-electron approximation in the Coulomb and exchange terms, the only real approximation has been the replacement of the atomic polyhedron by a sphere. Wigner and Seitz have investigated the latter approximation in detail and find that its effects are completely negligible. Of course, E_0 is just the average energy given by a total wave function consisting of a single determinant of one-electron functions. It is a very good approximation to the Hartree-Fock average energy, but yields a cohesive energy which is much too small. The calculated value of the cohesive energy of sodium, obtained by subtracting the minimum value of E_0 from $-I$, is only about 7 kcal/mole, compared with the experimental value of 26 kcal/mole. This is understandable, for we have already seen that the first two terms of E_0 *alone* (the value of α is so close to unity for sodium that it is immaterial whether α is included or not) yield a good value for the cohesive energy. It should be noted, in passing, that if we used a total wave function consisting of a *single product* of one-electron functions, that is, if we used the Hartree method, the only difference would be the omission of the exchange energy from E_0. Since the exchange energy is large and negative, E_0 would then be very much too high and there would theoretically be no cohesion at all. We have previously mentioned, in Chapter 7, that the principal advantage of the Hartree-Fock method is that it is an improvement on the Hartree method in cohesive energy calculations, but it is clearly not a sufficient improvement.

What E_0 still lacks is an energy term representing the effects of proper Coulomb correlations, which are neglected in the Hartree-Fock theory. We have seen that this theory accounts in some way for correlation between the positions of two electrons with parallel spins, but not at all for correlation between the positions of two electrons with antiparallel spins. The missing energy term, which is called the *correlation energy*, is therefore due principally to antiparallel spin correlations. It is not *entirely* due to these, however, for the parallel spin correlations which have been included are not proper Coulomb correlations, due to the Coulomb interaction of the electrons, but are more or less 'accidental' correlations due to the Pauli principle. In the following chapter we will describe one method of calculating the correlation energy, in which the Coulomb interaction is taken into account before the Pauli principle is applied, and it will be seen that the effect of the Pauli principle is then very much smaller. Meanwhile, we will devote a section to a general discussion of this energy term, before completing our account of the cohesive energy.

9.5. The Correlation Energy

The correlation energy may be defined, without any reference to electron spin, as follows:

the correlation energy is the total energy, calculated with proper allowance for Coulomb correlations, minus the Hartree-Fock energy.

We will denote the average correlation energy per electron by W.

The correlation energy is far more difficult to calculate than any of the other energy terms. Unlike the exchange energy, it is extremely difficult to calculate even for free electrons. However, for a free-electron gas (and hence, to a good approximation, for the valence electrons in the alkali metals) several more or less successful attempts have been made, and there is sufficient agreement among the various results to make us feel reasonably confident about the magnitude of the correlation energy. Before discussing these results, let us see what information we can get without any involved calculation.

We have previously remarked that a very good value of the cohesive energy of sodium is obtained by taking the average energy per electron to be the first two terms, $\varepsilon_0 + \alpha E_F$, of E_0 only. If our final cohesive energy is to be right, therefore, it is clear that the correlation energy must roughly cancel the Coulomb and exchange terms in E_0. That is to say, we must have, approximately,

$$W = -\frac{0.284}{r_s}\ \text{ryd}. \tag{9.77}$$

This might be taken as a semi-empirical formula for the correlation energy of a free-electron gas for electron densities such as occur in metals. Detailed calculation shows that this formula is not far wrong, but it is, of course, of little help to us, for in obtaining it we have made an assumption about the cohesive energy, which it is our object to calculate. None the less, it gives us some idea of what to expect. We note, in particular, that the correlation energy is of roughly the same magnitude as the cohesive energy, so that it is far from being negligible.

A quantity which can be calculated without difficulty is the correlation energy of a free-electron gas at *very low densities,* that is, for very large values of r_s. We know that the kinetic energy is inversely proportional to r_s^2, whereas the potential energy of the Coulomb interaction is inversely proportional to r_s. As r_s increases, therefore, the kinetic energy will eventually become negligible compared with the potential energy, and the electrons will tend to form a stable lattice. When this occurs the total energy may be calculated quite simply using the atomic sphere approximation. Remembering that in the free-electron model the electrons move in a uniform distribution of positive charge just sufficient to neutralize the electronic charge, we see that the energy per electron at very low densities is approximately that of an electron at the centre of a uniform spherical distribution of positive charge, of radius r_s and total charge e.

The density of the positive charge is $3e/4\pi r_s^3$. If an electron is at the centre of a sphere, of radius r, of positive charge of this density, the total charge within the sphere is

$$-e + \frac{4\pi}{3} r^3 \left(\frac{3e}{4\pi r_s^3}\right) = -e + \frac{er^3}{r_s^3},$$

and the potential at the surface is

$$\left(-1+\frac{r^3}{r_s^3}\right)\frac{e}{r}.$$

The energy required to bring a shell of positive charge, of thickness dr, from infinite distance is, therefore,

$$\left(\frac{r^3}{r_s^3}-1\right)\frac{e}{r}\frac{3e}{4\pi r_s^3}4\pi r^2\,\mathrm{d}r = \frac{3e^2}{r_s^3}\left(\frac{r^3}{r_s^3}-1\right)r\,\mathrm{d}r.$$

The energy per electron at very low densities is, thus,

$$\frac{3e^2}{r_s^3}\int_0^{r_s}\left(\frac{r^3}{r_s^3}-1\right)r\,\mathrm{d}r = -\frac{0.9e^2}{r_s}, \tag{9.78}$$

or, in atomic units,

$$-\frac{1.8}{r_s}\text{ ryd.} \tag{9.79}$$

Now, the energy per electron in the Hartree-Fock approximation [see equation (7.54)], if the kinetic energy is again ignored, is just the exchange energy,

$$-\frac{0.916}{r_s}\text{ ryd.}$$

The average correlation energy per electron at very low densities is, therefore

$$W = -\frac{1.8}{r_s}+\frac{0.916}{r_s} = -\frac{0.88}{r_s}\text{ ryd} \tag{9.80}$$

(the approximations used do not warrant the retention of more than two figures in the numerator).

This is not a semi-empirical result, but a straight-forward theoretical one which is correct for a free-electron gas at very low densities. It must be remembered, however, that the valence electrons in a metal only approximate to a free-electron gas at the densities normally occurring in solid metals (r_s lies between 3 and 6 B.u. for the alkali metals). When the interatomic spacing is very large, that is, when we have virtually a system of free atoms, the valence electron wave functions are very different from free-electron functions. The above formula therefore has no direct application. None the less, it is extremely useful in correlation energy calculations, for a reason which will become apparent.

A possible method of calculating the correlation energy which immediately suggests itself is by perturbation theory. The essential terms in the Hamiltonian of a free-electron gas are

$$-\frac{\hbar^2}{2m}\sum_{i=1}^{N}\nabla_i^2+\tfrac{1}{2}\sum_{i\neq j}^{N}\sum^{N}\frac{e^2}{r_{ij}}. \tag{9.81}$$

What has been omitted is a term representing the interaction of the electrons with the neutralizing uniform distribution of positive charge and the self-energy of this charge. If the second term were not present the eigenfunctions of (9.81) would be merely determinants of free-electron functions. It might therefore seem a simple matter to account for the second term, which includes the effects of all correlations, by perturbation theory. This has indeed been done, to various degrees of accuracy, but the task is by no means an easy one. This is because, although the first-order correction, which consists of the exchange energy and the Coulomb energy [the latter is cancelled by the two terms omitted from (9.81)], is obtained without difficulty, the second-order correction is found to diverge. A convergent result can only be obtained by including higher-order perturbation corrections, and, in fact, summing the whole perturbation series — this should, of course, give the energy with complete accuracy (see § 3.8), although certain approximations are required in practice.

The straightforward perturbation calculations are only valid at high densities ($r_s < 1$ B.u.), so that in order to obtain from them the correlation energy at actual metallic densities it is necessary to interpolate between the high density and low density limits — hence the utility of formula (9.80). The earliest interpolation formula of this sort was obtained by WIGNER [1934, 1938], which gave †

$$W = -\frac{0.88}{r_s+7.8}\text{ ryd.} \tag{9.82}$$

For sodium, with $r_s = 4$ B.u., this gives $W = -0.075$ ryd, which is very

† The formula originally given by Wigner was $W = -0.576/(r_s+5.1)$ ryd, but this, as Wigner [1938] himself pointed out, was based upon an incorrect low density limit. Formula (9.82) was given by Pines [1955] — it agrees with Wigner's result in the limit as $r_s \to 0$, and with formula (9.80) for very large r_s. Since Wigner claimed an accuracy of only 20 per cent for his formula, the correction resulting from the use of (9.82) is hardly significant.

close to the value -0.071 ryd, given by the semi-empirical formula (9.77). Wigner's formula has had so much success in cohesive energy calculations that it seems unlikely to be greatly in error, and more recent work bears this out. GELL-MANN and BRUECKNER [1957], for example, have recently made a calculation of the correlation energy of a free-electron gas which they claim to be perfectly accurate in the high density limit. This gives

$$W = 0.0622 \log r_s - 0.096 + O(r_s) \text{ ryd}, \tag{9.83}$$

the last term being very small and tending to zero with r_s. This formula is certainly wrong for low densities and for the densities occurring in actual metals, but for $r_s = 1$ B.u., ignoring the term $O(r_s)$, it gives $W = -0.096$ ryd, whereas formula (9.82) gives $W = -0.100$ ryd.

There have been other calculations of the correlation energy of a free-electron gas, based upon perturbation theory of infinite order, which we will not enumerate. In the following chapter, however, we will describe a method, due to Pines, which involves only second-order perturbation theory, because it uses the concept of *plasma oscillations* to reduce the effective range of the Coulomb interaction. The formula obtained by Pines, which is believed to be valid in the region of actual metallic densities, although not for very high or for very low densities, is

$$W = 0.031 \log r_s - 0.115 \text{ ryd}. \tag{9.84}$$

This gives values very close to those of formula (9.82) for r_s between 2 and 6 B.u. — for sodium, in particular, it gives $W = -0.072$ ryd.

9.6. Further Remarks on the Cohesive Energy

The final expression for the average energy per electron of an alkali metal, which we will denote by E, is thus

$$E(r_s) = \varepsilon_0(r_s) + \alpha \frac{2.21}{r_s^2} + \frac{0.284}{r_s} + W(r_s) \text{ ryd}, \tag{9.85}$$

where $W(r_s)$ is given by either (9.82) or (9.84). If we again denote by r_0 the atomic radius corresponding to the minimum value of E, then the cohesive energy per electron is

$$S = -I - E(r_0) \text{ ryd}, \tag{9.86}$$

where I is the ionization energy of a free atom. The calculated values of the cohesive energies and equilibrium atomic radii of the alkali metals, obtained in this way, are within a few per cent of the experimental values.

Other quantities which can be directly calculated from equation (9.85) are the *pressure* p and *compressibility* κ, at the absolute zero of temperature, for any value of r_s. If Ω is the volume of an atomic sphere, the pressure is given by

$$p = -\frac{\mathrm{d}E}{\mathrm{d}\Omega}, \tag{9.87}$$

and the compressibility by

$$\kappa = -\frac{1}{\Omega}\frac{\mathrm{d}\Omega}{\mathrm{d}p}. \tag{9.88}$$

Thus,

$$\frac{1}{\kappa} = -\Omega\frac{\mathrm{d}p}{\mathrm{d}\Omega} = \Omega\frac{\mathrm{d}^2E}{\mathrm{d}\Omega^2}, \tag{9.89}$$

or, since $\Omega = \frac{4}{3}\pi r_s^3$,

$$\frac{1}{\kappa} = \frac{1}{12\pi r_s}\frac{\mathrm{d}^2E}{\mathrm{d}r_s^2} - \frac{1}{6\pi r_s^2}\frac{\mathrm{d}E}{\mathrm{d}r_s}. \tag{9.90}$$

When $r_s = r_0$, the equilibrium atomic radius at zero temperature and pressure, we have $\mathrm{d}E/\mathrm{d}r_s = 0$, and

$$\frac{1}{\kappa} = \frac{1}{12\pi r_0}\left(\frac{\mathrm{d}^2E}{\mathrm{d}r_s^2}\right)_{r_s=r_0}. \tag{9.91}$$

The compressibilities of the alkali metals calculated by means of this formula again agree very well with the experimental values.

Equation (9.85) does not apply directly to the other monovalent metals, copper, silver, and gold, even though the valence electron wave functions in these metals approximate almost as closely to free-electron functions as they do in the alkali metals. This is because the ion-cores (and, in particular, the outermost d sub-shells) in copper, silver, and gold are so large that neighbouring cores overlap appreciably. It is therefore not permissible to treat the interaction of the ion-cores as if they were point charges, as we did in obtaining equation (9.85). Strictly speaking, the outermost d electrons in these metals should be treated in the same way as the valence electrons (see § 8.12), but, as the d electrons are by no means free, such a calculation is hardly possible at the present time. Some success has been obtained by simply adding on to E, as given in equation (9.85), a term representing the additional energy due to the overlapping of the ion-cores, which has been estimated using the Thomas-Fermi approximation; but we will not go into this.

Equation (9.85) applies only to monovalent metals (with small ion-cores), but it can easily be generalized to metals of any valency Z. If $\varepsilon_0(r_s)$ is again the eigenvalue of equation (9.10), subject to the same boundary condition (9.8), with $V(r)$ now the potential function of the *Z-times* ionized atom †, we obtain, for the average energy *per electron*,

$$E(r_s) = \varepsilon_0(r_s) + \alpha \frac{2.21Z^{\frac{2}{3}}}{r_s^2} + \frac{1.2Z}{r_s} - \frac{0.916Z^{\frac{1}{3}}}{r_s} + W(Z^{-\frac{1}{3}}r_s). \qquad (9.92)$$

The kinetic, exchange, and correlation energies are obtained, in the free-electron approximation, from those of a monovalent metal simply by substituting $Z^{-\frac{1}{3}}r_s$ for r_s. The Coulomb energy *per atom* is still given by expression (9.69), but now, in the free-electron approximation,

$$\rho(r) = \frac{3Z}{4\pi r_s^3}, \qquad (9.93)$$

so that the total Coulomb energy is given by (9.74) multiplied by Z^2. This leads to the expression $1.2Z/r_s$ for the Coulomb energy *per electron*.

We should, of course, expect equation (9.92) to be a very much worse approximation for a polyvalent metal, whatever the size of the ion-core, than it is for an alkali metal. This is because the electrons in a polyvalent metal occupy states in more than one Brillouin zone, and equation (9.53) for $\varepsilon(\boldsymbol{k})$ is only expected to hold near the centre of the first zone. Nor is it likely that the free-electron approximation will apply so well to the electronic interaction terms. None the less, remarkably good results have been obtained by this method (see Brooks [1958]) for polyvalent metals with small ion-cores, such as magnesium and aluminium. This suggests that, for such metals, in spite of the effects of the zone boundaries, the valence electrons are, in some respects, still very nearly free.

† The use of this potential function cannot be justified by the effects of Coulomb correlations, since it is clear that in the case of a polyvalent metal there must be on the average Z electrons in an atomic polyhedron. The justification is the fact, mentioned previously, that the wave function ψ_0 has been found to be virtually the same whether or not the self-consistent field of the electrons is included in $V(r)$.

9.7. The Quantum Defect Method

The purpose of the Quantum Defect Method is to obtain the energy levels of a valence electron in a metal directly from the observed energy levels in a free atom, without the necessity of constructing an ion-core field $V(r)$. In order to give the bases of the method in as simple a form as possible, we will confine our discussion to the state ψ_0 of lowest energy in the metal, although the method has been applied to other states.

We have remarked in § 9.4 that, outside the effective radius of the ion-core, which is small compared with the atomic radius, the potential function $V(r)$ of a monovalent metal ion is very nearly hydrogenic — that is to say, for practical purposes,

$$V(r) = -e^2/r. \tag{9.94}$$

This means that, outside the ion-core, and hence in the region where it is required to fit the boundary condition (9.8), equation (9.10) is just the hydrogen atom equation

$$\frac{\mathrm{d}^2\psi_0}{\mathrm{d}r^2} + \frac{2}{r}\frac{\mathrm{d}\psi_0}{\mathrm{d}r} + \frac{2m}{\hbar^2}\left(\varepsilon_0 + \frac{e^2}{r}\right)\psi_0 = 0, \tag{9.95}$$

or, in atomic units,

$$\frac{\mathrm{d}^2\psi_0}{\mathrm{d}r^2} + \frac{2}{r}\frac{\mathrm{d}\psi_0}{\mathrm{d}r} + \left(\varepsilon_0 + \frac{2}{r}\right)\psi_0 = 0. \tag{9.96}$$

The solutions of this equation are known in analytical form, so that it would seem an easy matter to fit the boundary condition (9.8). The difficulty is, however, that for each value of ε_0 there are two independent solutions, the general solution being an arbitrary linear combination of the two. The problem is thus to obtain the correct linear combination, which will join smoothly to the wave function inside the core for the same value of ε_0. It has been found possible to do this without knowing anything about the wave function inside the core, by making use of the experimentally determined *quantum defect*.

The energy levels of a hydrogen atom are given, in atomic units, by the formula

$$\varepsilon = -\frac{1}{n^2}\,\text{ryd}, \tag{9.97}$$

where n is an integer called the *principal quantum number*. It is found that the energy levels of the s states of the valence electron in an alkali atom can be expressed by the formula

$$\varepsilon = -\frac{1}{(n-\delta)^2}\ \text{ryd}, \tag{9.98}$$

where n is again the principal quantum number, and δ, which varies only slightly with n, is called the *quantum defect* (the same formula applies to p states, d states, and so on, with different values of the quantum defect, but in order to find ψ_0 we need only consider s states). The quantum defect is a smooth and slowly varying function of ε, which may be expressed very accurately by a polynomial of low degree, such as

$$\delta = a+b\varepsilon+c\varepsilon^2 \tag{9.99}$$

(for sodium, the values of the coefficients are, roughly, $a = 1.35$, $b = -0.06$, $c = 0.01$). The experimental values of ε form a discrete set, of course, but having obtained equation (9.99) we may use it to *define* the quantum defect for *any* value of ε. The energies ε_0 in which we are interested lie lower than the energy of the normal state of a valence electron in a free atom, which is the lowest energy for which we have an experimental value of δ, so that it is necessary to use equation (9.99) as an extrapolation formula.

Now, the general solution of equation (9.96), for a given ε_0, may be written

$$\psi_0(r) = AF(r)+BG(r), \tag{9.100}$$

where A and B are arbitrary constants and $F(r)$ and $G(r)$ are known, independent solutions. These solutions may be chosen in any number of ways, but we assume here that two particular functions have been chosen, which we will not specify in detail, except to say that $F(r)$ is finite at the origin while $G(r)$ becomes infinite there. We know that, when ε_0 is one of the free-atom energy levels, the correct linear combination of $F(r)$ and $G(r)$ must tend to zero as r tends to infinity. The function $\psi_0(r)$ given by equation (9.100) then represents the free-atom wave function outside the ion-core, for this particular ε_0, and so must necessarily join smoothly to the (unknown) wave function inside the core. The correct ratio B/A in this case is found, by analysis which is much too complicated for inclusion here, to be

$$\frac{B}{A} = -\tan \pi\delta. \tag{9.101}$$

It is then *assumed* that, for all the values of ε_0 in which we are interested, the ratio B/A for the function $\psi_0(r)$ outside the core, which joins smoothly to the true wave function inside the core, is given by the same formula, when δ is the extrapolated quantum defect defined by equation (9.99), with $\varepsilon = \varepsilon_0$. The value of r_s, lying outside the ion-core, for which the derivative of $\psi_0(r)$ vanishes, can then be found directly from (9.100). In this way, ε_0 is obtained as a function of r_s without ever solving the Schrödinger equation inside the ion-core. Although the values of the cohesive energies and equilibrium atomic radii of the alkali metals given by this method are in remarkably good agreement with experiment, the assumptions involved require further justification. For such justification, and a more detailed description of the method, interested readers are referred to the articles by HAM [1955] and BROOKS [1958].

The quantum defects of the p states of a valence electron in a free atom have also been used, with a modification of the foregoing method, to solve equation (9.35) for $P(r)$ outside the ion-core. This permits the quantity α to be found from equation (9.51), which only requires a knowledge of $P(r)$ in the vicinity of the surface of the atomic sphere. There appears to be one difficulty here, however, for the calculation of the factor γ requires that $u_0(r)$ be normalized, and this would seem to require a knowledge of $u_0(r)$ throughout the whole atomic sphere. It is an interesting fact that this is not so, provided $u_0(r)$ is known, outside the ion-core, for a range of values of ε_0. At a given value of r, it is clear that the value of the function $u_0(r)$ will vary with ε_0, and hence it may be differentiated with respect to ε_0. SILVERMAN [1952] has proved that, with $f(r) = ru_0(r)$ as before,

$$\int_0^{r_s} f^2 \, \mathrm{d}r = -\left[rf(r) \frac{\partial}{\partial r} \left(\frac{1}{r} \frac{\partial f}{\partial \varepsilon_0} \right) \right]_{r=r_s}. \tag{9.102}$$

This integral determines the normalization of $u_0(r)$, and we see that its evaluation only requires a knowledge of how the function $f(r)$ varies with ε_0 and with r outside the ion-core.

References

BARDEEN, J., 1938, J. Chem. Phys. **6**, 367.

BROOKS, H., 1953, Phys. Rev. **91**, 1027; 1958, Nuovo Cimento Suppl. **7**, No. 2, 165.

GELL-MANN, M., and K. A. BRUECKNER, 1957, Phys. Rev. **106**, 364.

HAM, F. S., 1955, Solid State Physics *1* (Academic Press, New York), p. 127.

PINES, D., 1955, Solid State Physics *1* (Academic Press, New York), p. 367.

SILVERMAN, R. A., 1952, Phys. Rev. ***85***, 227.

WIGNER, E., 1934, Phys. Rev. ***46***, 1002; 1938, Trans. Faraday Soc. ***34***, 678.

WIGNER, E., and F. SEITZ, 1933, Phys. Rev. ***43***, 804; 1934, *Ibid.* ***46***, 509.

CHAPTER 10

PLASMA OSCILLATIONS IN METALS

10.1. Introduction: Qualitative Description of Plasma Oscillations

In the previous chapter we showed how important it is to take proper account of Coulomb correlations in calculating the cohesive energy of a metal, but we also noted how difficult it is to do this, even in the case of free electrons. The principal difficulty is due to the fact that the Coulomb interaction of the electrons is so strong and of such long range that its effects cannot be calculated by ordinary perturbation theory. On the other hand, we saw in Chapter 7 that, as far as properties which depend only upon the *density of states in energy* are concerned, very good results can be obtained by treating the electrons as non-interacting particles — or, in the Hartree theory, by considering only the average effect of the electronic interaction. This *independent particle* approximation is the basis of nearly all band structure calculations — in our account of Brillouin zone theory it is implicit in the assumption [see equation (8.71)] of the same potential function $V(\boldsymbol{r})$ for all one-electron states.

During recent years a theory of the interaction of electrons in metals has been developed which offers a simple justification of the independent particle approximation, and, at the same time, permits the correlation energy to be calculated using ordinary second-order perturbation theory. This is the theory of *plasma oscillations* in metals, due to Bohm and Pines [1951, 1952, 1953], Pines [1953]. Although the qualitative ideas of the theory are now widely accepted, the detailed quantum-mechanical development is still in some dispute, so that the subject matter of the present chapter is rather more speculative than what has gone before. None the less, the basic principles of the theory are so simple, and its results are of such practical importance, that it has been thought worth while to include a brief account of this theory in the present work. A more complete account, which is still not too difficult, may be found in an article by the author (Raimes [1957]).

Any highly ionized gas, that is, a system composed of a large number of positive ions and virtually free electrons, with zero total charge, is called a *plasma*. Such plasmas, which occur in gas discharge tubes, have been studied both theoretically and experimentally for many years, and interest in them has lately intensified owing to their use in thermonuclear devices. However, it is clear that a metal may also be regarded as a plasma, for we have seen that a metal is a system of positive ions arranged on a crystal lattice, together with valence or conduction electrons which are more or less free to travel throughout the lattice. We know that the ions in a metal have a slight vibrational motion, but this may be neglected for most purposes and the ions regarded as static. Although it is formally possible to include the ion-core field of a metal in the quantum mechanical theory of plasma oscillations, accurate numerical results have so far been obtained only in the case of a free-electron gas, and we will restrict ourselves to this — we have seen in the previous chapter that, as far as the electronic interaction terms are concerned, the free-electron approximation may be expected to apply reasonably well to a number of metals. In this approximation the system of ion-cores is replaced by a uniform distribution of positive charge, which we will refer to as the *background* of positive charge, whose density is equal to the average electronic charge density, but of opposite sign.

The charge density of the positive background and electrons together is on the average zero, but the electrons are always in motion (we refer to this as the *thermal* motion, although it occurs even at the absolute zero of temperature), so that the electron density is, in fact, continually varying throughout the plasma. Now suppose that, as a result of a chance fluctuation in the thermal motion, the electronic charge density in some region is reduced below the average. The positive background is no longer neutralized in that region and the resulting positive charge attracts neighbouring electrons. The tendency is to restore charge neutrality, but the attracted electrons acquire momentum and so overshoot the mark — that is to say, more electrons accumulate in the region than are necessary to neutralize the positive charge. The excess negative charge thus created repels electrons outwards again, and so oscillations are set up. These longitudinal oscillations of the electron gas, analogous to sound waves, are called *plasma oscillations*.

The approximation of replacing the ions by a uniform distribution of positive charge has also been used in the case of gas discharge plasmas. There is, however, an important difference between gas discharge plasmas and metallic plasmas. In the former the density (of the order of 10^{12}/cc) of the electrons is so small that their motion may be treated by classical mechanics or Maxwell-Boltzmann statistics. The motion of the high density (of the order of 10^{23}/cc) electron gas in a metal, however, must properly be treated by quantum mechanics or Fermi-Dirac statistics. None the less, a useful qualitative picture of plasma oscillations in metals, and, as we shall see, even reasonable quantitative results, can be obtained by classical methods.

10.2. Elementary Classical Theory: The Plasma Frequency

Let us denote by n the *average* density of electrons, so that the average electronic charge density is $-en$, and the uniform charge density of the positive background is en. In order to obtain the frequency of plasma oscillation in as simple a way as possible, let us at first neglect the thermal motion of the electrons. We assume that the electrons are initially at rest and distributed with uniform density n, and are then displaced radially outwards from some point in the plasma, which we take to be the origin O. The displacement $\xi(r)$ is a function of r, the distance from O, and we will suppose this function and its gradient to be everywhere small. As a result of the displacement the number of electrons which leave a sphere of radius r, centred at O, is very nearly $4\pi nr^2\xi(r)$ — the number originally contained within a shell of thickness $\xi(r)$ at the surface of the sphere. Owing to the positive background, therefore, the sphere is left with the charge $4\pi enr^2\xi(r)$. The electric field at distance r from O is consequently of magnitude $4\pi en\xi(r)$ and directed radially outwards, so that each electron experiences a force $-4\pi e^2n\xi(r)$ radially outwards. This force must be equated to $m\ddot{\xi}(r)$, where m is as usual the mass of an electron and $\ddot{\xi}(r)$ is its outward acceleration, so that

$$\ddot{\xi}+\left(\frac{4\pi e^2 n}{m}\right)\xi = 0. \tag{10.1}$$

This is the equation of simple harmonic motion, and tells us that the electrons will oscillate about their equilibrium positions with angular frequency

$$\omega_{\mathrm{p}} = \left(\frac{4\pi e^2 n}{m}\right)^{\frac{1}{2}}, \tag{10.2}$$

which is called the *plasma frequency*. For a typical gas discharge plasma ω_{p} is of the order of 10^{10} radians/sec, whereas for a metal it is of the order of 10^{16} radians/sec.

Of course, we have ignored the thermal motion of the electrons in the foregoing work, except in so far as thermal fluctuations cause a departure from uniform electronic density and hence initiate plasma oscillation, but the result remains plausible if we regard the displacement as being a 'drift' displacement superimposed upon the random thermal motion. When proper allowance is made for the thermal motion it is found that the angular frequency of oscillation ω is very nearly ω_p for long waves, but increases as the wavelength λ decreases. The *dispersion relation* obtained by classical methods is, approximately,

$$\omega^2 = \omega_p^2 + k^2 \langle v_i^2 \rangle, \tag{10.3}$$

where $k(= 2\pi/\lambda)$ is the wave number of the plasma wave and $\langle v_i^2 \rangle$ is the average of the squared velocities of the electrons. The dispersion relation given by the quantum-mechanical theory is the same as this as far as terms of the second order in k.

In fact, the dispersion is not very great, ω never differing from ω_p by more than a few per cent, because there is an upper limit to k, which we will denote by k_c, for wave numbers above which plasma oscillations do not occur. It will be seen in the following section that the effect of the thermal motion is to disrupt the plasma oscillations and to prevent their occurrence with short wavelengths, so that there is a lower limit to the wavelength of plasma oscillation. That this must be so also follows simply from the corpuscular nature of the electron gas. It is meaningless to speak of organized oscillations of the latter with wavelengths smaller than the average interelectronic distance, which is a few ångström units in metals. We therefore expect k_c^{-1} to be of the order of 1Å, and this is borne out by calculation which takes into account the effect of the thermal motion.

10.3. A More Detailed Classical Theory

It is not our intention in this book to give a complete description of the quantum-mechanical theory of plasma oscillations, although we shall use the results of this theory and attempt to make them plausible. It will be helpful in the latter task if we first present a more detailed classical theory than that given above. This introduces several concepts which are used in the quantum-mechanical theory, and also clearly demonstrates the disruptive effect of the thermal motion on the plasma oscillations.

It is convenient for purposes of computation to assume that the metal is in the form of a cube of unit volume. In our free-electron model, then, we have n electrons in a cubic box of unit volume, which also contains a uniform distribution of positive charge of density en. It is our object to show that the Fourier coefficients of the electron density oscillate approximately with angular frequency ω_p, provided the wavelength is sufficiently long. To do this we must first of all expand the potential energy of the electrons in Fourier series within the box.

We write the potential energy due to the Coulomb interaction between the ith and jth electrons as follows:

$$\frac{e^2}{r_{ij}} = \sum_{\boldsymbol{k}} c_{\boldsymbol{k}} \mathrm{e}^{\mathrm{i}\boldsymbol{k}\cdot(\boldsymbol{r}_i - \boldsymbol{r}_j)}, \tag{10.4}$$

where

$$\boldsymbol{k} = 2\pi(n_1\boldsymbol{e}_1 + n_2\boldsymbol{e}_2 + n_3\boldsymbol{e}_3),$$

$\boldsymbol{e}_1$, $\boldsymbol{e}_2$, $\boldsymbol{e}_3$ being unit vectors along three mutually orthogonal edges of the cube, and n_1, n_2, n_3 being integers — the sum is thus a triple sum over all the positive and negative integral values of n_1, n_2, n_3, including zero. To determine the coefficients $c_{\boldsymbol{k}}$ we multiply both sides of equation (10.4) by $\exp[\mathrm{i}\boldsymbol{k}' \cdot (\boldsymbol{r}_j - \boldsymbol{r}_i)]$ and integrate with respect to $\boldsymbol{r}_j$ over the volume of the box; thus

$$e^2 \int \frac{\mathrm{e}^{\mathrm{i}\boldsymbol{k}'\cdot(\boldsymbol{r}_j - \boldsymbol{r}_i)}}{r_{ij}} \mathrm{d}\boldsymbol{r}_j = \sum_{\boldsymbol{k}} c_{\boldsymbol{k}} \int \mathrm{e}^{\mathrm{i}(\boldsymbol{k}-\boldsymbol{k}')\cdot(\boldsymbol{r}_i - \boldsymbol{r}_j)} \mathrm{d}\boldsymbol{r}_j. \tag{10.5}$$

The integral on the left-hand side is similar to that appearing in the expression (7.36), and may be evaluated in the same way. We find

$$\int \frac{\mathrm{e}^{\mathrm{i}\boldsymbol{k}'\cdot(\boldsymbol{r}_j - \boldsymbol{r}_i)}}{r_{ij}} \mathrm{d}\boldsymbol{r}_j = \frac{4\pi}{k'^2}. \tag{10.6}$$

The integral on the right-hand side of (10.5) is elementary, and has the value zero, unless $\boldsymbol{k} = \boldsymbol{k}'$, when it has the value unity, since the box is of unit volume. We have, finally,

$$c_{\boldsymbol{k}} = \frac{4\pi e^2}{k^2}, \tag{10.7}$$

except when $\boldsymbol{k} = \boldsymbol{0}$. Integration of equation (10.4) gives immediately

$$c_0 = e^2 \int \frac{\mathrm{d}\boldsymbol{r}_j}{r_{ij}}, \tag{10.8}$$

which is just the potential energy of the ith electron due to a uniform distribution of one *electronic* charge throughout the box. We may thus write the total potential energy of the ith electron, due to its interaction with all the other electrons *and* with the positive background, as

$$U(\boldsymbol{r}_i) = \sum_{j\neq i}\sum_{\boldsymbol{k}}{}' \frac{4\pi e^2}{k^2}\, \mathrm{e}^{\mathrm{i}\boldsymbol{k}\cdot(\boldsymbol{r}_i-\boldsymbol{r}_j)}, \qquad (10.9)$$

the prime indicating that the terms with $\boldsymbol{k} = \boldsymbol{0}$ are excluded, these terms being cancelled by the effect of the positive background.

The total force † exerted on the ith electron is

$$-\operatorname{grad}_i U(\boldsymbol{r}_i) \equiv -\left(\boldsymbol{e}_1 \frac{\partial}{\partial x_i} + \boldsymbol{e}_2 \frac{\partial}{\partial y_i} + \boldsymbol{e}_3 \frac{\partial}{\partial z_i}\right) U(\boldsymbol{r}_i),$$

and this may be equated to $m\dot{\boldsymbol{v}}_i$, where $\boldsymbol{v}_i = \dot{\boldsymbol{r}}_i$ is the velocity of the electron. We find

$$\dot{\boldsymbol{v}}_i = -\frac{4\pi e^2 \mathrm{i}}{m} \sum_j \sum_{\boldsymbol{k}}{}' \frac{\boldsymbol{k}}{k^2}\, \mathrm{e}^{\mathrm{i}\boldsymbol{k}\cdot(\boldsymbol{r}_i-\boldsymbol{r}_j)}, \qquad (10.10)$$

in which it is unnecessary to omit explicitly the term with $j = i$, since this is automatically zero owing to the symmetrical distribution of the $\boldsymbol{k}$ vectors.

Now let us consider the *actual* distribution of electronic charge at a given instant, by which we mean the discontinuous distribution represented by the instantaneous positions of all the electrons, and not a local volume average, which is usually implied. Regarding the electrons as point particles, the actual electronic charge density may be written $-e\rho(\boldsymbol{r})$, where

$$\rho(\boldsymbol{r}) = \sum_i \delta(\boldsymbol{r}-\boldsymbol{r}_i), \qquad (10.11)$$

$\delta(\boldsymbol{r}-\boldsymbol{r}_i)$ being the Dirac δ-function†† and the sum being over all the electrons.

---

† It should be noted that here, as in the calculation of the cohesive energy, we are neglecting *magnetic* forces, which are of a very much smaller order of magnitude than the electrostatic forces.

†† This is the three-dimensional form of the function defined on p. 214. It may be defined similarly by the relations $\delta(\boldsymbol{r}-\boldsymbol{r}_i) = 0$, for $\boldsymbol{r} \neq \boldsymbol{r}_i$, and $\int \delta(\boldsymbol{r}-\boldsymbol{r}_i)\mathrm{d}\boldsymbol{r} = 1$, the integration being throughout any region containing the point $\boldsymbol{r}_i$. The principal property of this function is expressed in the equation

$$\int f(\boldsymbol{r})\,\delta(\boldsymbol{r}-\boldsymbol{r}_i)\,\mathrm{d}\boldsymbol{r} = f(\boldsymbol{r}_i),$$

where $f(\boldsymbol{r})$ is an arbitrary function and the integration is again throughout any region containing $\boldsymbol{r}_i$.

The function $\rho(\boldsymbol{r})$, which we will call the *particle density* [the number of electrons in any region is obtained by integrating $\rho(\boldsymbol{r})$ throughout the region], may also be expanded formally in Fourier series within the box. Thus, we write

$$\rho(\boldsymbol{r}) = \sum_{\boldsymbol{k}} \rho_{\boldsymbol{k}} \mathrm{e}^{\mathrm{i}\boldsymbol{k}\cdot\boldsymbol{r}}, \tag{10.12}$$

where

$$\rho_{\boldsymbol{k}} = \int \rho(\boldsymbol{r}) \mathrm{e}^{-\mathrm{i}\boldsymbol{k}\cdot\boldsymbol{r}} \mathrm{d}\boldsymbol{r} = \sum_{i} \mathrm{e}^{-\mathrm{i}\boldsymbol{k}\cdot\boldsymbol{r}_i}. \tag{10.13}$$

$\rho_{\boldsymbol{0}}$, the Fourier coefficient with $\boldsymbol{k} = \boldsymbol{0}$, is just the average electron density n, and the other coefficients represent fluctuations about this average density. In terms of these density fluctuations equation (10.10) becomes

$$\dot{\boldsymbol{v}}_i = -\frac{4\pi e^2 \mathrm{i}}{m} \sum_{\boldsymbol{k}}{}' \frac{\boldsymbol{k}}{k^2} \rho_{\boldsymbol{k}} \mathrm{e}^{\mathrm{i}\boldsymbol{k}\cdot\boldsymbol{r}_i}. \tag{10.14}$$

Now, from equation (10.13) we have

$$\dot{\rho}_{\boldsymbol{k}} = -\mathrm{i} \sum_{i} (\boldsymbol{k}\cdot\boldsymbol{v}_i) \mathrm{e}^{-\mathrm{i}\boldsymbol{k}\cdot\boldsymbol{r}_i}, \tag{10.15}$$

and

$$\ddot{\rho}_{\boldsymbol{k}} = -\sum_{i} [(\boldsymbol{k}\cdot\boldsymbol{v}_i)^2 + \mathrm{i}\boldsymbol{k}\cdot\dot{\boldsymbol{v}}_i] \mathrm{e}^{-\mathrm{i}\boldsymbol{k}\cdot\boldsymbol{r}_i}. \tag{10.16}$$

Substitution of $\dot{\boldsymbol{v}}_i$ from equation (10.14) gives

$$\ddot{\rho}_{\boldsymbol{k}} = -\sum_{i} (\boldsymbol{k}\cdot\boldsymbol{v}_i)^2 \mathrm{e}^{-\mathrm{i}\boldsymbol{k}\cdot\boldsymbol{r}_i} - \frac{4\pi e^2}{m} \sum_{i} \sum_{\boldsymbol{k}'}{}' \frac{\boldsymbol{k}\cdot\boldsymbol{k}'}{k'^2} \rho_{\boldsymbol{k}'} \mathrm{e}^{\mathrm{i}(\boldsymbol{k}'-\boldsymbol{k})\cdot\boldsymbol{r}_i}. \tag{10.17}$$

The last term of this equation may be split into two parts, consisting of those terms of the double summation with $\boldsymbol{k}' = \boldsymbol{k}$ and those with $\boldsymbol{k}' \neq \boldsymbol{k}$ respectively, as follows:

$$-\frac{4\pi e^2 n}{m} \rho_{\boldsymbol{k}} - \frac{4\pi e^2}{m} \sum_{\boldsymbol{k}'\neq\boldsymbol{k}}{}' \frac{\boldsymbol{k}\cdot\boldsymbol{k}'}{k'^2} \rho_{\boldsymbol{k}'} \rho_{\boldsymbol{k}-\boldsymbol{k}'}. \tag{10.18}$$

We expect the Fourier coefficients $\rho_{\boldsymbol{k}}$, for $\boldsymbol{k} \neq \boldsymbol{0}$, to be very small compared with n, since there is a large number of electrons and they are more or less randomly situated. The *phase factors* $\exp(-\mathrm{i}\boldsymbol{k}\cdot\boldsymbol{r}_i)$ are complex numbers of unit modulus, and $\rho_{\boldsymbol{k}}$ is thus the sum of a large number of unit vectors with random directions in the complex plane — for each vector with a given direction there is one with very nearly the opposite direction, so that the sum must generally be small. It is also clear that the time average of $\rho_{\boldsymbol{k}}$ is zero. It is reasonable to suggest, therefore, that the second term in (10.18), which is a sum of products of two Fourier coefficients, will be small compared with the first, at least for small values of k. Admittedly, this is not entirely obvious, for the second term is an infinite sum, but detailed consideration (see BOHM and PINES [1952]) shows that it is indeed very small compared with the first term, for the small values of k which will concern us, and we will neglect it. This is called the *random phase approximation* by Bohm and Pines, and is also a central feature of their quantum-mechanical theory of plasma oscillations.

Using the random phase approximation, then, and formula (10.2) for ω_{p}, equation (10.17) becomes

$$\ddot{\rho}_{\boldsymbol{k}} = -\sum_i (\boldsymbol{k}\cdot\boldsymbol{v}_i)^2 \mathrm{e}^{-\mathrm{i}\boldsymbol{k}\cdot\boldsymbol{r}_i} - \omega_{\mathrm{p}}^2 \rho_{\boldsymbol{k}}. \tag{10.19}$$

The first term on the right does not involve the accelerations and would be present even if the electrons did not interact — it arises simply from the thermal motion of the electrons. The second term represents the effect of the electronic interactions. It is clear that, for sufficiently small values of k, the first term, which contains the factor k^2, may be neglected in comparison with the second, giving

$$\ddot{\rho}_{\boldsymbol{k}} + \omega_{\mathrm{p}}^2 \rho_{\boldsymbol{k}} = 0. \tag{10.20}$$

Thus we see that, for sufficiently long wavelengths, the Fourier coefficients of the electron density oscillate with the plasma frequency; which is another way of expressing the result obtained in § 10.2. Equation (10.19) tells us more than this, however, for it shows explicitly the effect of the random thermal motion of the electrons, and enables us to fix an approximate upper bound to the wave number of plasma oscillation. The equation may be written

$$\ddot{\rho}_{\boldsymbol{k}} = -\sum_i [(\boldsymbol{k}\cdot\boldsymbol{v}_i)^2 + \omega_{\mathrm{p}}^2] \mathrm{e}^{-\mathrm{i}\boldsymbol{k}\cdot\boldsymbol{r}_i}, \tag{10.21}$$

and we deduce that plasma oscillation may occur provided the wave number k is such that

$$\omega_{\mathrm{p}} \gg k v_0, \tag{10.22}$$

where v_0 is the velocity at the top of the Fermi distribution, that is, the maximum velocity of any electron at the absolute zero of temperature.

In other words, using the notation introduced in § 10.2, we may write, very roughly,

$$k_c \approx \omega_p / v_0. \tag{10.23}$$

This gives a value of k_c^{-1} for a typical metal of about an ångström unit, in agreement with our previous statement.

It must be remembered that classical methods, which are not strictly applicable to the electrons in a metal, have been used in the foregoing work. None the less, the results of the quantum-mechanical theory of plasma oscillations are found to be in essential agreement with those obtained above. Of course, (10.23) only provides a very rough upper bound to the wave number of plasma oscillation. In fact, owing to the presence of the first term on the right-hand side of equation (10.19), the density fluctuations ρ_k will never quite oscillate harmonically, even when k is small. However, it is possible to split ρ_k into two independent components, one of which represents the collective motion, that is, the plasma oscillations, and the other represents the random thermal motion. The first component predominates at long wavelengths, satisfying the condition (10.22), and, within the random phase approximation, is found to oscillate harmonically with angular frequency given approximately by the dispersion relation (10.3). We will not go into this in detail, as the treatment we have given is sufficient for our purposes — we have already remarked that, in any case, the dispersion is small.

10.4. Elementary Quantum Theory: The Excitation Energy of a Plasmon

We have seen in the foregoing section that the plasma oscillations can be represented approximately by a finite set of harmonic oscillators with angular frequency ω_p, and these may be thought of, roughly, as the density fluctuations ρ_k with $k < k_c$. According to elementary quantum theory, as shown in Chapter 1, the energy of such an oscillator must have one of the values given by the expression $(N+\frac{1}{2})\hbar\omega_p$, where N is a positive integer or zero. Pines has given the name *plasmon* to a quantized plasma oscillator, and we shall make use of this in the following work. The state with $N = 0$, or ground state, has energy $\frac{1}{2}\hbar\omega_p$, which is the *zero-point energy* of the plasmon. The energy required to raise the plasmon from one state to that of next higher energy, the *excitation energy*, is $\hbar\omega_p$. The success of the plasma theory as a computational tool depends crucially upon the magnitude of $\hbar\omega_p$, which we will now calculate.

The atomic radius r_s is defined by †

$$\frac{4\pi}{3} r_s^3 = \frac{1}{n}. \tag{10.24}$$

Thus, equation (10.2) gives

$$\omega_p^2 = \frac{4\pi e^2 n}{m} = \frac{3e^2}{mr_s^3}. \tag{10.25}$$

If, now, r_s is measured in Bohr units and energy in rydbergs, we obtain

$$\hbar\omega_p = \frac{2\sqrt{3}}{r_s^{\frac{3}{2}}} \text{ ryd.} \tag{10.26}$$

For sodium, with $r_s = 4$ B.u., this gives $\hbar\omega_p = 0.433$ ryd $= 5.9$ eV. In general, for the valence electrons in all metals, $\hbar\omega_p$ lies between about 3 and 25 eV.

It is more significant to compare $\hbar\omega_p$ with ζ_0, the maximum kinetic energy of any electron at 0°K, according to the Sommerfeld-Hartree theory of a free-electron gas. Equation (7.11) gives

$$\zeta_0 = \frac{\hbar^2}{2m}\left(\frac{9\pi}{4}\right)^{\frac{2}{3}} \frac{1}{r_s^2}, \tag{10.27}$$

which becomes, in atomic units,

$$\zeta_0 = \frac{3.68}{r_s^2} \text{ ryd.} \tag{10.28}$$

Thus, from (10.26) and (10.28),

$$\hbar\omega_p = 0.94 r_s^{\frac{1}{2}} \zeta_0, \tag{10.29}$$

when r_s is measured in Bohr units.

Now $0.94\, r_s^{\frac{1}{2}} > 1$ for all metals, so that $\hbar\omega_p > \zeta_0$. We have seen in Chapter 7 that, at normal temperatures T, only a few electrons in states near the Fermi surface are excited and their thermal energies are of the order of kT, which is very much smaller than ζ_0. We may therefore say

† As explained in § 7.2, this is strictly true only for a monovalent metal — for a metal of valency Z we must replace r_s, in (10.24) and any formula derived from it, by $Z^{-\frac{1}{3}} r_s$. However, in work on electronic interactions it is customary to *define* r_s by equation (10.24) regardless of the valency of the metal to which application might be made (n always being, of course, the valence electron density). This point must be borne in mind when making numerical calculations using published tables of atomic radii.

that $\hbar\omega_p$, the excitation energy of a plasmon, is very much greater than the thermal energy which any electron is able to give away at normal temperatures. This means that thermal excitation of plasmons can usually be neglected and the plasmons will remain in their ground states unless excited by some other method, such as the passage of a fast charged particle through the metal (see § 10.9).

The foregoing is the *most important fact in the plasma theory*. The practical utility of the theory depends upon it, for it means that the plasmons take no active part in many electronic processes and may often be ignored. Now, plasma oscillation is an organized motion of a large number of electrons and does not occur with wavelength smaller than a few ångström units. It may be inferred from this that the *long-range* part of the Coulomb interaction is responsible for the plasmons, so that in calculations where the latter may be ignored the former may also be ignored. We shall see in the following section that the remaining interaction has an effective range of about k_c^{-1}, which is of the order of 1 Å, and this is so short that reasonable results might often be expected by ignoring this interaction also, that is, by treating the electrons as non-interacting particles. The plasma theory thus offers a justification of the independent particle approximation, which has been used with much success in the theory of metals.

10.5. The Short-Range Interaction

The total potential energy due to the Coulomb interaction of the electrons is

$$\tfrac{1}{2}\sum_{i\neq j}\sum \frac{e^2}{r_{ij}}. \tag{10.30}$$

According to equation (10.9), this potential energy, together with that due to the background of positive charge, may be written

$$\tfrac{1}{2}\sum_i U(\boldsymbol{r}_i) = \sum_{i\neq j}\sum\sum_{\boldsymbol{k}}{}' \frac{2\pi e^2}{k^2}\,\mathrm{e}^{\mathrm{i}\boldsymbol{k}\cdot(\boldsymbol{r}_i-\boldsymbol{r}_j)}. \tag{10.31}$$

Now, from equation (10.13), we have

$$\rho_{\boldsymbol{k}}^*\rho_{\boldsymbol{k}} = \sum_i\sum_j \mathrm{e}^{\mathrm{i}\boldsymbol{k}\cdot(\boldsymbol{r}_i-\boldsymbol{r}_j)}, \tag{10.32}$$

so that (10.31) becomes

$$\sum_{\boldsymbol{k}}{}' \frac{2\pi e^2}{k^2}(\rho_{\boldsymbol{k}}^*\rho_{\boldsymbol{k}}-n), \tag{10.33}$$

the term $-n$ being due to the fact that $i \neq j$ in (10.31). The work of § 10.3 tells us that the density fluctuations $\rho_{\boldsymbol{k}}$, with $k < k_c$, are described by the plasmons. This suggests, as is confirmed by the quantum-mechanical theory, that, after the plasma oscillations have been accounted for, the potential energy due to the residual interaction, which we denote by $H_{\text{s.r.}}$, consists of those terms of (10.31) with $k > k_c$; thus

$$H_{\text{s.r.}} = \sum_{i \neq j} \sum_{\substack{\boldsymbol{k} \\ (k > k_c)}} \frac{2\pi e^2}{k^2} \mathrm{e}^{\mathrm{i}\boldsymbol{k} \cdot (\boldsymbol{r}_i - \boldsymbol{r}_j)}. \tag{10.34}$$

In other words, comparing (10.30) and (10.34), the potential energy of two electrons a distance r apart is no longer e^2/r, but

$$\sum_{\substack{\boldsymbol{k} \\ (k > k_c)}} \frac{4\pi e^2}{k^2} \mathrm{e}^{\mathrm{i}\boldsymbol{k} \cdot \boldsymbol{r}}. \tag{10.35}$$

If we replace the sum by an integral, remembering that the density of representative points in $\boldsymbol{k}$-space is $1/8\pi^3$, since the metal has unit volume, (10.35) becomes

$$\frac{e^2}{2\pi^2} \int_{(k > k_c)} \frac{1}{k^2} \mathrm{e}^{\mathrm{i}\boldsymbol{k} \cdot \boldsymbol{r}} \mathrm{d}\boldsymbol{k}$$

$$= \frac{e^2}{\pi} \int_{k_c}^{\infty} \mathrm{d}k \int_0^{\pi} \mathrm{e}^{\mathrm{i}kr \cos\theta} \sin\theta \,\mathrm{d}\theta$$

$$= \frac{2e^2}{\pi} \int_{k_c}^{\infty} \frac{\sin kr}{kr} \mathrm{d}k = \frac{e^2}{r} F(k_c r), \tag{10.36}$$

where

$$F(k_c r) = \frac{2}{\pi} \int_{k_c r}^{\infty} \frac{\sin x}{x} \mathrm{d}x = 1 - \frac{2}{\pi} \operatorname{Si}(k_c r), \tag{10.37}$$

with

$$\operatorname{Si}(y) = \int_0^y \frac{\sin x}{x} \mathrm{d}x. \tag{10.38}$$

The function $\operatorname{Si}(y)$ cannot be evaluated analytically, except for $y = 0$, when it has the value zero, and in the limit as $y \to \infty$, when it has the value $\pi/2$. However, tables of values exist, and when these are used the graph of the function $F(k_c r)$ is found to be as shown in figure 10.1. The graph of the function $\exp(-k_c r)$ is also shown for comparison. For values of $k_c r$ less than 2 the functions are very similar, falling rapidly from unity at the origin to nearly zero. At larger values of $k_c r$ the function $F(k_c r)$ oscillates with decreasing amplitude, but these oscillations are negligible when multiplied by e^2/r — they have no physical significance, but are due to the assumption that the plasmons cease abruptly at $k = k_c$, which rather oversimplifies the problem. We see, then, that the short-range interaction, that which remains when the long-range interaction has been accounted for by the plasmons, is a *screened* Coulomb interaction and the effective range, or *screening distance*, is roughly k_c^{-1}, that is, one or two ångström units.

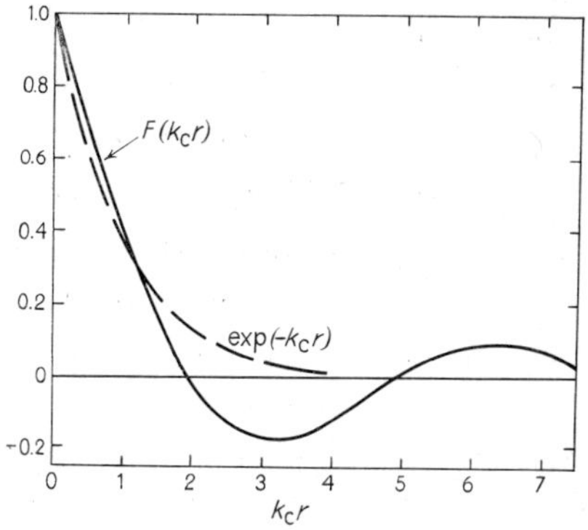

Fig. 10.1. The full curve represents the function $F(k_c r)$, equation (10.37), and the broken curve the function $\exp(-k_c r)$.

The total potential energy (10.34) due to the short-range interaction may be written

$$H_{\text{s.r.}} = \tfrac{1}{2} \sum_{i \neq j} \sum \frac{e^2}{r_{ij}} F(k_c r_{ij}), \tag{10.39}$$

In the following section we will calculate the exchange energy using this expression instead of the full Coulomb interaction (10.30).

Of course, a screening of the charge of an electron is expected simply as a result of the polarization of the surrounding plasma, that is to say, the repulsion of neighbouring electrons leaving an excess positive charge around the given electron. We calculated this screening by the Thomas-Fermi method in § 7.10.1. According to equations (7.81) and (7.83), the potential at distance r from a given electron is

$$-\frac{e}{r} \mathrm{e}^{-r/\lambda}, \tag{10.40}$$

where

$$\lambda = 0.64 r_s^{\frac{1}{2}} \text{ B.u.} \tag{10.41}$$

The screening function is thus of the exponential type, which was shown above to be very similar to the screening function of the plasma theory. However, we shall see that the screening distance λ, 0.68 Å for sodium, is about one half the value of k_c^{-1} required by the plasma theory, so that the Thomas-Fermi method rather exaggerates the screening effect of the electron gas.

10.6. The Exchange Energy due to the Short-Range Interaction, and the Density of States

The deficiencies of the Hartree-Fock theory have been discussed at some length in Chapter 7. This theory takes into account the 'accidental' correlations among the positions of electrons with parallel spins, due to the Pauli principle, but completely neglects proper Coulomb correlations. As a result, 'exchange' effects are very much exaggerated, and, in particular, the density of states curve is much too wide and has the wrong shape near the Fermi surface [see Figure 7.8]. Now, according to the theory developed in the present chapter, the effects of *long-range* Coulomb correlations, among the positions of *all* electrons, regardless of spin, are embodied in the plasmons. Furthermore, these plasmons are not normally excited and, for the purpose of calculating the density of one-electron states in energy, they may be ignored, except in so far as they permit us to dispense with the long-range part of the Coulomb interaction. We thus expect that the difficulties of the Hartree-Fock theory will be largely overcome if the residual *short-range* interaction is used in calculating the exchange energy, instead of the whole Coulomb interaction as before, because this is equivalent to taking into account long-range Coulomb correlations before applying the Pauli principle.

The exchange energy associated with the state $\boldsymbol{k}$ in the Hartree-Fock theory, from equation (7.36), *et seq.*, is

$$\varepsilon_x(\boldsymbol{k}) = -\frac{e^2}{v}\sum_{\boldsymbol{k}'}\int \frac{1}{r}\,\mathrm{e}^{\mathrm{i}(\boldsymbol{k}-\boldsymbol{k}')\cdot\boldsymbol{r}}\,\mathrm{d}\boldsymbol{r}, \tag{10.42}$$

the sum being over all the orbital states within the Fermi sphere. In order to find the exchange energy associated with the state $\boldsymbol{k}$ in the Bohm-Pines theory, which we will denote by $\varepsilon_{xs}(\boldsymbol{k})$, we must substitute the expression (10.35) for e^2/r in (10.42), and also set $v = 1$, since we are considering unit volume. This gives, with suitable adjustment of notation to avoid confusing the various $\boldsymbol{k}$ vectors,

$$\varepsilon_{xs}(\boldsymbol{k}) = -\sum_{\substack{\boldsymbol{k}_1\\(|\boldsymbol{k}_1|<k_0)}}\ \sum_{\substack{\boldsymbol{k}_2\\(|\boldsymbol{k}_2|>k_c)}} \frac{4\pi e^2}{|\boldsymbol{k}_2|^2}\int \mathrm{e}^{\mathrm{i}(\boldsymbol{k}-\boldsymbol{k}_1+\boldsymbol{k}_2)\cdot\boldsymbol{r}}\,\mathrm{d}\boldsymbol{r}. \tag{10.43}$$

The integral is throughout the unit cube, so that

$$\int e^{i(\boldsymbol{k}-\boldsymbol{k}_1+\boldsymbol{k}_2)\cdot\boldsymbol{r}} d\boldsymbol{r} = 0, \quad \text{if } \boldsymbol{k}_2 \neq \boldsymbol{k}_1-\boldsymbol{k}, \qquad (10.44)$$
$$= 1, \quad \text{if } \boldsymbol{k}_2 = \boldsymbol{k}_1-\boldsymbol{k},$$

and, hence,

$$\varepsilon_{xs}(\boldsymbol{k}) = -4\pi e^2 \sum_{\substack{\boldsymbol{k}_1 \\ (|\boldsymbol{k}_1|<k_0, \\ |\boldsymbol{k}_1-\boldsymbol{k}|>k_c)}} \frac{1}{|\boldsymbol{k}_1-\boldsymbol{k}|^2}. \qquad (10.45)$$

Substituting an integral for the sum, in the usual way, we find

$$\varepsilon_{xs}(\boldsymbol{k}) = -\frac{e^2}{2\pi^2}\int \frac{d\boldsymbol{k}_1}{|\boldsymbol{k}_1-\boldsymbol{k}|^2}, \qquad (10.46)$$

the region of integration being defined by

$$|\boldsymbol{k}_1| < k_0, \qquad |\boldsymbol{k}_1-\boldsymbol{k}| > k_c.$$

In evaluating this integral we consider the two cases, $k < k_0-k_c$, $k > k_0-k_c$, separately. It is convenient in both cases, however, to use the

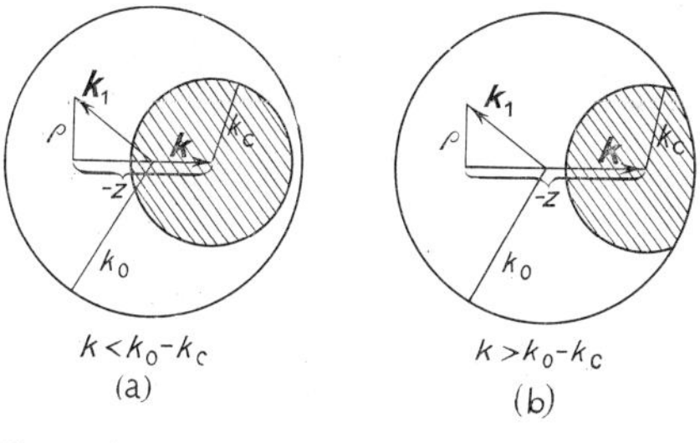

Fig. 10.2. The region of integration for $\boldsymbol{k}_1$ lies inside the Fermi sphere (large circle) and outside the shaded region, which, *in case* (a), represents a sphere of radius k_c, centred at $\boldsymbol{k}$, and, *in case* (b), represents a portion of such a sphere.

cylindrical coordinates (ρ, ϕ, z) with origin at $\boldsymbol{k}$ and z-axis in the direction of $\boldsymbol{k}$, ρ being the perpendicular distance from $\boldsymbol{k}_1$ to the z-axis, as shown in Figure 10.2. We then have

$$|\boldsymbol{k}_1-\boldsymbol{k}|^2 = \rho^2+z^2. \qquad (10.47)$$

Owing to the cylindrical symmetry the azimuthal angle ϕ need not appear explicitly, and we may take the volume element to be $2\pi\rho\,\mathrm{d}\rho\,\mathrm{d}z$.

The expression (10.46) thus assumes the following forms:

for $k < k_0 - k_c$,

$$\varepsilon_{xs}(\boldsymbol{k}) = -\frac{e^2}{\pi}\int_{-(k+k_0)}^{k_0-k} \mathrm{d}z \int_0^{[k_0^2-(z+k)^2]^{\frac{1}{2}}} \frac{\rho\,\mathrm{d}\rho}{\rho^2+z^2} + \frac{e^2}{\pi}\int_{-k_c}^{k_c} \mathrm{d}z \int_0^{(k_c^2-z^2)^{\frac{1}{2}}} \frac{\rho\,\mathrm{d}\rho}{\rho^2+z^2}; \tag{10.48}$$

for $k > k_0 - k_c$,

$$\varepsilon_{xs}(\boldsymbol{k}) = -\frac{e^2}{\pi}\int_{-(k+k_0)}^{-k_c} \mathrm{d}z \int_0^{[k_0^2-(z+k)^2]^{\frac{1}{2}}} \frac{\rho\,\mathrm{d}\rho}{\rho^2+z^2} - \frac{e^2}{\pi}\int_{-k_c}^{(k_0^2-k_c^2-k^2)/2k} \mathrm{d}z \int_{(k_c^2-z^2)^{\frac{1}{2}}}^{[k_0^2-(z+k)^2]^{\frac{1}{2}}} \frac{\rho\,\mathrm{d}\rho}{\rho^2+z^2}. \tag{10.49}$$

The integrations are all elementary, and we obtain, finally,

for $k < k_0 - k_c$,

$$\varepsilon_{xs}(\boldsymbol{k}) = -\frac{e^2}{2\pi}\left[2k_0 + \frac{k_0^2-k^2}{k}\log\left(\frac{k_0+k}{k_0-k}\right) - 4k_c\right], \tag{10.50}$$

for $k > k_0 - k_c$,

$$\varepsilon_{xs}(\boldsymbol{k}) = -\frac{e^2}{2\pi}\left[k_0 + \frac{k_0^2-k^2}{k}\log\left(\frac{k_0+k}{k_c}\right) + \frac{3k^2+k_c^2-k_0^2}{2k} - 2k_c\right]. \tag{10.51}$$

It should be noted that, in obtaining these expressions, we have assumed, as we shall continue to do in the following work, that $k_0 > k_c$.

The total one-electron energy $\varepsilon(\boldsymbol{k})$ is obtained by adding the free-electron kinetic energy to $\varepsilon_{xs}(\boldsymbol{k})$, that is,

$$\varepsilon(\boldsymbol{k}) = \frac{\hbar^2 k^2}{2m} + \varepsilon_{xs}(\boldsymbol{k}). \tag{10.52}$$

This is still a function of the magnitude k of the wave vector only, so that the energy surfaces remain spherical and the density of states is given by equation (7.32), namely,

$$\mathcal{N}(\varepsilon) = \frac{k^2}{2\pi^2} \bigg/ \frac{d\varepsilon}{dk}, \tag{10.53}$$

for unit volume. It can be seen immediately that $\mathcal{N}(\varepsilon)$ does not fall to zero at the Fermi surface, as it does in the Hartree-Fock theory. Near the Fermi surface we must use equation (10.51) for $\varepsilon_{xs}(\boldsymbol{k})$, which gives

$$\frac{d\varepsilon}{dk} = \frac{\hbar^2 k}{m} + \frac{e^2}{2\pi}\left[\frac{k_0^2+k^2}{k^2}\log\left(\frac{k_0+k}{k_c}\right) + \frac{k_c^2-k_0^2-2kk_0-k^2}{2k^2}\right]. \tag{10.54}$$

This does not tend to infinity as $k \to k_0$, but to the finite value

$$\frac{\hbar^2 k_0}{m} + \frac{e^2}{2\pi}\left[2\log\left(\frac{2k_0}{k_c}\right) + \frac{k_c^2}{2k_0^2} - 2\right]. \tag{10.55}$$

It is convenient to introduce the dimensionless constant β, defined by

$$\beta = k_c/k_0, \tag{10.56}$$

so that

$$\left(\frac{d\varepsilon}{dk}\right)_{k_0} = \frac{\hbar^2 k_0}{m} + \frac{e^2}{2\pi}\left(2\log\frac{2}{\beta} + \frac{\beta^2}{2} - 2\right). \tag{10.57}$$

Now, in the Sommerfeld-Hartree theory only the first term on the right appears, the other being due to the exchange energy. Thus, if we denote by $\mathcal{N}_0(\varepsilon)$ and $\mathcal{N}(\varepsilon)$ the densities of states in the Sommerfeld-Hartree and Bohm-Pines theories respectively, and by ζ_0 and ζ_1 the respective energies at the Fermi surface, we have, from (10.53),

$$\frac{\mathcal{N}_0(\zeta_0)}{\mathcal{N}(\zeta_1)} = 1 + \frac{e^2 m}{2\pi\hbar^2 k_0}\left(2\log\frac{2}{\beta} + \frac{\beta^2}{2} - 2\right). \tag{10.58}$$

Using formula (7.31), which gives

$$k_0 = 1.919/r_s, \tag{10.59}$$

and measuring r_s in Bohr units, (10.58) becomes

$$\frac{\mathcal{N}_0(\zeta_0)}{\mathcal{N}(\zeta_1)} = 1 + \frac{r_s}{12.06}\left(2\log\frac{2}{\beta} + \frac{\beta^2}{2} - 2\right). \tag{10.60}$$

We have not yet discussed in detail the evaluation of β, although a rough value is provided by equation (10.23). There is, in fact, no unique method of fixing this quantity precisely, but we shall see in § 10.8 that a reasonable value for *sodium* is about $\beta = 0.8$. This, with $r_s = 4$ B.u., gives

$$\frac{\mathcal{N}_0(\zeta_0)}{\mathcal{N}(\zeta_1)} = 1.05. \tag{10.61}$$

The density of states at the Fermi surface thus has very similar values in the two theories, and the same applies to any quantity which depends only upon this density. In particular, (10.61) is also the ratio of the calculated electronic specific heats in the two theories, so that these are very similar, and, furthermore, the difficulty regarding the temperature dependence of the electronic specific heat in the Hartree-Fock theory, discussed in § 7.7, no longer appears.

Now let us investigate the band width according to the Bohm-Pines theory. From (10.50), (10.51) and (10.52), we obtain

$$\varepsilon(k_0) = \frac{\hbar^2 k_0^2}{2m} - \frac{e^2 k_0}{2\pi}\left(2-2\beta+\frac{\beta^2}{2}\right), \tag{10.62}$$

and

$$\varepsilon(0) = -\frac{e^2 k_0}{2\pi}(4-4\beta), \tag{10.63}$$

provided, in the latter case, that $\beta < 1$, or $k_c < k_0$, as we have assumed. The band width is thus

$$\varepsilon(k_0)-\varepsilon(0) = \frac{\hbar^2 k_0^2}{2m} - \frac{e^2 k_0}{2\pi}\left(-2+2\beta+\frac{\beta^2}{2}\right). \tag{10.64}$$

Again using equation (10.59), and atomic units, this becomes

$$\varepsilon(k_0)-\varepsilon(0) = \frac{3.68}{r_s^2} - \frac{0.611}{r_s}\left(-2+2\beta+\frac{\beta^2}{2}\right) \text{ ryd.} \tag{10.65}$$

The first term on the right is the Sommerfeld-Hartree band width, and amounts to 0.23 ryd for sodium. If, as before, we take $\beta = 0.8$ for this metal, the value of the second term is 0.01 ryd, so that the Bohm-Pines band width is practically the same as the Sommerfeld-Hartree band width. Indeed, the two are equal when $\beta = 2(\sqrt{2}-1) = 0.828$, since the second term on the right of (10.65) vanishes for this value. The Bohm-Pines band width is thus in much better agreement with the experimental X-ray data, as discussed in § 7.9, than is that of the Hartree-Fock theory.

We have now established that the essential features of the Bohm-Pines and Sommerfeld-Hartree $\mathcal{N}(\varepsilon)$ curves are very similar. Of course, the detailed comparison of the two curves — whether one is lower and wider or higher and narrower than the other — depends upon the chosen value of β, and there is a certain latitude here. None the less, whatever the value of β, it is quite clear that the use of the short-range interaction, as justified by the plasma theory, overcomes the principal defects of the Hartree-Fock theory.

It should be noted that the Bohm-Pines density of states, coming from (10.52) and (10.53), still neglects the effect of *short-range* Coulomb correlations. If we regard the short-range interaction as a perturbation applied to a system of initially non-interacting particles, the exchange energy $\varepsilon_{xs}(\boldsymbol{k})$ is the *first-order* perturbation energy — the *second-order* energy would represent the effect of short-range correlations. FLETCHER and LARSON [1958] have calculated the latter and have found that, again dependent upon the value of β, it can have a considerable effect upon the $\mathcal{N}(\varepsilon)$ curve. The *qualitative* results we have obtained above remain true, however.

In the following section we shall be concerned with the total energy of the system, and, in preparation for this, we will now calculate the *total exchange energy* due to the short-range interaction. We will denote this by nE_{xs}, where E_{xs} is the *average* exchange energy per electron, and as in the Hartree-Fock theory, equation (7.49), we find

$$nE_{xs} = \sum_{\boldsymbol{k}} \varepsilon_{xs}(\boldsymbol{k}). \tag{10.66}$$

The sum is over all the orbital states within the Fermi sphere, and, replacing the sum by an integral, we obtain

$$\begin{aligned} nE_{xs} &= \frac{1}{8\pi^3}\int \varepsilon_{xs}(\boldsymbol{k})\,\mathrm{d}\boldsymbol{k} = \frac{1}{2\pi^2}\int_0^{k_0} \varepsilon_{xs}(\boldsymbol{k})\,k^2\,\mathrm{d}k \\ &= \frac{1}{2\pi^2}\int_0^{k_0-k_c} \varepsilon_{xs}(\boldsymbol{k})\,k^2\,\mathrm{d}k + \frac{1}{2\pi^2}\int_{k_0-k_c}^{k_0} \varepsilon_{xs}(\boldsymbol{k})\,k^2\,\mathrm{d}k. \end{aligned} \tag{10.67}$$

We have divided the range of integration with respect to k into two parts — $\varepsilon_{xs}(\boldsymbol{k})$ is given, in the first, by (10.50), and, in the second, by (10.51). Nothing worse than elementary integration by parts is involved, and the result is

$$nE_{xs} = -\frac{3e^2 k_0 n}{4\pi}\left(1-\frac{4\beta}{3}+\frac{\beta^2}{2}-\frac{\beta^4}{48}\right). \tag{10.68}$$

This gives the average exchange energy per electron, in atomic units, as

$$E_{xs} = -\frac{0.916}{r_s}\left(1-\frac{4\beta}{3}+\frac{\beta^2}{2}-\frac{\beta^4}{48}\right) \text{ ryd.} \tag{10.69}$$

Now, the average exchange energy in the Hartree-Fock theory is $-0.916/r_s$ (it is obtained from the Bohm-Pines result by setting $\beta = 0$). If we take $\beta = 0.8$, for sodium, the factor

$$\left(1-\frac{4\beta}{3}+\frac{\beta^2}{2}-\frac{\beta^4}{48}\right)$$

has the value 0.26, so that the Bohm-Pines exchange energy is considerably less than that of the Hartree-Fock theory. We have seen in Chapter 7 that the principal advantage of the Hartree-Fock theory over the simple Hartree theory lies in the lower total energy produced by the large negative exchange energy. It would therefore appear, at first sight, as if the Bohm-Pines theory were energetically less favourable than the Hartree-Fock theory. We shall see in the following section that this is not so, however; for the smaller exchange energy is compensated by other energy terms, so that the total energy in the Bohm-Pines theory is, in fact, *lower* than that in the Hartree-Fock theory, even when the former does not include the effect of short-range correlations.

10.7. The Correlation Energy

It is difficult to make the calculation of the total energy of the system entirely convincing without going into details of the quantum-mechanical theory of plasma oscillations, which we do not wish to do. Not only would this take us beyond the scheme of the present work, but, owing to the fact that the quantum-mechanical theory is still in some dispute, it would probably raise more difficulties than it would resolve. None the less, we believe that the essential features of this calculation can at least be made plausible within our prescribed framework.

According to the plasma theory, the system, which consists of n electrons and a uniform distribution of positive charge in a box of unit volume, can be described approximately as a set of n particles having a screened Coulomb interaction, together with a set of plasmons, one for each $\boldsymbol{k}$ with $k < k_c$. The number of plasmons is thus $k_c^3/6\pi^2$, the number of $\boldsymbol{k}$ vectors lying within a sphere of radius k_c, the density being $1/8\pi^3$. In the ground state of the system, and it is the energy of this state we wish to find, the plasmons are all in their ground states, each having zero point energy $\frac{1}{2}\hbar\omega_p$, and are represented by a product of ground state harmonic oscillator wave functions. Also, the screened interaction of the particles is of such short range that as a first approximation we may neglect it, in which case the particle wave function is a single determinant of free-electron functions including spin.

The ground state wave function of the system is thus approximately a product of ground state harmonic oscillator functions and a single determinant of free-electron functions. This is only an approximation for two main reasons: first, we have neglected a small coupling which exists between the plasmons and the electrons, and, second, we have neglected the effect of the short-range interaction term $H_{\text{s.r.}}$ on the particle wave function. A further difficulty may be noted here. The number of degrees of freedom of a system of n free particles is $3n$. By re-describing the system in terms of plasmons we have increased this number by $k_c^3/6\pi^2$, which is not permissible. It is, in fact, necessary to impose a number of so-called *subsidiary conditions*, equal to the number of plasmons, upon the system in order to maintain the number of degrees of freedom at $3n$. These conditions, which express the relationship between the plasmon and particle coordinates, complicate the formal quantum-mechanical problem considerably. However, BOHM, HUANG and PINES [1957] have shown that, as far as the calculation of the ground state energy of the system is concerned, the subsidiary conditions can be neglected, and so we will ignore them.

We therefore expect the approximate total energy of the system to be a sum of the kinetic energy of the particles, the exchange energy due to the short-range interaction, and the zero point energies of the plasmons. This would, indeed, make the energy *higher* than that of the Hartree-Fock theory, but an important negative energy term has, in fact, been overlooked. The necessity for this term may be understood by reference to formula (10.33) for the potential energy of the whole Coulomb interaction. When the potential energy of the short-range interaction (those terms with $k > k_c$) is removed from this, the remainder may be expressed in the form

$$\sum_{\substack{\boldsymbol{k}\\(k<k_c)}}{}' \frac{2\pi e^2}{k^2}\rho_{\boldsymbol{k}}^*\rho_{\boldsymbol{k}} - \sum_{\substack{\boldsymbol{k}\\(k<k_c)}}{}' \frac{2\pi e^2 n}{k^2}. \tag{10.70}$$

Now, we have remarked that the density fluctuations $\rho_{\boldsymbol{k}}$, with $k < k_c$, are described by the plasmons, so that the energy due to the first term of (10.70) is already included in the zero point energies of the plasmons. This does not apply to the second term, however, which is constant and must appear unchanged in the final energy expression.

If we denote by $E_{\rm BP}$ the *average* energy per electron in this approximation, the *total* energy of the system is, then,

$$\begin{aligned} nE_{\rm BP} &= nE_{\rm F} + nE_{\rm xs} + \sum_{\substack{\boldsymbol{k}\\(k<k_c)}}{}' \left(\frac{\hbar\omega_{\rm p}}{2} - \frac{2\pi e^2 n}{k^2}\right) \\ &= nE_{\rm F} + nE_{\rm xs} + \left(\frac{k_c^3}{6\pi^2}\right)\frac{\hbar\omega_{\rm p}}{2} - \frac{ne^2 k_c}{\pi}, \end{aligned} \tag{10.71}$$

on replacing the sum by an integral in the usual way. Using equations (10.56), (10.68) and the fact that $k_0^3 = 3\pi^2 n$, this gives

$$\begin{aligned} E_{\rm BP} &= E_{\rm F} - \frac{3e^2 k_0}{4\pi}\left(1 - \frac{4\beta}{3} + \frac{\beta^2}{2} - \frac{\beta^4}{48}\right) + \frac{\hbar\omega_{\rm p}}{4}\beta^3 - \frac{e^2 k_0}{\pi}\beta \\ &= E_{\rm F} - \frac{3e^2 k_0}{4\pi}\left(1 + \frac{\beta^2}{2} - \frac{\beta^4}{48}\right) + \frac{\hbar\omega_{\rm p}}{4}\beta^3. \end{aligned} \tag{10.72}$$

From equations (7.52), (10.26) and (10.59), we then have, in atomic units,

$$\begin{aligned} E_{\rm BP} &= \frac{2.21}{r_s^2} - \frac{0.916}{r_s}\left(1 + \frac{\beta^2}{2} - \frac{\beta^4}{48}\right) + \frac{\sqrt{3}}{2r_s^{\frac{3}{2}}}\beta^3 \text{ ryd} \\ &= \frac{2.21}{r_s^2} - \frac{0.916}{r_s} - \frac{0.458}{r_s}\beta^2 + \frac{0.866}{r_s^{\frac{3}{2}}}\beta^3 + \frac{0.019}{r_s}\beta^4 \text{ ryd}. \end{aligned} \tag{10.73}$$

The first two terms in (10.73) constitute the average energy per electron $E_{\rm HF}$ in the Hartree-Fock theory [see equation (7.54)]. If we take $\beta = 0.8$ and $r_s = 4$ B.u. for sodium, as in the previous section, the remaining three terms in (10.73) have the value -0.016 ryd, so that $E_{\rm BP}$ is *lower* than $E_{\rm HF}$. The reason for this lower energy is simply that the Bohm-Pines theory takes into account long-range correlations among the electronic positions, regardless of spin, while the Hartree-Fock theory does not. The difference

$E_{BP} - E_{HF}$ is called the *long-range correlation energy* per electron, and we will denote it by W_l; thus,

$$W_l = -\frac{0.458}{r_s}\beta^2 + \frac{0.866}{r_s^{\frac{3}{2}}}\beta^3 + \frac{0.019}{r_s}\beta^4 \text{ ryd.} \qquad (10.74)$$

This is not the whole of the correlation energy, as defined in § 9.5, because E_{BP} still neglects the effect of $H_{s.r.}$ on the particle wave function — in other words, the effect of short-range correlations. The term nE_{xs} is the *first-order* perturbation correction due to $H_{s.r.}$, obtained by using a single determinantal particle wave function, which would be correct only if $H_{s.r.}$ were zero. The correct particle wave function should be an infinite sum of determinants of free-electron functions, which are the eigenfunctions of the unperturbed system, with coefficients determined by $H_{s.r.}$. We have already remarked in § 9.5 that, if the whole Coulomb interaction term (10.30) is treated as a perturbation, the second-order energy correction diverges. Here, however, because the screened interaction is of such short range, the second-order perturbation energy turns out to be quite small, and it is not necessary to consider higher-order corrections. We call this second-order perturbation energy, which is of course negative, the *short-range correlation energy* and denote it per electron by W_s.

From equation (3.134) we thus find

$$W_s = -\frac{1}{n}\sum_{j\neq 0}\frac{|(H_{s.r.})_{0j}|^2}{E_j - E_0}, \qquad (10.74)$$

where

$$(H_{s.r.})_{0j} = \int \Psi_0^* H_{s.r.} \Psi_j \, d\tau', \qquad (10.75)$$

the normalized functions Ψ_0 and Ψ_j being nth-order determinants of free-electron functions, the former representing the ground state and the latter an excited state of the unperturbed system. E_0 and E_j are the corresponding kinetic energies, that is, the energies of the system of particles in the states Ψ_0 and Ψ_j when no interaction is present.

The calculation of the matrix elements (10.75) is too lengthy for inclusion here. However, it may be shown that the only non-zero matrix elements are those for which Ψ_j contains *two and only two* excited one-electron functions. That is to say, Ψ_j must be obtained from Ψ_0 by exciting *two* electrons to states lying outside the Fermi sphere. These excited electrons can have either parallel or antiparallel spins, but it is found that the matrix element is zero unless the spins of the excited states are the same as those of the initial states. Now, the terms in (10.74) corresponding to the excitation of two electrons with parallel spins give the part of the short-range correlation energy due to parallel spin correlations and the remaining terms give the part due to antiparallel spin correlations. We know, however, that the Pauli principle has the effect of keeping electrons with parallel spins apart, reducing the effectiveness of $H_{\text{s.r.}}$, so it is reasonable to assume that the parallel spin part of W_{s} will be small, and this is borne out by calculation. For simplicity, therefore, we will ignore the contribution of parallel spin correlations to W_{s}.

The only Ψ_j we need consider, then, are of the type obtained from Ψ_0 by raising two electrons with wave vectors $\boldsymbol{k}_1$ and $\boldsymbol{k}_2$, and opposite spins, to excited levels lying outside the Fermi sphere. It also appears in the calculation that the wave vectors of the excited states must be $\boldsymbol{k}_1+\boldsymbol{k}$ and $\boldsymbol{k}_2-\boldsymbol{k}$, with $k > k_{\text{c}}$, so that the total momentum is automatically conserved. We thus find

$$(H_{\text{s.r.}})_{0j} = 4\pi e^2/k^2, \tag{10.76}$$

$$\begin{aligned} E_j - E_0 &= \frac{\hbar^2}{2m}[(\boldsymbol{k}_1+\boldsymbol{k})^2+(\boldsymbol{k}_2-\boldsymbol{k})^2-\boldsymbol{k}_1^2-\boldsymbol{k}_2^2] \\ &= \frac{\hbar^2}{m}\boldsymbol{k}\cdot(\boldsymbol{k}_1-\boldsymbol{k}_2+\boldsymbol{k}), \end{aligned} \tag{10.77}$$

and, hence,

$$W_{\text{s}} = -\frac{1}{n}\sum_{\boldsymbol{k}}\sum_{\boldsymbol{k}_1}\sum_{\boldsymbol{k}_2}\frac{m(4\pi e^2)^2}{\hbar^2 k^4 \boldsymbol{k}\cdot(\boldsymbol{k}_1-\boldsymbol{k}_2+\boldsymbol{k})}, \tag{10.78}$$

where $k > k_{\text{c}}$, and $\boldsymbol{k}_1$, $\boldsymbol{k}_2$ lie inside the Fermi sphere while $\boldsymbol{k}_1+\boldsymbol{k}$ and $\boldsymbol{k}_2-\boldsymbol{k}$ lie outside it.

If we now replace the sums by integrals, we obtain

$$W_{\text{s}} = -\frac{m(4\pi e^2)^2}{n\hbar^2(8\pi^3)^3}\iiint\frac{\mathrm{d}\boldsymbol{k}\,\mathrm{d}\boldsymbol{k}_1\,\mathrm{d}\boldsymbol{k}_2}{k^4\boldsymbol{k}\cdot(\boldsymbol{k}_1-\boldsymbol{k}_2+\boldsymbol{k})}, \tag{10.79}$$

the region of integration being

$$|\boldsymbol{k}_1|,\ |\boldsymbol{k}_2| < k_0,\quad k > k_{\text{c}},\quad |\boldsymbol{k}_1+\boldsymbol{k}| > k_0,\quad |\boldsymbol{k}_2-\boldsymbol{k}| > k_0.$$

Finally, expressing k, $|\boldsymbol{k}_1|$ and $|\boldsymbol{k}_2|$ in units of k_0 and the energy in rydbergs, we have

$$W_s = -\frac{3}{16\pi^5}\iiint \frac{\mathrm{d}\boldsymbol{k}\,\mathrm{d}\boldsymbol{k}_1\,\mathrm{d}\boldsymbol{k}_2}{k^4\boldsymbol{k}\cdot(\boldsymbol{k}_1-\boldsymbol{k}_2+\boldsymbol{k})}\ \text{ryd}, \tag{10.80}$$

where $|\boldsymbol{k}_1|, |\boldsymbol{k}_2| < 1$, $k > \beta$, $|\boldsymbol{k}_1+\boldsymbol{k}| > 1$, $|\boldsymbol{k}_2-\boldsymbol{k}| > 1$. The integration is tedious and we merely quote the result given by PINES [1955]:

$$W_s = -(0.0254-0.0626\log\beta+0.006\,37\beta^2)\ \text{ryd}. \tag{10.81}$$

The total correlation energy per electron, the sum of W_l and W_s, is thus

$$W = -\frac{0.458}{r_s}\beta^2+\frac{0.866}{r_s^{\frac{3}{2}}}\beta^3+\frac{0.019}{r_s}\beta^4$$
$$-0.0254+0.0626\log\beta-0.006\,37\beta^2\ \text{ryd}. \tag{10.82}$$

Before applying this to any metal, let us consider in more detail the evaluation of β.

10.8. The Value of β

PINES [1955] originally proposed to choose that value of the parameter β which minimizes W_l, or, what is the same thing, the value which minimizes E_{BP}. This is a reasonable procedure, since it gives the greatest improvement of the Bohm-Pines total energy on that of the Hartree-Fock theory, without taking into account short-range correlations — in other words, it takes the greatest advantage of the inclusion of long-range correlations in the plasma theory. Neglecting the small term $0.019\beta^4/r_s$ in (10.74), we find

$$\frac{\partial W_l}{\partial\beta} = -\frac{0.916}{r_s}\beta+\frac{2.598}{r_s^{\frac{3}{2}}}\beta^2, \tag{10.83}$$

and equating this to zero gives

$$\beta = 0.35r_s^{\frac{1}{2}}, \tag{10.84}$$

or

$$k_c = 0.35r_s^{\frac{1}{2}}k_0 = 0.67r_s^{-\frac{1}{2}}, \tag{10.85}$$

where r_s is in Bohr units. According to this formula, $\beta = 0.70$ for sodium, and the screening distance is $k_c^{-1} = 3.0$ B.u. $= 1.6$ Å.

If the energy due to the interaction between the plasmons and electrons, which we have neglected in our calculation, is included in W_l before minimization (see PINES [1958]), a slightly larger value, roughly

$$\beta = 0.40 r_s^{\frac{1}{2}}, \tag{10.86}$$

is obtained. This gives $\beta = 0.80$ for sodium, which is the value we used in § 10.6.

As far as the calculation of the density of states is concerned it is clearly advantageous to have β as large as possible, for this will reduce the short-range interaction to a minimum and so improve the accuracy of the independent particle approximation. However, it is not possible to choose an arbitrarily large value of β. Equation (10.23) suggests, and this is borne out by quantum-mechanical considerations, that an upper bound to the value of β is

$$\beta = \frac{\omega_p}{k_0 v_0}. \tag{10.87}$$

Now

$$\zeta_0 = \frac{\hbar^2 k_0^2}{2m} = \tfrac{1}{2} m v_0^2, \tag{10.88}$$

and

$$\hbar k_0 = m v_0, \tag{10.89}$$

so that (10.87) becomes

$$\beta = \frac{\hbar \omega_p}{2\zeta_0}, \tag{10.90}$$

or

$$\beta = 0.47 r_s^{\frac{1}{2}}, \tag{10.91}$$

from equation (10.29). This gives $\beta = 0.94$ and $k_c^{-1} = 1.2$ Å for sodium.

If we insert any of these values of β in equation (10.82) and retain only the significant terms for actual metallic densities (that is, for values of r_s lying between 2 and 6 B.u.), we obtain

$$W = C + 0.031 \log r_s, \tag{10.92}$$

approximately, the constant C having a value in the neighbourhood of -0.1. NOZIÈRES and PINES [1958] have considered the correlation energy in more detail, taking into account the interaction between plasmons and electrons, and have concluded that, with a probable error of less than 15 %,

$$W = -0.115 + 0.031 \log r_s \tag{10.93}$$

in the region of actual metallic densities. This is the formula quoted in § 9.5; it gives $W = -0.072$ ryd for sodium, in good agreement with the value $-$ 0.075 ryd given by the formula (9.82) of Wigner.

It is of interest to note that the value of β according to the Thomas-Fermi theory, if we take k_c^{-1} to be the screening distance λ given by equation (10.41), is

$$\beta_{\mathrm{TF}} = 0.81 r_s^{\frac{1}{2}}, \tag{10.94}$$

which is nearly twice as great as the largest value permitted by the plasma theory.

10.9. Experimental Evidence of Plasma Oscillations in Solids

So far the validity of the plasma theory has rested upon its ability to justify the independent particle approximation, which we know to be in reasonable agreement with experiment, and to provide a value of the correlation energy of the size required in cohesive energy calculations. More direct evidence of the existence of plasma oscillations in metals is provided by the energy losses of fast electrons in penetrating thin metallic films.

It has been shown in § 10.4 that plasmons are unlikely to be excited by heating, since even at quite high temperatures no electron has thermal energy $\hbar\omega_p$ to give away. However, if a very fast electron enters a metal from outside, there is a good chance that it will excite one or more plasmons. Thus, if a beam of high energy electrons is shot through a metallic film, and we assume that the electrons in the metal are practically free, we should expect some of the emergent electrons to have lost energy $\hbar\omega_p$, others $2\hbar\omega_p$, others $3\hbar\omega_p$, and so on, according to the number of plasmons they have excited. Of course, even in a free-electron gas, the energy losses will not be in multiples of *exactly* $\hbar\omega_p$, owing to dispersion [see equation (10.3)], but this will merely broaden the spectral lines slightly.

In fact, many experiments have now been carried out (for a summary of the experimental results see PINES [1955] or [1956]) in which beams of electrons with energies of several kilovolts are passed through metallic films, generally of the order of 100 Å in thickness, and the energy loss spectra determined. Such high energies are not strictly required in order to excite plasmons, since $\hbar\omega_p$ is in the region of 10 eV, but they are used in order that the electrons will be scattered through only a small angle in passing through the film, which makes the emergent beam easier to handle.

It is found that, for some metals, in particular beryllium, magnesium, and aluminium, there are characteristic energy losses at almost exact integral multiples of $\hbar\omega_p$, the electron density used in computing ω_p being that of the *valence* electrons in the metal, that is, two per atom for Be and Mg and three per atom for Al. The energy loss spectrum of aluminium, found by BLACKSTOCK, RITCHIE and BIRKHOFF [1955], is shown in Figure 10.3; $\hbar\omega_p$ is 16 eV for this metal and peaks appear at intervals of very nearly 15 eV. However, the energy loss spectra of many other metals, and several non-metals, such as carbon, silicon and germanium, show at least one pronounced peak at about $\hbar\omega_p$, where again the density of valence electrons, four per atom for C, Si and Ge, is used in computing ω_p.

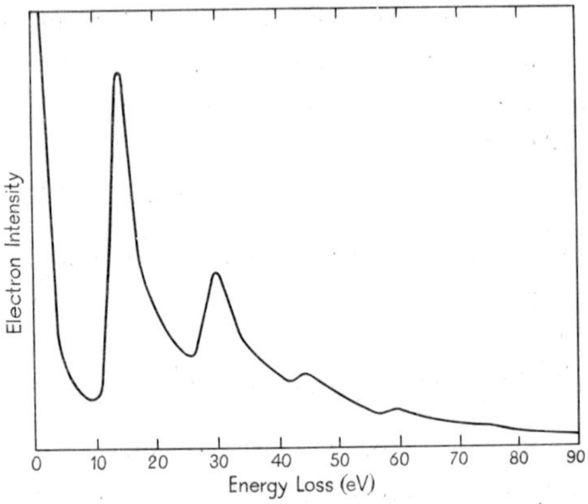

Fig. 10.3. Energy loss spectrum of 45 keV electrons after passing through an aluminium film of thickness about 550 Å. Peaks occur at intervals of approximately 15 eV, while $\hbar\omega_p$ for this metal is 16 eV (after BLACKSTOCK, RITCHIE and BIRKHOFF [1955]).

On the other hand, agreement between the free-electron plasma theory and the experimental loss spectra is completely lacking for metals such as copper, silver, gold and the transition metals with well-filled d sub-shells. Copper, for instance, has a single broad peak at about $2\hbar\omega_p$, when the electron density is taken to be one per atom. This is not very surprising, for where the ion-cores are large the distinction between valence and core electrons tends to break down, and we should expect a direct participation by the core electrons in the plasma oscillations. The core electrons, even in the d sub-shells of the transition metals, are by no means free, however, so that we should not expect the free-electron plasma theory to apply in this case.

Even in metals such as sodium, magnesium and aluminium, in which the ion-cores are small, the periodic field of the ionic lattice is expected to have *some* effect on the plasma oscillations, for it causes the one-electron wave functions to differ in some degree from free-electron functions. It might be imagined that the plasma frequency in an alkali metal, for example, could be obtained quite simply by substituting the effective mass m^*, discussed in § 9.3, for the ordinary electronic mass m in the formula for ω_p, According to a theory due originally to Mott (see, for example, RAIMES [1957]), however, this is not so, and the plasma frequency in such metals should rather be simply the free-electron frequency, with a small correction for the polarizability of the ion-cores.

This theory, which is now known as the *dielectric theory* of plasma oscillations, has been extensively developed by a number of people. It promises to be a powerful means of studying the effects of electronic interactions in solids, but so far little progress has been made owing to lack of the necessary experimental data. However, one of the elementary results of the theory is that the frequency-dependent dielectric constant $1+4\pi\alpha$, where α is the polarizability of the metal, must vanish at the plasma frequency. Unfortunately, optical data in the relevant frequency range, the far ultra-violet, exist only for the alkali metals, but for these metals it is indeed found that the dielectric constant vanishes, that is to say, the metal becomes transparent, for light of almost exactly the angular frequency ω_p. This is further confirmation of the applicability of the free-electron plasma theory to such metals.

In conclusion, we would emphasize once more that the theory we have described in this chapter is not free from difficulties, and it may prove to be quantitatively unreliable without many tedious refinements which would detract from its elegance and practical utility. None the less, even if only qualitatively valid, it will have served a most useful purpose in providing a long-needed justification for the independent particle approximation.

References

BLACKSTOCK, A. W., R. H. RITCHIE and R. D. BIRKHOFF, 1955, Phys. Rev. ***100***, 1078.

BOHM, D., K. HUANG and D. PINES, 1957, Phys. Rev. ***107***, 71.

BOHM, D. and D. PINES, 1951, Phys. Rev. ***82***, 625; 1952, Ibid. ***85***, 338; 1953, Ibid. ***92***, 609.

FLETCHER, J. G. and D. C. LARSON, 1958, Phys. Rev. ***111***, 455.

NOZIÈRES, P. and D. PINES, 1958, Phys. Rev. ***111***, 442.

PINES, D., 1953, Phys. Rev. ***92***, 626;
1955, Solid State Physics ***1*** (Academic Press, New York), p. 367;
1956, Rev. Mod. Phys. ***28***, 184;
1958, Nuovo Cimento Suppl. ***7***, No. 2, 329.

RAIMES, S., 1957, Reports on Progress in Physics ***20***, 1.

CHAPTER 11

TIME-DEPENDENCE AND TRANSITION PROBABILITIES

11.1. The Time-Dependent Schrödinger Equation

We have reserved a discussion of the time-dependence of states until this final chapter, not because it is more difficult than the previous work, nor because a knowledge of all that has gone before is required for its understanding, but simply in order to emphasize that we have so far been dealing only with *stationary states*, whose dependence on time is trivial. We have, in fact, only considered *conservative* systems, whose Hamiltonians do not contain the time explicitly. However, a problem which frequently arises in atomic physics is that of a system, initially in a given stationary state, which is subject to a perturbation of only temporary duration or varying with time. This might, for example, be due to the passage of a charged particle or a light wave through the system. There is then a finite probability that in a certain time the system will have made a transition to some other stationary state. This is called a *transition probability*, and in order to calculate it we need to use a modified Schrödinger equation which applies when the energy of the system is not necessarily constant.

The form of the required equation is suggested by considerations like those introduced in § 2.1. The classical Hamiltonian H and energy E are now both functions of the time t, so that the energy equation is

$$H(q, p, t) = E(t) \tag{11.1}$$

(for compactness we use q and p to denote the whole set of cartesian coordinates and conjugate momenta of the system). Let us define the function $\mathscr{H}$ by

$$\mathscr{H}(q, p, t, E) = H(q, p, t) - E.$$

It can immediately be verified that $\mathscr{H}$ may be used as the Hamiltonian of the system, for

$$\frac{\partial \mathscr{H}}{\partial p} = \frac{\partial H}{\partial p} = \dot{q}, \tag{11.2a}$$

and

$$-\frac{\partial \mathscr{H}}{\partial q} = -\frac{\partial H}{\partial q} = \dot{p} \tag{11.2b}$$

— in other words, Hamilton's equations have the same form whether $\mathscr{H}$ or H is used. However, we now have the two further equations

$$\frac{\partial \mathscr{H}}{\partial E} = -1 = \dot{t}, \tag{11.3a}$$

and

$$\frac{\partial \mathscr{H}}{\partial t} = \frac{\partial H}{\partial t}.$$

The latter equation may be written, using (11.1),

$$-\frac{\partial \mathscr{H}}{\partial(-t)} = \dot{E}. \tag{11.3b}$$

Comparing (11.3a) and (11.3b) with (11.2a) and (11.2b) respectively, we deduce that E is conjugate to $-t$. Now, in obtaining the Schrödinger equation from the classical energy equation, we replace the momentum p conjugate to q by the operator $-\mathrm{i}\hbar\, \partial/\partial q$. The foregoing suggests that E should also be replaced by the operator $-\mathrm{i}\hbar\, \partial/\partial(-t)$; that is, we should write

$$E = \mathrm{i}\hbar \frac{\partial}{\partial t}. \tag{11.4}$$

Substituting in equation (11.1), and operating with both sides upon a function † $\Psi(q, t)$, we obtain

$$H\left(q, \frac{\hbar}{\mathrm{i}}\frac{\partial}{\partial q}, t\right)\Psi = \mathrm{i}\hbar\frac{\partial \Psi}{\partial t}, \tag{11.5}$$

which is the *time-dependent Schrödinger equation*. The function Ψ must, of course, satisfy the conditions imposed upon ψ in § 2.2.

For a system of N particles with a potential energy V which depends explicitly upon the time, the equation is thus

† Throughout the present chapter we shall use Ψ to denote a function of the particle coordinates and the time, and ψ to denote a function of the particle coordinates only.

$$\left[-\sum_{i=1}^{N}\frac{\hbar^2}{2m_i}\nabla_i^2+V(x_1, y_1, z_1, \dots x_N, y_N, z_N, t)\right]\Psi(x_1, \dots z_N, t)$$

$$= \mathrm{i}\hbar\frac{\partial}{\partial t}\Psi(x_1, \dots z_N, t). \qquad (11.6)$$

It should be emphasized that we have *not* given a rigorous derivation of the Schrödinger time-dependent equation from classical mechanics. No such derivation exists, any more than it does for the time-free equation considered previously. Nor is a derivation necessary — it is sufficient to postulate equation (11.5) as one of the basic equations of wave mechanics. We have merely been concerned to remove a little of the arbitrariness from such a postulate, but, as always, the justification lies in the results.

Of course, equation (11.5) must remain valid even when we are dealing with a conservative system. In this case H does not contain t, and the equation is separable. We write

$$\Psi(q, t) = \psi(q)f(t), \qquad (11.7)$$

substitute in (11.5), and divide through by Ψ, obtaining

$$\frac{1}{\psi}H\psi = \frac{\mathrm{i}\hbar}{f}\frac{\mathrm{d}f}{\mathrm{d}t}. \qquad (11.8)$$

The left-hand side is a function of q only and the right-hand side a function of t only, so that both must equal the same *separation constant* λ. Thus,

$$H\psi = \lambda\psi. \qquad (11.9)$$

But this is just the ordinary (time-free) Schrödinger equation, and λ must therefore be one of the energy eigenvalues, E_n say, and ψ the corresponding eigenfunction ψ_n. The equation for f is then

$$\frac{1}{f}\frac{\mathrm{d}f}{\mathrm{d}t} = -\frac{\mathrm{i}}{\hbar}E_n, \qquad (11.10)$$

with the general solution

$$f(t) = A\mathrm{e}^{-\mathrm{i}E_n t/\hbar}, \qquad (11.11)$$

where A is an arbitrary constant. A separable solution of (11.5) for a conservative system is therefore

$$\Psi_n(q, t) = A\psi_n(q)\mathrm{e}^{-\mathrm{i}E_n t/\hbar}, \qquad (11.12)$$

and, since the equation is linear, the general solution may be expressed as a sum of such solutions for all the states ψ_n; that is,

$$\Psi(q, t) = \sum_n A_n \psi_n(q) e^{-iE_n t/\hbar}, \tag{11.13}$$

the coefficients A_n being constants. When $t = 0$, we have

$$\Psi(q, 0) = \sum_n A_n \psi_n(q),$$

and, if the ψ_n are normalized as well as orthogonal, we find by the method of Appendix 2

$$A_n = \int \psi_n^*(q) \Psi(q, 0) dq, \tag{11.14}$$

the integration being over the configuration space of the system.

In the general case of a non-conservative system, let us suppose that ψ_n and E_n are the eigenfunctions and corresponding eigenvalues of the equation

$$H_0 \psi = E \psi, \tag{11.15}$$

where

$$H_0 = H \left(q, \frac{\hbar}{i} \frac{\partial}{\partial q}, 0 \right),$$

the Hamiltonian at time $t = 0$ (we can choose $t = 0$ to be any convenient instant). Then the general solution of equation (11.5) may be written

$$\Psi(q, t) = \sum_n A_n(t) \psi_n(q) e^{-iE_n t/\hbar}, \tag{11.16}$$

where the coefficients A_n are now functions of t. This is because, at any fixed time t, it is always possible to expand the function $\Psi(q, t)$ in terms of a complete orthogonal set of functions of q, but the coefficients will, of course, depend upon the value of t. The exponential factors in (11.16) are really superfluous so long as the $A_n(t)$ are not specified, but are included so that, in the case of a conservative system, the expansion reduces to (11.13) with A_n constant.

11.2. Probability Density and Expectation Values

If Ψ is normalized according to

$$\int |\Psi(q, t)|^2 dq = 1, \tag{11.17}$$

then $|\Psi|^2$, or $\Psi^* \Psi$, is interpreted as a probability density. In other words,

$|\Psi(q, t)|^2 \mathrm{d}q$ *is the probability that the configuration of the system will lie in the small interval* dq *about* q *at the time* t.

It is implicit in the normalizing equation (11.17) that the integral of $|\Psi(q, t)|^2$ over the configuration space of the system must be a constant, independent of t. This is easily seen to be true for the function Ψ_n given in equation (11.12), but we will now prove it to be so in general. The Schrödinger equation and its complex conjugate are

$$H\Psi = \mathrm{i}\hbar \frac{\partial \Psi}{\partial t}, \tag{11.18}$$

$$H^*\Psi^* = -\mathrm{i}\hbar \frac{\partial \Psi^*}{\partial t}. \tag{11.19}$$

Multiplying the former by Ψ^* and subtracting the latter multiplied by Ψ gives

$$\frac{1}{\mathrm{i}\hbar}(\Psi^* H\Psi - \Psi H^* \Psi^*) = \Psi^* \frac{\partial \Psi}{\partial t} + \Psi \frac{\partial \Psi^*}{\partial t} = \frac{\partial}{\partial t}(\Psi^* \Psi). \tag{11.20}$$

Hence

$$\frac{\partial}{\partial t}\int |\Psi|^2 \mathrm{d}q = \frac{1}{\mathrm{i}\hbar}\int (\Psi^* H\Psi - \Psi H^* \Psi^*)\mathrm{d}q. \tag{11.21}$$

However, owing to the Hermitian character of H [see equation (3.58)],

$$\int \Psi^* H \Psi \,\mathrm{d}q = \int \Psi H^* \Psi^* \,\mathrm{d}q, \tag{11.22}$$

so that

$$\frac{\partial}{\partial t}\int |\Psi|^2 \mathrm{d}q = 0, \tag{11.23}$$

and this is what we wished to prove.

The *expectation value* $\langle f \rangle$ of an operator $f(q, p)$ is defined as in § 2.7 by

$$\langle f \rangle = \int \Psi^*(q, t) f\left(q, \frac{\hbar}{\mathrm{i}}\frac{\partial}{\partial q}\right) \Psi(q, t)\mathrm{d}q, \tag{11.24}$$

when Ψ is normalized.

For a *conservative* system in the state given by equation (11.13) the expectation value of the energy is

$$\begin{aligned}\langle H\rangle &= \int \Psi^*(q,t)H\left(q,\frac{\hbar}{\mathrm{i}}\frac{\partial}{\partial q}\right)\Psi(q,t)\mathrm{d}q \\ &= \int (\sum_n A_n^*\psi_n^*\mathrm{e}^{\mathrm{i}E_nt/\hbar})\mathrm{i}\hbar\frac{\partial}{\partial t}(\sum_m A_m\psi_m\mathrm{e}^{-\mathrm{i}E_mt/\hbar})\mathrm{d}q \\ &= \sum_n\sum_m A_n^*A_mE_m\mathrm{e}^{\mathrm{i}(E_n-E_m)t/\hbar}\int \psi_n^*\psi_m\mathrm{d}q \\ &= \sum_n |A_n|^2E_n, \end{aligned} \tag{11.25}$$

assuming that the ψ_n are normalized as well as orthogonal. This formula is only true provided Ψ is normalized, that is to say,

$$\begin{aligned}\int |\Psi(q,t)|^2\mathrm{d}q &= \sum_n\sum_m A_n^*A_m\mathrm{e}^{\mathrm{i}(E_n-E_m)t/\hbar}\int \psi_n^*\psi_m\mathrm{d}q \\ &= \sum_n |A_n|^2 = 1. \end{aligned} \tag{11.26}$$

Now, a measurement of the energy of the system must yield one of the energy eigenvalues E_n. We therefore deduce from (11.25) and (11.26) that $|A_n|^2$ is to be interpreted as the probability that the measured value of the energy will be E_n.

For the particular state

$$\Psi_n(q,t) = \psi_n(q)\mathrm{e}^{-\mathrm{i}E_nt/\hbar} \tag{11.27}$$

of a conservative system, we note that the energy is *certain* to have the value E_n. Also

$$|\Psi_n(q,t)|^2 = |\psi_n(q)|^2, \tag{11.28}$$

so that the probability density does not change with time, and the above probability interpretation of $|\Psi|^2$ reduces to the one we used earlier in the book. Such a state is what we have referred to as a *stationary state.* Since it is $|\Psi|^2$ and not Ψ itself which has physical meaning, it is clear that so long as we only consider stationary states the time-dependence is not significant.

11.3. The Current Density

Let us for simplicity consider a single electron moving in an electric field, with potential energy $V(\boldsymbol{r})$. The Hamiltonian is

$$H = -\frac{\hbar^2}{2m}\nabla^2+V(\boldsymbol{r}), \tag{11.29}$$

and equation (11.20) becomes

$$\frac{\partial}{\partial t}|\Psi|^2 = -\frac{\hbar}{2mi}(\Psi^*\nabla^2\Psi - \Psi\nabla^2\Psi^*). \tag{11.30}$$

This is the same as

$$\frac{\partial}{\partial t}|\Psi|^2 = -\frac{\hbar}{2mi}\operatorname{div}(\Psi^*\nabla\Psi - \Psi\nabla\Psi^*), \tag{11.31}$$

since

$$\nabla\cdot(\Psi^*\nabla\Psi) = \nabla\Psi^*\cdot\nabla\Psi + \Psi^*\nabla^2\Psi.$$

It will now be convenient to use the *charge cloud* interpretation of $|\Psi|^2$, introduced for $|\psi|^2$ in § 2.6, which is closely related to the probability interpretation. Thus, we assume that the charge $-e$ of the electron is spread out into a charge cloud of density

$$\rho = -e|\Psi|^2, \tag{11.32}$$

which in general is a function of position and of time. The *electric current density* $\boldsymbol{j}$ is then related to ρ by the *equation of continuity*

$$\frac{\partial\rho}{\partial t} = -\operatorname{div}\boldsymbol{j}, \tag{11.33}$$

which merely expresses the fact that the rate at which charge is emerging from a volume element must equal the rate at which the charge within the element is decreasing. Comparing (11.33) with (11.31), we find that

$$\boldsymbol{j} = -\frac{e\hbar}{2mi}(\Psi^*\nabla\Psi - \Psi\nabla\Psi^*). \tag{11.34}$$

If $\mathrm{d}S$ is a small plane element of area and j_n is the component of $\boldsymbol{j}$ perpendicular to the element, then $j_n\,\mathrm{d}S$ is the amount of charge passing through $\mathrm{d}S$ per unit time.

Of course, it is not necessary to use the charge cloud interpretation. If we omitted the charge $-e$ from (11.32) and (11.34), then $\boldsymbol{j}$ would be the *probability current density*. On the other hand, if we substituted m for $-e$, then $\boldsymbol{j}$ would be the *mass current density*.

Since $\boldsymbol{j} = \rho\boldsymbol{v}$, where $\boldsymbol{v}$ is the *mean velocity* of charge or mass at any point, we have

$$\boldsymbol{v} = \frac{\hbar}{2mi}(\Psi^*\nabla\Psi - \Psi\nabla\Psi^*)/|\Psi|^2. \tag{11.35}$$

We note that, unless a state Ψ is a complex function of the spatial coordinates, there is no current associated with it. For example, the eigenfunctions of a free particle moving along the x-axis are

$$\psi_k(x) = \mathrm{e}^{ikx}, \tag{11.36}$$

with unquantized energies

$$\varepsilon(k) = \frac{\hbar^2 k^2}{2m}. \tag{11.37}$$

The time-dependent wave function of a stationary state is, thus,

$$\Psi_k(x, t) = \mathrm{e}^{ikx}\mathrm{e}^{-\mathrm{i}\varepsilon(k)t/\hbar}. \tag{11.38}$$

This is not normalized, but none the less may be substituted in equation (11.35), since normalization would multiply the numerator and the denominator by the same constant. We find

$$\begin{aligned} v &= \frac{\hbar}{2m\mathrm{i}}\left(\Psi_k^* \frac{\mathrm{d}\Psi_k}{\mathrm{d}x} - \Psi_k \frac{\mathrm{d}\Psi_k^*}{\mathrm{d}x}\right) \Big/ |\Psi|^2 \\ &= \frac{\hbar}{2m\mathrm{i}}\left(\mathrm{e}^{-ikx}\frac{\mathrm{d}}{\mathrm{d}x}\mathrm{e}^{ikx} - \mathrm{e}^{ikx}\frac{\mathrm{d}}{\mathrm{d}x}\mathrm{e}^{-ikx}\right) \\ &= \frac{\hbar k}{m}. \end{aligned} \tag{11.39}$$

For a particle in a one-dimensional box, however, with eigenfunctions

$$\psi_k(x) = \sin kx, \tag{11.40}$$

and the same time factor as in (11.38), we find $v = 0$.

For a stationary state of any conservative system, with wave function of the form

$$\Psi(q, t) = \psi(q)\mathrm{e}^{-\mathrm{i}Et/\hbar}, \tag{11.41}$$

it is easily seen that

$$\boldsymbol{v} = \frac{\hbar}{2m\mathrm{i}}(\psi^*\nabla\psi - \psi\nabla\psi^*)/|\psi|^2. \tag{11.42}$$

11.4. The Average Velocity Associated with a One-Electron State in a Metal

We assume that a valence electron in a metal is in a stationary state whose Bloch wave function is

$$\psi_{\boldsymbol{k}}(\boldsymbol{r}) = e^{i\boldsymbol{k}\cdot\boldsymbol{r}} u_{\boldsymbol{k}}(\boldsymbol{r}), \tag{11.43}$$

satisfying the Schrödinger equation

$$\nabla^2\psi_{\boldsymbol{k}} + \frac{2m}{\hbar^2}[\varepsilon(\boldsymbol{k}) - V(\boldsymbol{r})]\psi_{\boldsymbol{k}} = 0. \tag{11.44}$$

We wish to determine the average velocity $\langle \boldsymbol{v}_{\boldsymbol{k}} \rangle$ of the electron, taken throughout the volume of the metal, which, according to equation (11.42), is given by

$$\begin{aligned}\langle \boldsymbol{v}_{\boldsymbol{k}} \rangle &= \int \boldsymbol{v}_{\boldsymbol{k}} |\psi_{\boldsymbol{k}}|^2 \,\mathrm{d}\boldsymbol{r} \\ &= \frac{\hbar}{2mi}\int (\psi_{\boldsymbol{k}}^* \nabla\psi_{\boldsymbol{k}} - \psi_{\boldsymbol{k}} \nabla\psi_{\boldsymbol{k}}^*)\,\mathrm{d}\boldsymbol{r},\end{aligned} \tag{11.45}$$

provided $\psi_{\boldsymbol{k}}$ is normalized, so that

$$\int |\psi_{\boldsymbol{k}}|^2 \,\mathrm{d}\boldsymbol{r} = \int |u_{\boldsymbol{k}}|^2 \,\mathrm{d}\boldsymbol{r} = 1. \tag{11.46}$$

Differentiating (11.44) partially with respect to k_1, the x-component of $\boldsymbol{k}$, we obtain

$$\nabla^2 \frac{\partial \psi_{\boldsymbol{k}}}{\partial k_1} + \frac{2m}{\hbar^2}\left[\psi_{\boldsymbol{k}} \frac{\partial \varepsilon}{\partial k_1} + (\varepsilon - V)\frac{\partial \psi_{\boldsymbol{k}}}{\partial k_1}\right] = 0. \tag{11.47}$$

But, from (11.43), we have

$$\frac{\partial \psi_{\boldsymbol{k}}}{\partial k_1} = ix\psi_{\boldsymbol{k}} + e^{i\boldsymbol{k}\cdot\boldsymbol{r}} \frac{\partial u_{\boldsymbol{k}}}{\partial k_1}, \tag{11.48}$$

so that

$$\nabla^2 \frac{\partial \psi_{\boldsymbol{k}}}{\partial k_1} = 2i \frac{\partial \psi_{\boldsymbol{k}}}{\partial x} + ix\nabla^2\psi_{\boldsymbol{k}} + \nabla^2\left(e^{i\boldsymbol{k}\cdot\boldsymbol{r}} \frac{\partial u_{\boldsymbol{k}}}{\partial k_1}\right). \tag{11.49}$$

Equation (11.47) thus becomes

$$2i \frac{\partial \psi_{\boldsymbol{k}}}{\partial x} + \frac{2m}{\hbar^2}\psi_{\boldsymbol{k}} \frac{\partial \varepsilon}{\partial k_1} + \left[\nabla^2 + \frac{2m}{\hbar^2}(\varepsilon - V)\right]\left(e^{i\boldsymbol{k}\cdot\boldsymbol{r}} \frac{\partial u_{\boldsymbol{k}}}{\partial k_1}\right) = 0, \tag{11.50}$$

using (11.44). Multiplying by $\psi_{\boldsymbol{k}}^*$, and integrating throughout the volume of the metal, gives

$$\mathrm{i}\int \psi_{\boldsymbol{k}}^{*} \frac{\partial \psi_{\boldsymbol{k}}}{\partial x}\,\mathrm{d}\boldsymbol{r} = -\frac{m}{\hbar^2}\frac{\partial \varepsilon}{\partial k_1}, \tag{11.51}$$

the contribution from the last term of (11.50) being zero for the following reason. According to Green's theorem [Appendix 1, equation (A1.23)],

$$\int \left[\psi_{\boldsymbol{k}}^{*}\nabla^2\left(\mathrm{e}^{\mathrm{i}\boldsymbol{k}\cdot\boldsymbol{r}}\frac{\partial u_{\boldsymbol{k}}}{\partial k_1}\right) - \left(\mathrm{e}^{\mathrm{i}\boldsymbol{k}\cdot\boldsymbol{r}}\frac{\partial u_{\boldsymbol{k}}}{\partial k_1}\right)\nabla^2\psi_{\boldsymbol{k}}^{*}\right]\mathrm{d}\boldsymbol{r}$$
$$= \int \left[\psi_{\boldsymbol{k}}^{*}\frac{\partial}{\partial n}\left(\mathrm{e}^{\mathrm{i}\boldsymbol{k}\cdot\boldsymbol{r}}\frac{\partial u_{\boldsymbol{k}}}{\partial k_1}\right) - \left(\mathrm{e}^{\mathrm{i}\boldsymbol{k}\cdot\boldsymbol{r}}\frac{\partial u_{\boldsymbol{k}}}{\partial k_1}\right)\frac{\partial}{\partial n}\psi_{\boldsymbol{k}}^{*}\right]\mathrm{d}S. \tag{11.52}$$

The latter integral is over the surface of the metal, and vanishes owing to the periodicity of the integrand. Hence,

$$\int \psi_{\boldsymbol{k}}^{*}\left[\nabla^2 + \frac{2m}{\hbar^2}(\varepsilon - V)\right]\left(\mathrm{e}^{\mathrm{i}\boldsymbol{k}\cdot\boldsymbol{r}}\frac{\partial u_{\boldsymbol{k}}}{\partial k_1}\right)\mathrm{d}\boldsymbol{r}$$
$$= \int \left(\mathrm{e}^{\mathrm{i}\boldsymbol{k}\cdot\boldsymbol{r}}\frac{\partial u_{\boldsymbol{k}}}{\partial k_1}\right)\left[\nabla^2 + \frac{2m}{\hbar^2}(\varepsilon - V)\right]\psi_{\boldsymbol{k}}^{*}\,\mathrm{d}\boldsymbol{r} = 0, \tag{11.53}$$

since $\psi_{\boldsymbol{k}}^{*}$ also satisfies equation (11.44).

There are two equations similar to (11.51), corresponding to the other two components of $\boldsymbol{k}$, and all three equations may be combined to give

$$\mathrm{i}\int \psi_{\boldsymbol{k}}^{*}\nabla\psi_{\boldsymbol{k}}\,\mathrm{d}\boldsymbol{r} = -\frac{m}{\hbar^2}\,\mathrm{grad}_{\boldsymbol{k}}\,\varepsilon(\boldsymbol{k}) = -\frac{m}{\hbar^2}\nabla_{\boldsymbol{k}}\varepsilon(\boldsymbol{k}), \tag{11.54}$$

where

$$\nabla_{\boldsymbol{k}} = \boldsymbol{e}_1\frac{\partial}{\partial k_1} + \boldsymbol{e}_2\frac{\partial}{\partial k_2} + \boldsymbol{e}_3\frac{\partial}{\partial k_3}.$$

The energy is real, and so we must also have

$$-\mathrm{i}\int \psi_{\boldsymbol{k}}\nabla\psi_{\boldsymbol{k}}^{*}\,\mathrm{d}\boldsymbol{r} = -\frac{m}{\hbar^2}\nabla_{\boldsymbol{k}}\varepsilon(\boldsymbol{k}). \tag{11.55}$$

Substituting (11.54) and (11.55) in (11.45), we obtain, finally,

$$\langle \boldsymbol{v}_{\boldsymbol{k}}\rangle = \frac{1}{\hbar}\nabla_{\boldsymbol{k}}\varepsilon(\boldsymbol{k}). \tag{11.56}$$

This is the relation we used in our discussion of metallic conduction in § 8.12. It shows, among other things, that a perfect lattice has no resistance, for an electron in a state $\boldsymbol{k}$ will always have the same average velocity.

In the case of a free electron, with $V(\boldsymbol{r}) = 0$, we have

$$\varepsilon(\boldsymbol{k}) = \frac{\hbar^2 k^2}{2m}, \tag{11.57}$$

and equation (11.56) gives

$$\langle \boldsymbol{v}_{\boldsymbol{k}} \rangle = \frac{\hbar \boldsymbol{k}}{m}. \tag{11.58}$$

Equation (11.42) tells us, in fact, that $\boldsymbol{v}_{\boldsymbol{k}}$ is constant, with the above value.

As a second example, let us consider the tight-binding method applied to a simple cubic lattice. Equation (8.116) gives the energy of the state $\boldsymbol{k}$ as

$$\varepsilon(\boldsymbol{k}) = \varepsilon_0 - \alpha - 2\gamma\,(\cos k_1 a + \cos k_2 a + \cos k_3 a),$$

so that

$$\nabla_{\boldsymbol{k}}\, \varepsilon(\boldsymbol{k}) = 2\gamma a(\boldsymbol{e}_1 \sin k_1 a + \boldsymbol{e}_2 \sin k_2 a + \boldsymbol{e}_3 \sin k_3 a). \tag{11.59}$$

The x-component $\langle v_x \rangle$ of the average velocity, for example, depends upon k_1 as shown in Figure 11.1. It is zero not only at the centre of the zone, but also at the zone boundaries $k_1 = \pm\pi/a$.

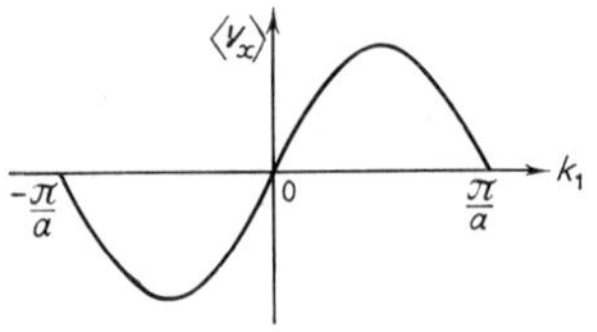

Fig. 11.1. The x-component of the average velocity as a function of k_1, according to the tight binding theory for a simple cubic lattice.

More sophisticated models give similar results. When the energy surfaces intersect the zone faces orthogonally, the component of $\langle \boldsymbol{v}_{\boldsymbol{k}} \rangle$ normal to a zone face must be zero over the whole face.

11.5. Wave Packets

Let us consider a free particle moving along the x-axis. The time-dependent Schrödinger equation is

$$-\frac{\hbar^2}{2m}\frac{\partial^2 \Psi}{\partial x^2} = i\hbar \frac{\partial \Psi}{\partial t}, \tag{11.60}$$

with the particular solution

$$\Psi_k(x, t) = e^{i(kx-\omega t)}, \tag{11.61}$$

a plane wave with wavelength $2\pi/k$ and angular frequency

$$\omega(k) = \frac{\varepsilon(k)}{\hbar} = \frac{\hbar k^2}{2m}. \tag{11.62}$$

The energy $\varepsilon(k)$ may have any value, so that the general solution of (11.60) is

$$\Psi(x, t) = \int_{-\infty}^{\infty} A(k) e^{i(kx-\omega t)} dk. \tag{11.63}$$

This is known as a *wave packet*. $A(k)$ is an arbitrary function (it must, of course, be such that the integral will converge), but the most useful wave packets are those for which $A(k)$ is large for only a small range of values of k.

As a specific example, let us suppose that $A(k)$ is the *Gaussian function*

$$A(k) = c e^{-a^2(k-K)^2}, \tag{11.64}$$

where c, a and K are constants. The value of $A(k)$ is a maximum when

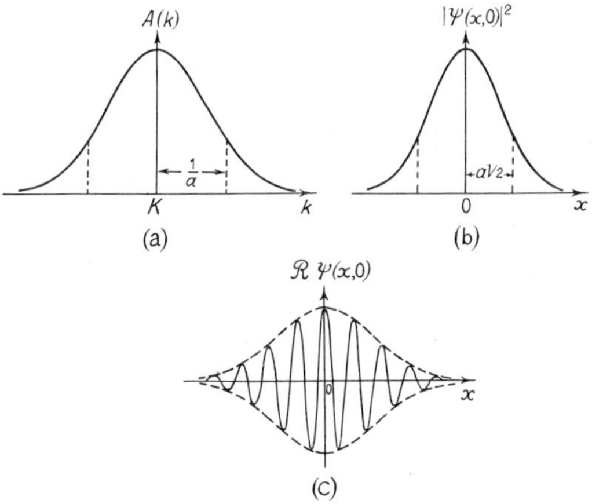

Fig. 11.2. Graphs of the functions $A(k)$, $|\Psi(x, 0)|^2$, and $\mathscr{R}\Psi(x, 0)$, the real part of $\Psi(x, 0)$.

$k = K$, and falls to $1/e$ times this value when $k-K = \pm 1/a$, tending rapidly to zero for larger values of $|k-K|$, as shown in Figure 11.2 (a). The range of k which contributes significantly to the integral (11.63) is thus roughly of width $2/a$ and symmetrical about K.

Substituting (11.64) in (11.63), we obtain

$$\Psi(x, t) = c\int_{-\infty}^{\infty} e^{\{-a^2(k-K)^2+i[kx-(\hbar k^2/2m)t]\}}\,dk. \tag{11.65}$$

Now let us write $\xi = k-K$, so that

$$\begin{aligned} -a^2\xi^2+i\left(kx-\frac{\hbar k^2}{2m}t\right) \\ &= -a^2\xi+ix(K+\xi)-\frac{i\hbar t}{2m}(K+\xi)^2 \\ &= -\alpha\xi^2-2\beta\xi-\gamma, \end{aligned} \tag{11.66}$$

where

$$\alpha = a^2+\frac{i\hbar t}{2m},$$

$$\beta = \frac{i}{2}\left(-x+\frac{\hbar tK}{m}\right),$$

and

$$\gamma = iK\left(-x+\frac{\hbar tK}{2m}\right).$$

Then

$$\begin{aligned} \Psi(x, t) &= c\int_{-\infty}^{\infty} e^{-\alpha\xi^2-2\beta\xi-\gamma}\,d\xi \\ &= c e^{(\beta^2/\alpha)-\gamma}\int_{-\infty}^{\infty} e^{-\alpha(\xi+\beta/\alpha)^2}\,d\xi \\ &= c e^{(\beta^2/\alpha)-\gamma}\int_{-\infty}^{\infty} e^{-\alpha u^2}\,du = c\sqrt{\frac{\pi}{\alpha}}\, e^{(\beta^2/\alpha)-\gamma} \\ &= \frac{c\sqrt{\pi}}{\sqrt{\left(a^2+\dfrac{i\hbar t}{2m}\right)}}\exp\left[-\frac{\left(x-\dfrac{\hbar tK}{m}\right)^2}{4\left(a^2+\dfrac{i\hbar t}{2m}\right)}+iK\left(x-\frac{\hbar tK}{2m}\right)\right]. \end{aligned} \tag{11.67}$$

In particular,

$$\Psi(x, 0) = \frac{c\sqrt{\pi}}{a}\, e^{-x^2/4a^2}\, e^{ixK}, \tag{11.68}$$

the real part of which is shown in Figure 11.2 (c). The factor exp $(\mathrm{i}xK)$ is a plane wave profile, with wavelength $2\pi/K$, and its amplitude is *modulated* by the factor exp $(-x^2/4a^2)$.

The probability density at $t = 0$ is

$$|\Psi(x, 0)|^2 = \frac{|c|^2\pi}{a^2}\,\mathrm{e}^{-x^2/2a^2}. \tag{11.69}$$

This is the Gaussian function shown in Figure 11.2(b), with its maximum at $x = 0$. It falls to $1/\mathrm{e}$ times its maximum value when $x = \pm a\sqrt{2}$. Nearly the whole of the area under the curve (c must be chosen so that this is unity) comes from the range $-a\sqrt{2} < x < a\sqrt{2}$. We may therefore say that, at $t = 0$, a particle in the state Ψ will almost certainly be found within a distance $a\sqrt{2}$ of the origin. We may therefore take

$$\Delta x = a\sqrt{2} \tag{11.70}$$

to be the *uncertainty* in the position of the particle at $t = 0$.

Now equation (11.39) tells us that the momentum of a free particle in a stationary state k is $p = mv = \hbar k$. The state Ψ is not a stationary state, however, and the k values are spread over an infinite range, but the most important k values lie within $1/a$ of K. We may thus take the uncertainty Δk in the value of k to be $1/a$, and the uncertainty in the momentum of the particle to be

$$\Delta p = \hbar\Delta k = \hbar/a. \tag{11.71}$$

From (11.70) and (11.71), we have

$$\Delta x \cdot \Delta p = \hbar\sqrt{2}, \tag{11.72}$$

at $t = 0$, in agreement with the uncertainty principle of Heisenberg, which states that

$$\Delta x \cdot \Delta p \geqq \tfrac{1}{2}\hbar \tag{11.73}$$

(in obtaining this expression, in § 2.10, we defined Δx and Δp as the root-mean-square values of the deviations from the mean, which are smaller than the values used above).

It follows from (11.67) that

$$|\Psi(x, t)|^2 = \frac{|c|^2\pi}{\sqrt{\left(a^4 + \dfrac{\hbar^2t^2}{4m^2}\right)}}\exp\left[-\frac{a^2\left(x - \dfrac{\hbar tK}{m}\right)^2}{2\left(a^4 + \dfrac{\hbar^2t^2}{4m^2}\right)}\right]. \tag{11.74}$$

At any time t the maximum of this function occurs at $x = \hbar tK/m$, so that the maximum probability density, or the *centre* of the wave packet, is moving in the positive x-direction with velocity

$$v_g = \frac{\hbar K}{m}. \tag{11.75}$$

This is known as the *group velocity* of the packet. We also note that, as t increases, the curve of $|\Psi|^2$ against x flattens out and broadens gradually, but remains Gaussian, with the same total area.

Since $\omega = \hbar k^2/2m$, we have

$$v_g = \left(\frac{d\omega}{dk}\right)_{k=K}. \tag{11.76}$$

We will now show that this formula for the group velocity remains true whatever the dependence of ω upon k.

Let us first consider a single plane wave

$$e^{i(kx-\omega t)}. \tag{11.77}$$

This function has value unity when $kx = \omega t$. The wave profile (see § 1.3) thus travels with velocity

$$u = \omega/k, \tag{11.78}$$

which is called the *phase velocity* or *wave velocity*.

Now let us add to (11.77) another plane wave, specified by $k+\delta k$, $\omega+\delta\omega$. We obtain

$$\begin{aligned} e^{i(kx-\omega t)} &+ e^{i[(k+\delta k)x-(\omega+\delta\omega)t]} \\ &= [e^{-\frac{1}{2}i(x\delta k-t\delta\omega)}+e^{\frac{1}{2}i(x\delta x-t\delta\omega)}]e^{i[(k+\frac{1}{2}\delta k)x-(\omega+\frac{1}{2}\delta\omega)t]} \\ &= 2\cos\tfrac{1}{2}(x\delta k-t\delta\omega)e^{i[(k+\frac{1}{2}\delta k)x-(\omega+\frac{1}{2}\delta\omega)t]}. \end{aligned} \tag{11.79}$$

If δk and $\delta\omega$ are small, this is virtually the wave (11.77) with its amplitude modulated by the function $2\cos(\frac{1}{2}x\delta k - t\,\delta\omega)$. The real parts of the two wave profiles and their sum are shown in Figure 11.3. Formula (11.79) thus represents a series of wave groups whose maximum amplitude moves in the positive x-direction with the group velocity

$$v_g = \frac{\delta\omega}{\delta k}. \tag{11.80}$$

If ω is a function of k, then in the limit as δk tends to zero, we may write

$$v_g = \frac{d\omega}{dk}. \tag{11.81}$$

If we form a wave packet, as in (11.63), from plane waves whose k values all lie close to a given value K, then the same argument will apply to any pair of waves, and the group velocity will be given by (11.76).

We note that the *phase velocity* of the waves in (11.63) is

$$\frac{\omega}{k} = \frac{\hbar k}{2m}, \tag{11.82}$$

which for the essential k values is nearly enough $\hbar K/2m$, that is to say, only one half of the group velocity.

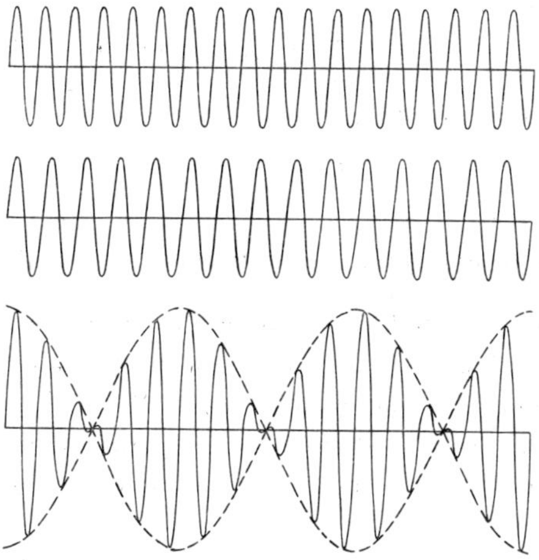

Fig. 11.3. Two plane wave profiles with slightly differing wavelengths, and their sum.

The classical velocity of the particle must be identified with the *group velocity* of a packet, and not the phase velocity of a single wave. The mean wavelength is

$$\lambda = \frac{2\pi}{K} = \frac{h}{mv_g}, \tag{11.83}$$

from (11.75), which agrees with the de Broglie formula (1.5) only if the particle velocity is taken to be v_g.

Finally, we may use the concept of group velocity to obtain another uncertainty relation of Heisenberg, which we have not yet considered. The uncertainty Δt in the *time* at which a particle associated with a wave packet passes a given point on the x-axis must equal the uncertainty in x divided by the group velocity; thus,

$$\Delta t = \frac{\Delta x}{v_g} = \frac{\hbar \Delta x}{\mathrm{d}\varepsilon/\mathrm{d}k}, \tag{11.84}$$

since $\omega = \varepsilon/\hbar$. However, the uncertainty $\Delta\varepsilon$ in the *energy* of the particle is related to the uncertainty Δk by

$$\Delta\varepsilon = \frac{\mathrm{d}\varepsilon}{\mathrm{d}k} \Delta k, \tag{11.85}$$

assuming Δk to be small, so that

$$\Delta t \cdot \Delta\varepsilon = \hbar \Delta x \cdot \Delta k = \Delta x \cdot \Delta p. \tag{11.86}$$

Hence, from (11.73), we have

$$\Delta t \cdot \Delta\varepsilon \geqq \tfrac{1}{2}\hbar. \tag{11.87}$$

11.6. Equation of Motion of a Wave Packet

We have so far been talking about wave packets which represent the motion of a free particle. Now let us consider the more general case of a particle moving under the action of a field. We will, for simplicity, still restrict ourselves to motion along the x-axis, the potential energy of the particle due to the field being $V(x)$. The time-dependent Schrödinger equation is now

$$-\frac{\hbar^2}{2m}\frac{\partial^2 \Psi}{\partial x^2} + V(x)\Psi = \mathrm{i}\hbar \frac{\partial \Psi}{\partial t}. \tag{11.88}$$

A particular solution is

$$\Psi_k(x, t) = \psi_k(x)\mathrm{e}^{-\mathrm{i}\varepsilon(k)t/\hbar}, \tag{11.89}$$

where ψ_k is an eigenfunction, and $\varepsilon(k)$ the corresponding eigenvalue, of

$$-\frac{\hbar^2}{2m}\frac{\mathrm{d}^2\psi}{\mathrm{d}x^2} + V(x)\psi = \varepsilon\psi. \tag{11.90}$$

The general solution may be written

$$\Psi(x, t) = \sum_k A_k \psi_k(x) e^{-i\varepsilon(k)t/\hbar}, \tag{11.91}$$

the coefficients A_k being constants. If the energy spectrum is continuous, or if the discrete energy levels are sufficiently closely spaced, the sum in (11.91) may be replaced by an integral:

$$\Psi(x, t) = \int A(k) \psi_k(x) e^{-i\varepsilon(k)t/\hbar} dk. \tag{11.92}$$

We will not consider a specific function Ψ, but will merely assume that this has the form of a wave packet, that is to say, $|\Psi|$ is virtually zero except in a small range of values of x at any time. The average x-coordinate, or the centre of the packet, is given by

$$\langle x \rangle = \int_{-\infty}^{\infty} x \Psi^* \Psi dx. \tag{11.93}$$

The rate of change of this with time is the group velocity of the packet, that is,

$$\frac{d\langle x \rangle}{dt} = \int_{-\infty}^{\infty} \left(x\Psi^* \frac{\partial \Psi}{\partial t} + x\Psi \frac{\partial \Psi^*}{\partial t} \right) dx. \tag{11.94}$$

We multiply equation (11.88) by $x\Psi^*$, subtract the complex conjugate equation multiplied by $x\Psi$, and integrate over all x, obtaining

$$\begin{aligned} i\hbar \frac{d\langle x \rangle}{dt} &= \int_{-\infty}^{\infty} -\frac{\hbar^2}{2m} \left(x\Psi^* \frac{\partial^2 \Psi}{\partial x^2} - x\Psi \frac{\partial^2 \Psi^*}{\partial x^2} \right) dx \\ &= \frac{\hbar^2}{2m} \int_{-\infty}^{\infty} \left(\Psi^* \frac{\partial \Psi}{\partial x} - \Psi \frac{\partial \Psi^*}{\partial x} \right) dx \\ &= \frac{\hbar^2}{m} \int_{-\infty}^{\infty} \Psi^* \frac{\partial \Psi}{\partial x} dx, \end{aligned} \tag{11.95}$$

after two integrations by parts, using the fact that Ψ vanishes at infinity.

Differentiating again with respect to time, we obtain

$$m \frac{d^2\langle x \rangle}{dt^2} = \frac{\hbar}{i} \int_{-\infty}^{\infty} \left(\frac{\partial \Psi^*}{\partial t} \frac{\partial \Psi}{\partial x} + \Psi^* \frac{\partial^2 \Psi}{\partial x \partial t} \right) dx,$$

and integration by parts of the second term in brackets gives

$$m \frac{d^2\langle x \rangle}{dt^2} = \frac{\hbar}{i} \int_{-\infty}^{\infty} \left(\frac{\partial \Psi^*}{\partial t} \frac{\partial \Psi}{\partial x} - \frac{\partial \Psi}{\partial t} \frac{\partial \Psi^*}{\partial x} \right) dx. \tag{11.96}$$

Substituting for $\partial\Psi/\partial t$ and $\partial\Psi^*/\partial t$ from the Schrödinger equation (11.88) and its complex conjugate, we obtain

$$m\frac{\mathrm{d}^2\langle x\rangle}{\mathrm{d}t^2} = -\frac{\hbar^2}{2m}\int_{-\infty}^{\infty}\left(\frac{\partial^2\Psi^*}{\partial x^2}\frac{\partial\Psi}{\partial x}+\frac{\partial^2\Psi}{\partial x^2}\frac{\partial\Psi^*}{\partial x}\right)\mathrm{d}x$$

$$+\int_{-\infty}^{\infty}V(x)\left(\Psi^*\frac{\partial\Psi}{\partial x}+\Psi\frac{\partial\Psi^*}{\partial x}\right)\mathrm{d}x$$

$$= -\int_{-\infty}^{\infty}\frac{\partial V}{\partial x}\Psi^*\Psi\,\mathrm{d}x = -\left\langle\frac{\partial V}{\partial x}\right\rangle, \tag{11.97}$$

again integrating by parts and remembering that Ψ and $\partial\Psi/\partial x$ vanish at infinity.

We have thus shown that the mean values of the acceleration and the force satisfy the classical equation of motion. In the limiting case of a very narrow wave packet, when $\Psi^*\Psi$ is practically a δ-function, the uncertainty in x will be negligible, and $\langle x\rangle$ may be identified with the classical value of the coordinate of the particle. In this case also the right hand side of (11.97) may be identified with the classical value of the force on the particle at position x, so that a very narrow wave packet satisfies the classical equation of motion.

The extension of this work to three dimensions is straightforward.

11.7. Wave Packets from Bloch Functions

In § 11.4 we determined the mean value of the velocity of an electron in a Bloch state $\boldsymbol{k}$. This may be obtained in a different way, by constructing a wave packet from Bloch functions with wave vectors in the vicinity of $\boldsymbol{k}$, and determining the group velocity of this packet. It is worth considering this method in detail, as it leads quite easily to an expression for the acceleration of a conduction electron in an external field.

Multiplying $\psi_{\boldsymbol{k}}$ in (11.43) by the appropriate time factor, we obtain the time-dependent Bloch function

$$\Psi_{\boldsymbol{k}}(\boldsymbol{r}, t) = u_{\boldsymbol{k}}(\boldsymbol{r})\mathrm{e}^{\mathrm{i}\boldsymbol{k}\cdot\boldsymbol{r}}\mathrm{e}^{-\mathrm{i}\varepsilon(\boldsymbol{k})t/\hbar}. \tag{11.98}$$

Let us construct a wave packet from such functions, with wave vectors close to $\boldsymbol{k}$; that is, we write

$$\Psi(\boldsymbol{r}, t) = \int A(\boldsymbol{k}')u_{\boldsymbol{k}'}(\boldsymbol{r})\mathrm{e}^{\mathrm{i}[\boldsymbol{k}'\cdot\boldsymbol{r}-\varepsilon(\boldsymbol{k}')t/\hbar]}\mathrm{d}\boldsymbol{k}', \tag{11.99}$$

where $|A(\boldsymbol{k}')|$ has a sharp maximum at $\boldsymbol{k}' = \boldsymbol{k}$ and falls rapidly to zero on either side. The integration is throughout the region in which $A(\boldsymbol{k}')$ is appreciably different from zero.

Expanding $\varepsilon(\boldsymbol{k}')$ in Taylor's series about $\boldsymbol{k}$, we obtain

$$\varepsilon(\boldsymbol{k}') = \varepsilon(\boldsymbol{k}) + (\boldsymbol{k}' - \boldsymbol{k}) \cdot \nabla_{\boldsymbol{k}} \varepsilon(\boldsymbol{k}) + \dots. \tag{11.100}$$

Since $|\boldsymbol{k}' - \boldsymbol{k}|$ is very small in the region of integration, we may neglect the remaining terms in the series, and, as a good approximation, write

$$\Psi(\boldsymbol{r}, t) = \mathrm{e}^{\mathrm{i}[\boldsymbol{k} \cdot \boldsymbol{r} - \varepsilon(\boldsymbol{k})t/\hbar]} \int A(\boldsymbol{k}') u_{\boldsymbol{k}'}(\boldsymbol{r}) \mathrm{e}^{\mathrm{i}(\boldsymbol{r} - t\nabla_{\boldsymbol{k}} \varepsilon/\hbar) \cdot (\boldsymbol{k}' - \boldsymbol{k})} \mathrm{d}\boldsymbol{k}'.$$

Also $u_{\boldsymbol{k}'}(\boldsymbol{r})$ may be assumed to change very little with $\boldsymbol{k}'$ in the region of integration, and so may be set equal to $u_{\boldsymbol{k}}(\boldsymbol{r})$ and taken outside the integral. We then have

$$\Psi(\boldsymbol{r}, t) = \Psi_{\boldsymbol{k}}(\boldsymbol{r}, t) \int A(\boldsymbol{k}') \mathrm{e}^{\mathrm{i}(\boldsymbol{r} - t\nabla_{\boldsymbol{k}} \varepsilon/\hbar) \cdot (\boldsymbol{k}' - \boldsymbol{k})} \mathrm{d}\boldsymbol{k}', \tag{11.101}$$

where $\Psi_{\boldsymbol{k}}$ is the Bloch function given in (11.98).

The integral in (11.101) has constant value so long as $\boldsymbol{r} - t\nabla_{\boldsymbol{k}} \varepsilon/\hbar$ is constant. Thus, if we ignore the periodic variation of $u_{\boldsymbol{k}}(\boldsymbol{r})$, which is independent of time, we may say that points at which $|\Psi|^2$ has a given value move with the constant velocity

$$\boldsymbol{v} = \frac{1}{\hbar} \nabla_{\boldsymbol{k}} \varepsilon(\boldsymbol{k}), \tag{11.102}$$

which is the group velocity of the packet. Comparison with equation (11.56) shows that $\boldsymbol{v}$ is equal to the average velocity of an electron in the stationary state $\boldsymbol{k}$. It must be remembered that, owing to the concentration of the function $A(\boldsymbol{k}')$ about $\boldsymbol{k}$, the wave packet must extend throughout several Wigner-Seitz cells, but it may still be small compared with the dimensions of the metal as a whole.

11.8. Acceleration of the Electrons in a Metal due to an External Electric Field

Now let us consider the effect of an electrostatic field $\boldsymbol{E}$ applied to a metal. The mean wave vector $\boldsymbol{k}$ of a wave packet representing an electron will now change with time; that is to say, the electron will be accelerated. We may assume, however, that the electron energy $\varepsilon(\boldsymbol{k})$ remains within the same zone — the fields which can be applied to metals are so weak that there is little probability of their causing an electron to make a transition to a higher zone, although such a transition is not entirely ruled out. We also assume that (11.102) remains true in the presence of an applied field, and make use of the fact proved in § 11.6, namely, that a wave packet moves like a classical particle.

The work done by the field on the electron per unit time is, then,

$$-e\boldsymbol{E}\cdot\boldsymbol{v} = -\frac{e}{\hbar}\boldsymbol{E}\cdot\nabla_{\boldsymbol{k}}\,\varepsilon(\boldsymbol{k}), \tag{11.103}$$

and this must be equated to the rate of change of the electron energy, which is

$$\frac{\mathrm{d}\varepsilon}{\mathrm{d}t} = \frac{\mathrm{d}\boldsymbol{k}}{\mathrm{d}t}\cdot\nabla_{\boldsymbol{k}}\,\varepsilon(\boldsymbol{k}). \tag{11.104}$$

We therefore find

$$\frac{\mathrm{d}\boldsymbol{k}}{\mathrm{d}t} = -\frac{e}{\hbar}\boldsymbol{E} \tag{11.105}$$

for the rate of change of the mean wave vector $\boldsymbol{k}$ of a wave packet due to the field. The wave vector increases uniformly with time in the direction of the applied force, so that the point which represents an electron in $\boldsymbol{k}$-space will travel with constant velocity, until it eventually reaches a zone face. We assume that there is an energy gap here which it is unlikely that the electron will jump. Hence, the representative point must reappear at the corresponding position on the opposite face of the zone, and continue to move with the same velocity. In the one-dimensional case shown in Figure 11.4, if $-e\boldsymbol{E}$ is in the positive k-direction, the representative point will travel along the energy curve until it reaches A, and will then reappear at A′ and again travel along the same curve to A. In extended k-space (see Figure 8.4) the point would continue to move in the positive k-direction along the oscillating energy curve of the same zone.

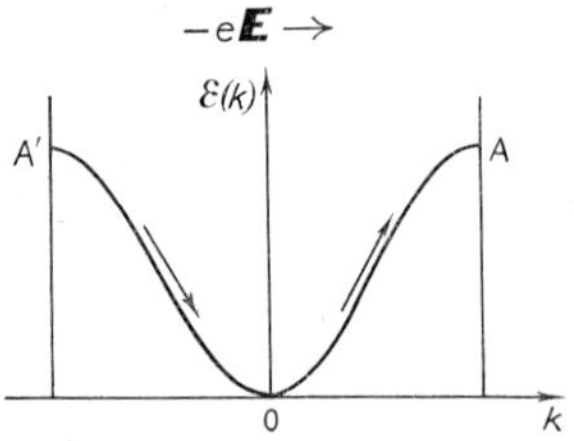

Fig. 11.4. Energy curve for a Brillouin zone of a one-dimensional metal. It is assumed that there are finite energy gaps at the zone boundaries A and A′. A point representing an electron moves in the direction shown by the arrows under the action of an electric field $\boldsymbol{E}$ in the negative k-direction.

The *acceleration* of a wave packet is

$$\frac{\mathrm{d}\boldsymbol{v}}{\mathrm{d}t} = \frac{1}{\hbar}\frac{\mathrm{d}}{\mathrm{d}t}\nabla_{\boldsymbol{k}}\,\varepsilon(\boldsymbol{k}) = \frac{1}{\hbar}\nabla_{\boldsymbol{k}}\left(\frac{\mathrm{d}\varepsilon}{\mathrm{d}t}\right)$$

$$= -\frac{e}{\hbar^2}\nabla_{\boldsymbol{k}}[\boldsymbol{E}\cdot\nabla_{\boldsymbol{k}}\,\varepsilon(\boldsymbol{k})], \tag{11.106}$$

using (11.103). The rectangular Cartesian components of the acceleration are, thus,

$$\frac{dv_1}{dt} = -\frac{e}{\hbar^2}\left(\frac{\partial^2\varepsilon}{\partial k_1^2}E_1 + \frac{\partial^2\varepsilon}{\partial k_1 \partial k_2}E_2 + \frac{\partial^2\varepsilon}{\partial k_1 \partial k_3}E_3\right),$$

$$\frac{dv_2}{dt} = -\frac{e}{\hbar^2}\left(\frac{\partial^2\varepsilon}{\partial k_2 \partial k_1}E_1 + \frac{\partial^2\varepsilon}{\partial k_2^2}E_2 + \frac{\partial^2\varepsilon}{\partial k_2 \partial k_3}E_3\right),$$

$$\frac{dv_3}{dt} = -\frac{e}{\hbar^2}\left(\frac{\partial^2\varepsilon}{\partial k_3 \partial k_1}E_1 + \frac{\partial^2\varepsilon}{\partial k_3 \partial k_2}E_2 + \frac{\partial^2\varepsilon}{\partial k_3^2}E_3\right),$$

and these equations may be written compactly in the form

$$\frac{dv_i}{dt} = -\frac{e}{\hbar^2}\sum_j \frac{\partial^2\varepsilon}{\partial k_i \partial k_j}E_j, \qquad i, j = 1, 2, 3. \tag{11.107}$$

The classical equation of motion of an electron in the field $\boldsymbol{E}$ is

$$\frac{d\boldsymbol{v}}{dt} = -\frac{e}{m}\boldsymbol{E}. \tag{11.108}$$

Now, if the one-electron energy is given by

$$\varepsilon(\boldsymbol{k}) = \frac{\hbar^2 k^2}{2m^*} = \frac{\hbar^2}{2m^*}(k_1^2 + k_2^2 + k_3^2), \tag{11.109}$$

with m^* constant, as is very nearly the case in sodium, for example, equation (11.106) reduces to

$$\frac{d\boldsymbol{v}}{dt} = -\frac{e}{m^*}\boldsymbol{E}, \tag{11.110}$$

which is the classical equation (11.108) with the *effective mass* m^* substituted for m. In a slightly more general case, if

$$\varepsilon(\boldsymbol{k}) = \frac{\hbar^2}{2}\left(\frac{k_1^2}{m_1^*} + \frac{k_2^2}{m_2^*} + \frac{k_3^2}{m_3^*}\right), \tag{11.111}$$

equations (11.107) reduce to

$$\frac{dv_i}{dt} = -\frac{e}{m_i^*}E_i, \qquad i = 1, 2, 3, \tag{11.112}$$

and m_1^*, m_2^*, m_3^* are called the *effective masses for motion in the x-, y- and z-directions* respectively.

In accordance with the foregoing, equation (11.106) is often written in the form

$$\frac{\mathrm{d}\boldsymbol{v}}{\mathrm{d}t} = -e\left(\frac{1}{\boldsymbol{m}^*}\right)\cdot\boldsymbol{E}, \tag{11.113}$$

where $(1/\boldsymbol{m}^*)$ is the *reciprocal mass tensor*, having the nine components specified by

$$\left(\frac{1}{\boldsymbol{m}^*}\right)_{ij} = \frac{1}{\hbar^2}\frac{\partial^2\varepsilon}{\partial k_i \partial k_j} \tag{11.114}$$

— the rule for multiplying the tensor by the vector is simply that contained in equations (11.107).

The acceleration is generally not in the direction of the force $-e\boldsymbol{E}$, and may, in fact, be opposed to it. For example, in the case of *one-dimensional motion*, we have

$$\frac{\mathrm{d}v}{\mathrm{d}t} = -\frac{eE}{\hbar^2}\frac{\mathrm{d}^2\varepsilon}{\mathrm{d}k^2}, \tag{11.115}$$

and the effective mass is the *scalar*

$$m^* = \hbar^2 \Big/ \frac{\mathrm{d}^2\varepsilon}{\mathrm{d}k^2}. \tag{11.116}$$

If the graph of $\varepsilon(k)$ is of the type shown in Figure 11.4, we see that $\mathrm{d}^2\varepsilon/\mathrm{d}k^2$ is negative near the zone boundaries, so that here the electron has *negative effective mass*, and the acceleration is in the opposite sense to the force $-e\boldsymbol{E}$.

If, in addition to the electric field $\boldsymbol{E}$, there is also an applied magnetic field $\boldsymbol{H}$, a natural generalization of the foregoing results is to substitute for the force $-e\boldsymbol{E}$ the *Lorentz force*

$$-e\left(\boldsymbol{E}+\frac{1}{c}\boldsymbol{v}\wedge\boldsymbol{H}\right).$$

In other words, we replace equation (11.105) by

$$\frac{\mathrm{d}\boldsymbol{k}}{\mathrm{d}t} = -\frac{e}{\hbar}\left(\boldsymbol{E}+\frac{1}{c}\boldsymbol{v}\wedge\boldsymbol{H}\right), \tag{11.117}$$

where $\boldsymbol{v}$ is again given by (11.102). Detailed consideration shows that this equation is correct for most purposes. However, according to classical mechanics, the orbit of an electron in a combined electric and magnetic field is a helix. Since the work of the present section is based upon the representation of an electron by a wave packet, the dimensions of which cannot be smaller than those of a Wigner-Seitz cell, it is expected that equation (11.117) will fail when the radius of the helix becomes comparable with the atomic radius, that is, for sufficiently strong magnetic fields.

Finally, let us briefly consider the *conductivity* of a metal. We have already noted that a perfect crystal has no resistance, for an electron in a given stationary state always has the same average velocity. Hence, an electric current, which is due to an asymmetrical distribution of occupied states in $\boldsymbol{k}$-space, will continue unchanged until the distribution is changed — that is to say, until some electrons have made transitions to new states. Although, under the action of an applied electric field $\boldsymbol{E}$, the current may at first increase with time, according to (11.106), it will not increase indefinitely, owing to the effect of the zone structure. However, the steady state required by Ohm's Law will never be achieved.

This would be true, of course, only for perfect crystals. Real crystals are never perfect. In the first place, even at very low temperatures, the ions are in a state of thermal vibration about their mean positions, which destroys the exact periodicity of the lattice. Secondly, there are generally impurities present, that is, dissolved atoms of foreign elements — it is hardly possible to get rid of these entirely, although they may be reduced to very small traces. Thirdly, there are generally flaws in the crystal structure itself, due to some local disarrangement of the ionic patterns — examples of such flaws are *dislocations*, *stacking faults*, and *grain boundaries.*

The departures from perfect periodicity of the lattice field may be regarded as perturbations which cause some electrons to make transitions to different states — we say that the electrons have *collisions* with, or are *scattered* by, the lattice irregularities — and this is the reason for the electrical resistance of the metal. Only *some* electrons can make such transitions, namely, those near the Fermi surface. Owing to the fact that the electrons are so much lighter than the ions, their energy changes very little in collisions with the lattice, and hence electrons in states well below the Fermi surface cannot be scattered, because there are no vacant states of nearby energy to which they can transfer. The scattering is thus limited by the Pauli principle.

When an electric field is applied, the whole Fermi distribution begins to move, according to (11.105), but this movement is opposed by the scattering, which tends to restore the original symmetrical distribution. Very soon a state of equilibrium is reached, when the Fermi distribution becomes static but displaced from its original position, and the result is a steady current.

The calculation of the probability of scattering per unit time, or *transition probability*, of an electron from a state $\boldsymbol{k}$ to a state $\boldsymbol{k}'$ by a lattice irregularity is thus the central problem of the theory of conductivity. It is also an extremely difficult problem, for which only approximate solutions have been obtained. It would take us too far afield to attempt to give an adequate account of this theory here, and it is not necessary to do so, since several excellent books and review articles are available (see Bibliography), which cover the subject exhaustively. We will, however, give a brief description of the general method of calculating transition probabilities, in order to prepare the reader for the more advanced treatises.

11.9. Transition Probabilities

Although we shall, throughout the present section, refer to the electrons in a metal, subject to a perturbation due to lattice irregularities, it must be understood that the method we shall use, known as *time-dependent perturbation theory*, is quite general, and may be applied to any perturbed system — a free atom in the presence of a light wave, for example.

Let us write the time-dependent Schrödinger equation of an electron in a metal in the form

$$(H+U)\Psi = i\hbar \frac{\partial \Psi}{\partial t}, \tag{11.118}$$

where H is the Hamiltonian of an electron in the perfectly periodic lattice, and $U(\boldsymbol{r}, t)$ is the *difference* between the potential energy in the actual lattice and the potential energy $V(\boldsymbol{r})$ in the perfect lattice. We shall assume that $U(\boldsymbol{r}, t)$ is a small perturbation.

As usual, we let $\psi_{\boldsymbol{k}}(\boldsymbol{r})$ and $\varepsilon(\boldsymbol{k})$ denote the eigenfunctions and corresponding eigenvalues of H, so that

$$H\psi_{\boldsymbol{k}} \equiv \left[-\frac{\hbar^2}{2m}\nabla^2 + V(\boldsymbol{r})\right]\psi_{\boldsymbol{k}} = \varepsilon(\boldsymbol{k})\psi_{\boldsymbol{k}}, \tag{11.119}$$

and assume that the $\psi_{\boldsymbol{k}}$ are normalized in the volume of the metal, that is,

$$\int |\psi_{\boldsymbol{k}}(\boldsymbol{r})|^2 \,\mathrm{d}\boldsymbol{r} = 1, \tag{11.120}$$

the integration being throughout the volume of the metal. According to the discussion at the end of § 11.1, we may then write the general solution of equation (11.118) in the form

$$\Psi(\boldsymbol{r}, t) = \sum_{\boldsymbol{k}} A_{\boldsymbol{k}}(t)\psi_{\boldsymbol{k}}(\boldsymbol{r})\mathrm{e}^{-\mathrm{i}\varepsilon(\boldsymbol{k})t/\hbar}. \tag{11.121}$$

Substituting this into (11.118), we obtain

$$\sum_{\boldsymbol{k}} A_{\boldsymbol{k}}(H\psi_{\boldsymbol{k}} + U\psi_{\boldsymbol{k}})\mathrm{e}^{-\mathrm{i}\varepsilon(\boldsymbol{k})t/\hbar} = \sum_{\boldsymbol{k}} \left[A_{\boldsymbol{k}}\varepsilon(\boldsymbol{k})\psi_{\boldsymbol{k}} + \mathrm{i}\hbar\frac{\mathrm{d}A_{\boldsymbol{k}}}{\mathrm{d}t}\psi_{\boldsymbol{k}}\right]\mathrm{e}^{-\mathrm{i}\varepsilon(\boldsymbol{k})t/\hbar}. \tag{11.122}$$

Owing to equation (11.119), the first term in the summand on the left cancels that on the right, and we are left with

$$\sum_{\boldsymbol{k}} A_{\boldsymbol{k}} U\psi_{\boldsymbol{k}}\mathrm{e}^{-\mathrm{i}\varepsilon(\boldsymbol{k})t/\hbar} = \mathrm{i}\hbar\sum_{\boldsymbol{k}}\frac{\mathrm{d}A_{\boldsymbol{k}}}{\mathrm{d}t}\psi_{\boldsymbol{k}}\mathrm{e}^{-\mathrm{i}\varepsilon(\boldsymbol{k})t/\hbar}.$$

We multiply this equation through by $\psi^*_{\boldsymbol{k}'}$, and integrate throughout the volume of the metal. Remembering that the $\psi_{\boldsymbol{k}}$ are orthogonal as well as normalized, we find

$$\frac{\mathrm{d}A_{\boldsymbol{k}'}}{\mathrm{d}t} = \frac{1}{\mathrm{i}\hbar}\sum_{\boldsymbol{k}} A_{\boldsymbol{k}} U_{\boldsymbol{k}'\boldsymbol{k}}\mathrm{e}^{\mathrm{i}[\varepsilon(\boldsymbol{k}') - \varepsilon(\boldsymbol{k})]t/\hbar}, \tag{11.123}$$

where

$$U_{\boldsymbol{k}'\boldsymbol{k}} = \int \psi^*_{\boldsymbol{k}'} U\psi_{\boldsymbol{k}}\mathrm{d}\boldsymbol{r}. \tag{11.124}$$

Now we will suppose that at time $t = 0$ the electron is in the state $\boldsymbol{k}_i$, so that, $\Psi(\boldsymbol{r}, t)$ being normalized,

$$A_{\boldsymbol{k}}(0) = \begin{cases} 1, & \boldsymbol{k} = \boldsymbol{k}_i, \\ 0, & \boldsymbol{k} \neq \boldsymbol{k}_i. \end{cases} \tag{11.125}$$

Furthermore, provided the interval t is not *too* long, we may assume that the coefficients $A_{\boldsymbol{k}}(t)$ in equation (11.123) retain their values at $t = 0$. We are then neglecting the products $A_{\boldsymbol{k}} U_{\boldsymbol{k}'\boldsymbol{k}}$, with $\boldsymbol{k} \neq \boldsymbol{k}_i$, which are *second-order* terms, since $U_{\boldsymbol{k}'\boldsymbol{k}}$ is also small. Thus, equation (11.123) becomes

$$\frac{\mathrm{d}A_{\boldsymbol{k}'}}{\mathrm{d}t} = \frac{1}{\mathrm{i}\hbar} U_{\boldsymbol{k}'\boldsymbol{k}_i}\mathrm{e}^{\mathrm{i}[\varepsilon(\boldsymbol{k}') - \varepsilon(\boldsymbol{k}_i)]t/\hbar},$$

which gives,

$$A_{\boldsymbol{k}'}(t) = \frac{1}{\mathrm{i}\hbar}\int_0^t U_{\boldsymbol{k}'\boldsymbol{k}_i}\mathrm{e}^{\mathrm{i}[\varepsilon(\boldsymbol{k}') - \varepsilon(\boldsymbol{k}_i)]t/\hbar}\mathrm{d}t \tag{11.126}$$

for $\boldsymbol{k}' \neq \boldsymbol{k}_i$. Extending the argument of § 11.2 to non-conservative systems, we interpret $|A_{\boldsymbol{k}'}(t)|^2$ as the *probability that at time t the electron will be in the state* $\boldsymbol{k}'$ — in other words, it is the *transition probability* from the state

$\boldsymbol{k}_i$ to the state $\boldsymbol{k}'$ in time t. We shall in future drop the subscript i on $\boldsymbol{k}_i$. and take the initial state to be the state $\boldsymbol{k}$.

The result (11.126) is true for any small, time-dependent perturbation $U(\boldsymbol{r}, t)$. In treating the scattering due to lattice vibrations, however, it is usual, in order to simplify the working, to calculate the transition probability for a *fixed* displacement of the ions, and then to average over all possible displacements at a given temperature. Let us therefore proceed on the assumption that U is *independent of time* (the result will, of course, be the same if the perturbation is switched on at $t = 0$ and off after time t but is otherwise constant). $U_{\boldsymbol{k}'\boldsymbol{k}}$ is then also independent of time, and (11.126) becomes (with $\boldsymbol{k}$ instead of $\boldsymbol{k}_i$)

$$A_{\boldsymbol{k}'}(t) = \frac{U_{\boldsymbol{k}'\boldsymbol{k}}}{\varepsilon(\boldsymbol{k}')-\varepsilon(\boldsymbol{k})}\{1-\mathrm{e}^{\mathrm{i}[\varepsilon(\boldsymbol{k}')-\varepsilon(\boldsymbol{k})]t/\hbar}\}. \tag{11.127}$$

The probability that, starting in the state $\boldsymbol{k}$, the electron will be found in the state $\boldsymbol{k}'$ after an interval t is, thus,

$$|A_{\boldsymbol{k}'}(t)|^2 = |U_{\boldsymbol{k}'\boldsymbol{k}}|^2\,\frac{4\sin^2(\omega_{\boldsymbol{k}'\boldsymbol{k}}t/2)}{\hbar^2\omega_{\boldsymbol{k}'\boldsymbol{k}}^2}, \tag{11.128}$$

where

$$\omega_{\boldsymbol{k}'\boldsymbol{k}} = [\varepsilon(\boldsymbol{k}')-\varepsilon(\boldsymbol{k})]/\hbar. \tag{11.129}$$

For large values of t [which may still be small enough to justify the assumption leading to equation (11.126)] $|A_{\boldsymbol{k}'}(t)|^2$ has a sharp maximum when $\omega_{\boldsymbol{k}'\boldsymbol{k}} = 0$ — in other words, transitions in which energy is conserved are most likely. For such transitions we see that $|A_{\boldsymbol{k}'}(t)|^2$ is proportional to t^2, for

$$\lim_{\omega_{\boldsymbol{k}'\boldsymbol{k}}\to 0}\frac{\sin^2(\omega_{\boldsymbol{k}'\boldsymbol{k}}t/2)}{\omega_{\boldsymbol{k}'\boldsymbol{k}}^2} = \frac{t^2}{4}. \tag{11.130}$$

This is somewhat surprising, as we should have expected the transition probability to increase linearly with time. However, it must be remembered that the distribution of one-electron states in $\boldsymbol{k}$-space is practically a continuum, so that there is a large number of final states with approximately the same wave vector $\boldsymbol{k}'$ and the same energy. What is of physical significance is thus the probability of a transition from the state $\boldsymbol{k}$ to one or another of a group of final states with approximately the same wave vector $\boldsymbol{k}'$, and with energy almost the same as that of the initial state (these may lie, for example, near a particular element of the Fermi surface): we will now show that this is proportional to t.

For convenience we denote the energy $\varepsilon(\boldsymbol{k}')$ of a final state by ε'. We also denote by $\mathcal{N}_{\mathrm{f}}(\varepsilon')$ the density of the final states in energy, so that $\mathcal{N}_{\mathrm{f}}(\varepsilon')\mathrm{d}\varepsilon'$ is the number of final states having energies in the small interval $\mathrm{d}\varepsilon'$ about ε'. The probability that in time t an electron initially in the state $\boldsymbol{k}$ will make a transition to one or another of this group of final states is then

$$\frac{4}{\hbar^2}\int |U_{\boldsymbol{k}'\boldsymbol{k}}|^2 \frac{\sin^2(\omega_{\boldsymbol{k}'\boldsymbol{k}}t/2)}{\omega_{\boldsymbol{k}'\boldsymbol{k}}^2} \mathcal{N}_{\mathrm{f}}(\varepsilon')\mathrm{d}\varepsilon'. \tag{11.131}$$

The integration is over the energy range of the final states considered, but most of the contribution to it comes from a narrow interval about $\varepsilon' = \varepsilon(\boldsymbol{k})$, or $\omega_{\boldsymbol{k}'\boldsymbol{k}} = 0$. Since we are considering a group of states with almost the same wave vector $\boldsymbol{k}'$, we may therefore take $|U_{\boldsymbol{k}'\boldsymbol{k}}|^2 \mathcal{N}_{\mathrm{f}}(\varepsilon)$ outside the integral sign, and write (11.131) as

$$\frac{4}{\hbar}|U_{\boldsymbol{k}'\boldsymbol{k}}|^2 \mathcal{N}_{\mathrm{f}}(\varepsilon)\int_{-\infty}^{\infty} \frac{\sin^2(\omega_{\boldsymbol{k}'\boldsymbol{k}}t/2)}{\omega_{\boldsymbol{k}'\boldsymbol{k}}^2}\mathrm{d}\omega_{\boldsymbol{k}'\boldsymbol{k}} \tag{11.132}$$

(little error is introduced by taking the integration over an infinite range, rather than over a finite range including $\omega_{\boldsymbol{k}'\boldsymbol{k}} = 0$). The integral is

$$\frac{t}{2}\int_{-\infty}^{\infty}\frac{\sin^2 x}{x^2}\mathrm{d}x = \frac{\pi t}{2}, \tag{11.133}$$

so that (11.132) becomes

$$\frac{2\pi}{\hbar}|U_{\boldsymbol{k}'\boldsymbol{k}}|^2 \mathcal{N}_{\mathrm{f}}(\varepsilon)t, \tag{11.134}$$

which is proportional to t, as required. The *transition probability per unit time* from the state $\boldsymbol{k}$ to one or another of a group of final states with wave vectors near $\boldsymbol{k}'$, and with almost the same energy as the initial state, is thus

$$\frac{2\pi}{\hbar}|U_{\boldsymbol{k}'\boldsymbol{k}}|^2 \mathcal{N}_{\mathrm{f}}(\varepsilon). \tag{11.135}$$

We will leave our discussion of transition probabilities here. For the methods of calculating the matrix element $U_{\boldsymbol{k}'\boldsymbol{k}}$ the reader is referred to the more advanced works mentioned in the Bibliography.

Appendix 1

VECTOR ANALYSIS

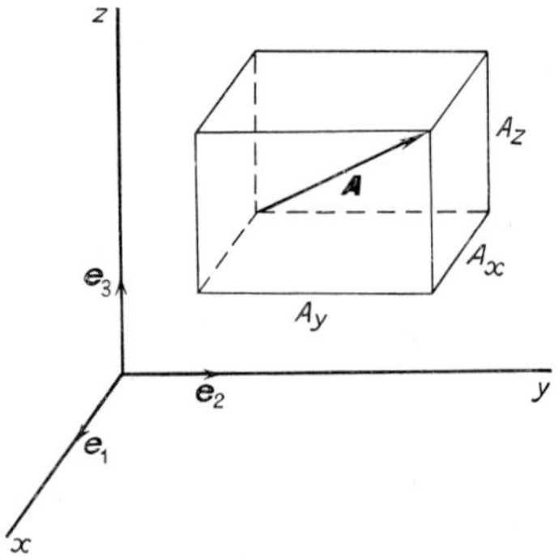

Fig. 1.

The components (A_x, A_y, A_z) of a vector $\boldsymbol{A}$, with respect to some system of rectangular Cartesian coordinates, are the projections of the vector on the axes. The *length*, or *magnitude*, of the vector $\boldsymbol{A}$, denoted by A or $|\boldsymbol{A}|$, is given by

$$A = \sqrt{(A_x^2+A_y^2+A_z^2)}, \tag{A1.1}$$

and is always taken to be positive.

If $\boldsymbol{e}_1$, $\boldsymbol{e}_2$, $\boldsymbol{e}_3$ are unit vectors, that is, vectors of length unity, in the directions of the x, y, and z axes respectively, then the vector $\boldsymbol{A}$ may be written

$$\boldsymbol{A} = A_x\boldsymbol{e}_1+A_y\boldsymbol{e}_2+A_z\boldsymbol{e}_3. \tag{A1.2}$$

In most text-books these unit vectors are denoted by $\boldsymbol{i}$, $\boldsymbol{j}$, $\boldsymbol{k}$, but we have avoided these symbols as they are rather overworked in the theory of metals.

The *radius vector* or *position vector* of a point P(x, y, z), with respect to the origin O, is the vector

$$\boldsymbol{r} = x\boldsymbol{e}_1+y\boldsymbol{e}_2+z\boldsymbol{e}_3. \tag{A1.3}$$

The distance of the point from O is, thus,

$$\text{OP} = r = \sqrt{(x^2+y^2+z^2)}. \tag{A1.4}$$

The *scalar product* $\boldsymbol{A} \cdot \boldsymbol{B}$ of two vectors $\boldsymbol{A}$ and $\boldsymbol{B}$, inclined at an angle θ to each other, is defined as

$$\boldsymbol{A} \cdot \boldsymbol{B} = AB \cos \theta. \tag{A1.5}$$

Hence,

$$\boldsymbol{e}_1 \cdot \boldsymbol{e}_1 = \boldsymbol{e}_2 \cdot \boldsymbol{e}_2 = \boldsymbol{e}_3 \cdot \boldsymbol{e}_3 = 1, \tag{A1.6}$$

and

$$\boldsymbol{e}_1 \cdot \boldsymbol{e}_2 = \boldsymbol{e}_2 \cdot \boldsymbol{e}_3 = \boldsymbol{e}_3 \cdot \boldsymbol{e}_1 = 0. \tag{A1.7}$$

In terms of the components of $\boldsymbol{A}$ and $\boldsymbol{B}$, it follows that

$$\boldsymbol{A} \cdot \boldsymbol{B} = A_x B_x + A_y B_y + A_z B_z. \tag{A1.8}$$

In particular,

$$\boldsymbol{A} \cdot \boldsymbol{A} = A^2 = A_x^2 + A_y^2 + A_z^2, \tag{A1.9}$$

in agreement with (A1.1).

The *vector product* $\boldsymbol{A} \wedge \boldsymbol{B}$ is defined as the vector $\boldsymbol{C}$ whose magnitude is

$$C = AB \sin \theta, \tag{A1.10}$$

where θ is the *smaller* of the angles of inclination, and whose direction is perpendicular to the plane containing $\boldsymbol{A}$ and $\boldsymbol{B}$, in the sense defined by the right-handed screw rule with respect to a rotation of $\boldsymbol{A}$ towards $\boldsymbol{B}$ through the angle θ. Hence,

$$\boldsymbol{e}_1 \wedge \boldsymbol{e}_1 = \boldsymbol{e}_2 \wedge \boldsymbol{e}_2 = \boldsymbol{e}_3 \wedge \boldsymbol{e}_3 = 0, \tag{A1.11}$$

and

$$\boldsymbol{e}_1 \wedge \boldsymbol{e}_2 = \boldsymbol{e}_3, \ \boldsymbol{e}_2 \wedge \boldsymbol{e}_3 = \boldsymbol{e}_1, \ \boldsymbol{e}_3 \wedge \boldsymbol{e}_1 = \boldsymbol{e}_2. \tag{A1.12}$$

Also,

$$\boldsymbol{A} \wedge \boldsymbol{B} = -\boldsymbol{B} \wedge \boldsymbol{A}. \tag{A1.13}$$

It follows that the components of $\boldsymbol{C}$ are

$$\left.\begin{aligned} C_x &= A_y B_z - A_z B_y, \\ C_y &= A_z B_x - A_x B_z, \\ C_z &= A_x B_y - A_y B_x, \end{aligned}\right\} \tag{A1.14}$$

or, alternatively, the vector $\mathbf{C}$ may be written in the determinantal form (see Appendix 3)

$$\boldsymbol{C} = \boldsymbol{A} \wedge \boldsymbol{B} = \begin{vmatrix} \boldsymbol{e}_1 & \boldsymbol{e}_2 & \boldsymbol{e}_3 \\ A_x & A_y & A_z \\ B_x & B_y & B_z \end{vmatrix}. \tag{A1.15}$$

The *scalar triple product* $\boldsymbol{F} \cdot \boldsymbol{A} \wedge \boldsymbol{B}$ is found from (A1.15) to be

$$\boldsymbol{F} \cdot \boldsymbol{A} \wedge \boldsymbol{B} = \begin{vmatrix} F_x & F_y & F_z \\ A_x & A_y & A_z \\ B_x & B_y & B_z \end{vmatrix}, \tag{A1.16}$$

and we deduce (as may be proved geometrically, using the definition of $\boldsymbol{A} \wedge \boldsymbol{B}$) that $\boldsymbol{F} \cdot \boldsymbol{A} \wedge \boldsymbol{B}$ is numerically equal to the volume of a parallelepiped with $\boldsymbol{F}$, $\boldsymbol{A}$, and $\boldsymbol{B}$ as concurrent edges.

The vector operator ∇ (*del*) is defined as

$$\nabla = \boldsymbol{e}_1 \frac{\partial}{\partial x} + \boldsymbol{e}_2 \frac{\partial}{\partial y} + \boldsymbol{e}_3 \frac{\partial}{\partial z}. \tag{A1.17}$$

The *gradient* of a scalar point function, or scalar field, $\psi(\boldsymbol{r})$ is defined as

$$\text{grad}\, \psi = \nabla\psi = \boldsymbol{e}_1 \frac{\partial \psi}{\partial x} + \boldsymbol{e}_2 \frac{\partial \psi}{\partial y} + \boldsymbol{e}_3 \frac{\partial \psi}{\partial z}, \tag{A1.18}$$

and it may be shown that, if $\boldsymbol{n}$ is a unit vector, $\boldsymbol{n} \cdot \nabla\psi$ is the derivative of ψ in the direction of $\boldsymbol{n}$, which may be denoted by $\partial\psi/\partial n$.

The *divergence* of a vector point function, or vector field, $\boldsymbol{F}(\boldsymbol{r})$ is defined as

$$\text{div}\, \boldsymbol{F} = \nabla \cdot \boldsymbol{F} = \frac{\partial F_x}{\partial x} + \frac{\partial F_y}{\partial y} + \frac{\partial F_z}{\partial z}. \tag{A1.19}$$

If we set $\boldsymbol{F} = \nabla\psi$ in equation (A1.19), we obtain

$$\nabla \cdot \nabla\psi = \nabla^2\psi = \frac{\partial^2 \psi}{\partial x^2} + \frac{\partial^2 \psi}{\partial y^2} + \frac{\partial^2 \psi}{\partial z^2}. \tag{A1.20}$$

The operator

$$\nabla^2 = \frac{\partial^2}{\partial x^2} + \frac{\partial^2}{\partial y^2} + \frac{\partial^2}{\partial z^2} \tag{A1.21}$$

is called the *Laplacian operator* †.

Green's theorem, in its most useful form, states that, if $\psi(\boldsymbol{r})$ and $\phi(\boldsymbol{r})$ are scalar point functions,

$$\int_v (\psi\nabla^2\phi - \phi\nabla^2\psi)\mathrm{d}\boldsymbol{r} = \int_S (\psi\nabla\phi - \phi\nabla\psi) \cdot \boldsymbol{n}\,\mathrm{d}S, \tag{A1.22}$$

the integral on the left being taken throughout the volume v within the

† The symbol $\triangle$ is often used in place of ∇^2 to represent the Laplacian operator.

closed surface S, that on the right being a surface integral over S, and $\boldsymbol{n}$ being a unit vector along the outward normal to S at the position of the element dS. If $\partial/\partial n$ denotes differentiation in the direction of $\boldsymbol{n}$, (A1.22) may be written

$$\int_v (\psi\nabla^2\phi - \phi\nabla^2\psi)\mathrm{d}\boldsymbol{r} = \int_S \left(\psi\frac{\partial\phi}{\partial n} - \phi\frac{\partial\psi}{\partial n}\right)\mathrm{d}S. \qquad \text{(A1.23)}$$

Finally, the compactness of vector notation is demonstrated in its application to Taylor's series for a function of three variables, which is used in Chapter 9. Thus, the Taylor's series

$$f(x+a, y+b, z+c) = f(x, y, z) + \left(a\frac{\partial}{\partial x} + b\frac{\partial}{\partial y} + c\frac{\partial}{\partial z}\right) f(x, y, z) + \frac{1}{2!}\left(a\frac{\partial}{\partial x} + b\frac{\partial}{\partial y} + c\frac{\partial}{\partial z}\right)^2 f(x, y, z) + \ldots \qquad \text{(A1.24)}$$

becomes

$$f(\boldsymbol{r}+\boldsymbol{l}) = f(\boldsymbol{r}) + \boldsymbol{l}\cdot\nabla f(\boldsymbol{r}) + \frac{1}{2!}(\boldsymbol{l}\cdot\nabla)^2 f(\boldsymbol{r}) + \ldots, \qquad \text{(A1.25)}$$

where

$$\boldsymbol{l} = a\boldsymbol{e}_1 + b\boldsymbol{e}_2 + c\boldsymbol{e}_3.$$

Appendix 2

EXPANSIONS IN SERIES OF ORTHOGONAL FUNCTIONS

A set of functions $\psi_1(x)$, $\psi_2(x)$, $\psi_3(x)$, ... is *orthonormal*, that is, orthogonal and normalized, in the interval (a, b), if

$$\int_a^b \psi_m^*(x)\psi_n(x)\,\mathrm{d}x = \delta_{mn} \tag{A2.1}$$

for all m and n — δ_{mn} having the value unity if $m = n$ and zero if $m \neq n$. It is said to be a *complete* set if there is no function, not identically zero, which is orthogonal to all the functions ψ_n — in other words, no function $\phi(x)$ exists such that

$$\int_a^b \psi_m^*(x)\phi(x)\,\mathrm{d}x = 0, \quad \text{for } all \ m,$$

except $\phi(x) \equiv 0$. In this case it is possible to expand an arbitrary function $f(x)$, in the interval (a, b), as an infinite series of the form

$$\begin{aligned} f(x) &= a_1\psi_1(x)+a_2\psi_2(x)+a_3\psi_3(x)+\ldots \\ &= \sum_n a_n\psi_n(x). \end{aligned} \tag{A2.2}$$

The constant coefficients a_n, which may be complex numbers, are easily determined by multiplying both sides of (A2.2) by $\psi_m^*(x)$ and integrating over (a, b). This gives

$$\int_a^b \psi_m^*(x)f(x)\,\mathrm{d}x = \sum_n a_n \int_a^b \psi_m^*(x)\psi_n(x)\,\mathrm{d}x,$$

and, according to (A2.1), all the terms on the right hand side vanish except that with $n = m$, and for this term the value of the integral is unity. We thus find

$$a_m = \int_a^b \psi_m^*(x)f(x)\,\mathrm{d}x, \tag{A2.3}$$

which determines the coefficients uniquely. If the functions ψ_n are orthogonal but not normalized, then the right hand side of (A2.3) must be divided by

$$\int_a^b |\psi_m(x)|^2 \mathrm{d}x.$$

In order that such an expansion be possible, that is to say, in order that the series (A2.2) may *converge* to $f(x)$ in (a, b), the function $f(x)$ must, in fact, satisfy certain analytical conditions. These are very wide, however, and certainly less stringent than the conditions which a wave function must satisfy, so we will not consider them explicitly.

It may be noticed that the foregoing is merely a generalization of the familiar method of expanding a function in *Fourier series*. The functions

$$\frac{1}{\sqrt{2\pi}}, \quad \frac{1}{\sqrt{\pi}} \cos nx, \quad \frac{1}{\sqrt{\pi}} \sin nx,$$

where $n = 1, 2, 3, \ldots$, constitute a complete orthonormal set in the interval $(-\pi, \pi)$, and the expansion

$$f(x) = \frac{a_0}{\sqrt{2\pi}} + \frac{1}{\sqrt{\pi}} \sum_{n=1}^{\infty} a_n \cos nx + \frac{1}{\sqrt{\pi}} \sum_{n=1}^{\infty} b_n \sin nx,$$

where

$$a_0 = \frac{1}{\sqrt{2\pi}} \int_{-\pi}^{\pi} f(x) \mathrm{d}x,$$

$$a_n = \frac{1}{\sqrt{\pi}} \int_{-\pi}^{\pi} f(x) \cos nx \mathrm{d}x,$$

$$b_n = \frac{1}{\sqrt{\pi}} \int_{-\pi}^{\pi} f(x) \sin nx \mathrm{d}x,$$

as given by (A2.3), is just the Fourier series representing $f(x)$ in the interval $(-\pi, \pi)$. It is evident from this example that not all the functions of the set need appear in the expansion; that is, some of the coefficients may be zero. For instance, if we expand the function x, which is an *odd* function, in Fourier series, the coefficients a_0 and all the a_n are found to be zero, so that the series consists of sine terms only — it is, in fact

$$x = \sum_{n=1}^{\infty} \frac{2}{n} (-1)^{n+1} \sin nx.$$

This series represents a saw-toothed function, with period 2π, which is equal to x in the interval $(-\pi, \pi)$.

The set of all the wave functions of a system having only discrete energy levels is a complete orthogonal set of the type we have been considering, and these functions may, of course, be normalized. Examples of such systems are the linear harmonic oscillator and the particle in a box. In the latter case, the normalized wave functions are found in Chapter 1 to be

$$\psi_n(x) = \sqrt{\frac{2}{L}} \sin \frac{n\pi x}{L}, \qquad n = 1, 2, 3, \ldots,$$

and these functions constitute a complete orthonormal set in the interval $(0, L)$. We may therefore expand a function $f(x)$ in a series of the form

$$f(x) = \sqrt{\frac{2}{L}} \sum_{n=1}^{\infty} a_n \sin \frac{n\pi x}{L},$$

valid in $(0, L)$, where

$$a_n = \sqrt{\frac{2}{L}} \int_0^L f(x) \sin \frac{n\pi x}{L} \,\mathrm{d}x.$$

If periodic boundary conditions, as defined in § 7.3, are applied to this system, the resulting normalized wave functions have the form

$$\psi_n(x) = \frac{1}{\sqrt{L}} \mathrm{e}^{2\pi i n x/L}, \qquad n = 0, \pm 1, \pm 2, \ldots,$$

which again constitute a complete orthonormal set in the interval $(0, L)$. Since both positive and negative values of n occur, the expansion of a function $f(x)$ in $(0, L)$ is now

$$f(x) = \frac{1}{\sqrt{L}} \sum_{n=-\infty}^{\infty} a_n \mathrm{e}^{2\pi i n x/L},$$

where

$$a_n = \frac{1}{\sqrt{L}} \int_0^L f(x) \mathrm{e}^{-2\pi i n x/L} \mathrm{d}x.$$

A slight complication occurs when, in addition to a discrete series of eigenvalues, a system also has a continuous distribution, or *continuous spectrum*, of eigenvalues. Corresponding to the latter there is a continuous range of eigenfunctions which must be included in the expansion of an arbitrary function. This may be done by adding on to the sum (A2.2) an integral over the continuous range of eigenfunctions. We will omit explicit details, however, as the formal procedure we have described is very little altered. This may be understood from the fact that an integral is just the limit of a sum — we have seen in Chapter 7 that, even when a discrete set of eigenfunctions exists, provided their eigenvalues are sufficiently closely spaced, it is often convenient to replace a sum over them by an integral, and this process may be reversed.

When some of the eigenfunctions are degenerate, it must be ensured that all the independent functions are included in the expansion, and these must be orthogonalized, if necessary, by the method described in § 2.7.2.

Of course, although we have only referred to functions of a single variable, everything we have said applies also to orthogonal sets of functions of any number of variables — the wave functions of a particle in three dimensions, for example, or those of a many-particle system. It is only necessary that the integration in equation (A2.3) be taken over the whole configuration space of the system.

Appendix 3

DETERMINANTS AND SIMULTANEOUS EQUATIONS

A determinant is generally denoted by a square array of symbols, called *elements*, enclosed between vertical lines, the *order* of the determinant being the number of rows (or columns) of elements. The elements may be numbers or functions, and the determinant is equal to a sum of products of elements, called the *expansion* of the determinant, which may be obtained by the application of fixed rules. For example, the expansion of a *second-order determinant* is given by

$$\begin{vmatrix} a_1 & a_2 \\ b_1 & b_2 \end{vmatrix} = a_1 b_2 - a_2 b_1.$$

The expansion of a *third-order determinant* is given by

$$\begin{vmatrix} a_1 & a_2 & a_3 \\ b_1 & b_2 & b_3 \\ c_1 & c_2 & c_3 \end{vmatrix} = a_1 \begin{vmatrix} b_2 & b_3 \\ c_2 & c_3 \end{vmatrix} - a_2 \begin{vmatrix} b_1 & b_3 \\ c_1 & c_3 \end{vmatrix} + a_3 \begin{vmatrix} b_1 & b_2 \\ c_1 & c_2 \end{vmatrix}$$

$$= a_1 b_2 c_3 - a_1 b_3 c_2 - a_2 b_1 c_3 + a_2 b_3 c_1 + a_3 b_1 c_2 - a_3 b_2 c_1. \quad \text{(A3.1)}$$

We note that each term is of the type $a_i b_j c_k$, where (ijk) is a permutation of the numbers (123), and all possible permutations are included. It may be seen also that the permutation (132) can be obtained from (123) by a single *interchange* of the numbers 2 and 3; the permutation (213) is also obtained by a single interchange, of 1 and 2; and the permutation (321) may be obtained by three interchanges, for example, 1 and 2, then 1 and 3, then 2 and 3. These permutations, requiring an odd number of interchanges, are called *odd* permutations — although they may be obtained from (123) by different successions of interchanges, the number will always be found to be odd. All the other permutations may be obtained by an even number of interchanges, and are called *even* permutations — for example, (231) is obtained from (123) by interchanging 1 and 2 and then 1 and 3. Now, the terms for which (ijk) is an odd permutation of (123) have negative sign, and the others have positive sign. Thus, if we introduce a *permutation operator* P to act upon the subscripts, such that $\mathrm{P}a_1b_2c_3 = a_2b_3c_1$, for example, and let p be the number of interchanges making up this permutation, then we may write (A3.1) concisely as

$$\sum_{\mathrm{P}} (-1)^p \mathrm{P} a_1 b_2 c_3,$$

the sum being over all six permutation operators, including the identity operator which leaves (123) unchanged.

If the elements of the determinant are functions, as in Chapter 5, we have

$$\begin{vmatrix} \phi_1(\boldsymbol{x}_1) & \phi_1(\boldsymbol{x}_2) & \phi_1(\boldsymbol{x}_3) \\ \phi_2(\boldsymbol{x}_1) & \phi_2(\boldsymbol{x}_2) & \phi_2(\boldsymbol{x}_3) \\ \phi_3(\boldsymbol{x}_1) & \phi_3(\boldsymbol{x}_2) & \phi_3(\boldsymbol{x}_3) \end{vmatrix}$$

$$\begin{aligned} &= \phi_1(\boldsymbol{x}_1)\phi_2(\boldsymbol{x}_2)\phi_3(\boldsymbol{x}_3) - \phi_1(\boldsymbol{x}_1)\phi_2(\boldsymbol{x}_3)\phi_3(\boldsymbol{x}_2) \\ &\quad - \phi_1(\boldsymbol{x}_2)\phi_2(\boldsymbol{x}_1)\phi_3(\boldsymbol{x}_3) + \phi_1(\boldsymbol{x}_2)\phi_2(\boldsymbol{x}_3)\phi_3(\boldsymbol{x}_1) \\ &\quad + \phi_1(\boldsymbol{x}_3)\phi_2(\boldsymbol{x}_1)\phi_3(\boldsymbol{x}_2) - \phi_1(\boldsymbol{x}_3)\phi_2(\boldsymbol{x}_2)\phi_3(\boldsymbol{x}_1) \\ &= \sum_{\mathrm{P}} (-1)^p \mathrm{P} \phi_1(\boldsymbol{x}_1)\phi_2(\boldsymbol{x}_2)\phi_3(\boldsymbol{x}_3). \end{aligned}$$

It may easily be verified that here the operator P may act upon *either* the subscripts of the ϕ_i *or* the subscripts of the $\boldsymbol{x}_i$. A determinant of any order may be expanded in the same way, so that

$$\sum_{\mathrm{P}} (-1)^p \mathrm{P} \phi_1(\boldsymbol{x}_1)\phi_2(\boldsymbol{x}_2) \ldots \phi_n(\boldsymbol{x}_n)$$

is an *nth order determinant*, the sum being over the $n!$ permutations of the subscripts $(123 \ldots n)$ of either the ϕ_i or the $\boldsymbol{x}_i$, p again being the number of interchanges in the permutation P.

It follows that, if two rows (or two columns) of the determinant are interchanged, the sign of the determinant is changed, for in order to obtain the same permutations of the subscripts p must then in every case be increased by 1, multiplying each term of the original expansion by -1. It also follows that, if the corresponding elements in two rows (or two columns) are the same, the determinant is zero, for an interchange of these rows (or columns) cannot alter the determinant, yet we have just seen that such an interchange must change the sign — if the determinant is unaltered by changing its sign, it must be zero. Other properties of determinants may be obtained in the same way, but these are the essential ones required in the text.

An application of determinants, which we have used in Chapter 3, is to the solution of simultaneous linear equations. For example, let us consider the pair of linear equations

$$a_1x+a_2y = 0,$$
$$b_1x+b_2y = 0,$$

in the two unknowns x and y, the coefficients being constants. Such equations are said to be *homogeneous*, because all the terms are of the same type — in particular, there is no term not containing x or y. One solution is $x = y = 0$, but this is generally of no physical significance. However, this is the *only* solution, unless

$$\frac{a_1}{b_1} = \frac{a_2}{b_2},$$

that is, unless

$$\begin{vmatrix} a_1 & a_2 \\ b_1 & b_2 \end{vmatrix} = 0.$$

If this is so, the equations have a non-zero solution and are said to be *consistent*. It should be noticed, however, that they cannot be solved for x and y separately, but only for the ratio x/y; thus,

$$\frac{x}{y} = -\frac{a_2}{a_1} = -\frac{b_2}{b_1}.$$

As a slightly less trivial example, let us consider the three homogeneous equations

$$a_1x+a_2y+a_3z = 0,$$
$$b_1x+b_2y+b_3z = 0,$$
$$c_1x+c_2y+c_3z = 0,$$

in the three unknowns x, y, and z. One solution is, again, $x = y = z = 0$, but we want the condition for the existence of a non-zero solution. By straightforward solution of the last two equations for the ratios x/z and y/z, we find

$$\frac{x}{\begin{vmatrix} b_2 & b_3 \\ c_2 & c_3 \end{vmatrix}} = \frac{-y}{\begin{vmatrix} b_1 & b_3 \\ c_1 & c_3 \end{vmatrix}} = \frac{z}{\begin{vmatrix} b_1 & b_2 \\ c_1 & c_2 \end{vmatrix}},$$

and substitution in the first equation gives

$$a_1\begin{vmatrix} b_2 & b_3 \\ c_2 & c_3 \end{vmatrix} - a_2\begin{vmatrix} b_1 & b_3 \\ c_1 & c_3 \end{vmatrix} + a_3\begin{vmatrix} b_1 & b_2 \\ c_1 & c_2 \end{vmatrix} = 0,$$

or

$$\begin{vmatrix} a_1 & a_2 & a_3 \\ b_1 & b_2 & b_3 \\ c_1 & c_2 & c_3 \end{vmatrix} = 0,$$

which is the condition for consistency. Similarly, in the case of n homogeneous equations in n unknowns, a non-zero solution exists *only if the determinant of the coefficients vanishes.* Even if consistent, however, the equations can only be solved for the ratios of the unknowns.

Appendix 4

SOME USEFUL INTEGRALS

1. $$\int_0^\infty x^n e^{-ax} dx = \frac{n!}{a^{n+1}}, \qquad n > -1, \quad a > 0.$$

2. $$\int_0^\infty e^{-ax^2} dx = \tfrac{1}{2}\sqrt{\frac{\pi}{a}}.$$

3. $$\int_0^\infty \frac{\sin x}{x} dx = \frac{\pi}{2}.$$

4. An integral of the type

$$\iint \frac{\rho(r_1)\rho(r_2)}{|\boldsymbol{r}_1 - \boldsymbol{r}_2|} d\boldsymbol{r}_1 d\boldsymbol{r}_2,$$

where $\rho(r)$ is a spherically symmetrical function, and the integrations are over all space, may be evaluated using the fact that it represents *twice* the self-potential energy of a spherically symmetrical charge distribution of density $\rho(r)$.

Let us consider the work which must be done in building up this charge distribution outwards from the origin, and let us assume that a sphere of charge of radius r has already been completed. The potential at the surface of this sphere is

$$\frac{1}{r}\int_0^r 4\pi r^2 \rho(r) dr.$$

The work which must be done to bring sufficient charge from infinity to form a shell of thickness dr, and density $\rho(r)$, at the surface of the sphere is, therefore,

$$4\pi r^2 \rho(r) dr \cdot \frac{1}{r}\int_0^r 4\pi r^2 \rho(r) dr,$$

and it follows that the self-potential energy of the whole distribution is

$$\int_0^\infty 4\pi r \rho(r) dr \int_0^r 4\pi r^2 \rho(r) dr.$$

The required value of the integral is twice this, namely,

$$32\pi^2 \int_0^\infty r\rho(r)\,\mathrm{d}r \int_0^r r^2 \rho(r)\,\mathrm{d}r.$$

As an example, in § 3.3 it is required to evaluate

$$\iint \frac{1}{r_{12}} \mathrm{e}^{-2\alpha(r_1+r_2)}\,\mathrm{d}\boldsymbol{r}_1\,\mathrm{d}\boldsymbol{r}_2.$$

Here $\rho(r) = \mathrm{e}^{-2\alpha r}$, so that the value of the integral is

$$32\pi^2 \int_0^\infty r\mathrm{e}^{-2\alpha r}\,\mathrm{d}r \int_0^r r^2 \mathrm{e}^{-2\alpha r}\,\mathrm{d}r$$

$$= 32\pi^2 \int_0^\infty r\mathrm{e}^{-2\alpha r} \left[\frac{1}{4\alpha^3} - \left(\frac{r^2}{2\alpha} + \frac{r}{2\alpha^2} + \frac{1}{4\alpha^3}\right)\mathrm{e}^{-2\alpha r}\right]\mathrm{d}r$$

$$= 32\pi^2 \left[\frac{1}{4\alpha^3}\frac{1}{(2\alpha)^2} - \frac{1}{2\alpha}\frac{6}{(4\alpha)^4} - \frac{1}{2\alpha^2}\frac{2}{(4\alpha)^3} - \frac{1}{4\alpha^3}\frac{1}{(4\alpha)^2}\right]$$

$$= \frac{5\pi^2}{8\alpha^5}.$$

If the integrals are not over all space, but are to be taken throughout a sphere, centred at the origin, and of radius R, it is only necessary to substitute R for ∞ in the upper limit of integration.

Bibliography

The following bibliography is not intended to be exhaustive, but is merely a short guide to further reading.

A. QUANTUM MECHANICS AND ATOMIC PHYSICS

BORN, M., Atomic Physics, 6th ed. (Blackie, 1957).

HARTREE, D. R., The Calculation of Atomic Structures (Wiley, 1957). (Contains an account of the theory and practical application to atoms of the Hartree and Hartree-Fock methods).

MOTT, N. F., and I. N. SNEDDON, Wave Mechanics and its Applications, (Oxford University Press, 1948).

PAULING, L. and E. B. WILSON, Introduction to Quantum Mechanics. (McGraw-Hill, 1935).

SCHIFF, L. I., Quantum Mechanics, 2nd ed. (McGraw-Hill, 1952).

TOLMAN, R. C., The Principles of Statistical Mechanics (Oxford University Press, 1938). (Chapter 2 remains one of the most elegant and readable introductions to formal quantum mechanics).

B. INTRODUCTORY WORKS ON SOLID STATE PHYSICS, INCLUDING THE ELECTRON THEORY OF METALS

COTTRELL, A. H., Theoretical Structural Metallurgy, 2nd ed., (Arnold, 1955). (This book and the following one contain little mathematics. They are recommended for background reading before studying the present book.)

HUME-ROTHERY, W., Atomic Theory for Students of Metallurgy, 2nd ed. (The Institute of Metals, 1952).

KITTEL, C., Introduction to Solid State Physics, 2nd ed. (Wiley, 1956). (Chapters 10—12 contain an elementary account of the electron theory of metals.)

SLATER, J. C., Quantum Theory of Matter (McGraw-Hill, 1951). (An excellent introduction to solid state theory.)

C. ADVANCED WORKS ON SOLID STATE PHYSICS, INCLUDING THE ELECTRON THEORY OF METALS

JONES, H., The Theory of Brillouin Zones and Electronic States in Crystals (North-Holland, 1960). (A valuable account of the one-electron approximation in the theory of solids, containing a full treatment of the group theory required in the calculation of wave functions.)

MOTT, N. F. and H. JONES, The Theory of the Properties of Metals and Alloys (Oxford University Press, 1936). (A classic work which is still indispensable to metal theorists.)

PEIERLS, R. E., Quantum Theory of Solids (Oxford University Press, 1955). (A compact work which concentrates on basic theory, rather than on applications. It presupposes a fair knowledge of quantum mechanics.)

SEITZ, F., The Modern Theory of Solids (McGraw-Hill, 1940). (This remains the most comprehensive work on solid state theory, but is by no means easy for a beginner.)

WILSON, A. H., The Theory of Metals, 2nd ed. (Cambridge University Press, 1953). (Another classic work, containing a detailed treatment of the theory of conductivity.)

ZIMAN, J. M., Electrons and Phonons (Oxford University Press, 1960). (The most complete account of the theory of conductivity to date, containing also a useful introduction to the electron theory of metals.)

D. USEFUL REVIEW ARTICLES, NOT MENTIONED IN THE TEXT

JONES, H., Theory of Electrical and Thermal Conductivity in Metals, Handbuch der Physik, vol. 19 (Springer, Berlin, 1957) p. 227.

LÖWDIN, P. O., Quantum Theory of Cohesive Properties of Solids, Advances in Physics, vol. 5, no. 17 (1956).

PIPPARD, A. B., Experimental Analysis of the Electronic Structure of Metals, Reports on Progress in Physics, vol. 23 (1960) p. 176.

REITZ, J. R., Methods of the One-Electron Theory of Solids, Solid State Physics, vol. 1 (Academic Press, New York, 1955) p. 1.

PROBLEMS

Problems (Chapter 1)

1.1. The most rapidly moving valence electron in metallic sodium, at the absolute zero of temperature, has a kinetic energy of about 3 eV. Show that its de Broglie wavelength is roughly 7Å.

[1 eV $= 1.6020 \times 10^{-12}$ ergs, $h = 6.624 \times 10^{-27}$ erg sec, $m = 9.1066 \times 10^{-28}$ g.]

1.2. Show that the wave functions of a system are unchanged if the potential energy is increased by the same amount everywhere. What happens to the energy levels?

1.3. Equation (1.28) may be solved graphically, for given L and V_0, by plotting both sides as functions of E and finding the values of E at which the two graphs intersect. By considering this graphical method of solution, show that, for a particle in a one-dimensional well, there is always at least one bound state, no matter how small V_0 may be.

1.4. Show that the wave functions of the three states of lowest energy of the harmonic oscillator, given in equations (1.64), (1.65) and (1.66), are normalized and orthogonal.

1.5. In the problem of the particle in a one-dimensional box, discussed in § 1.5, suppose that L is so large that the energy levels (1.29) form practically a continuum. Find the number of states with energies less than E, and by differentiating this with respect to E, show that the density of states (that is, the number of states per unit energy range) at energy E is

$$\frac{L}{\hbar\pi}\sqrt{\frac{m}{2E}}.$$

[This is the one-dimensional analogue of the problem discussed in § 7.2.]

Problems (Chapter 2)

2.1. Find the wave functions and energy levels of the particle in a box, discussed in § 2.3, if the box has unequal sides a, b, c.

2.2. The potential energy of a three-dimensional isotropic harmonic oscillator is

$$V(r) = \tfrac{1}{2}m\omega_0^2 r^2.$$

Write down the Schrödinger equation for this system in Cartesian coordinates, and separate it into three ordinary equations. Hence, using the results of § 1.8, find the three lowest energy levels, and state the degeneracy of each.

2.3. Show that the average value of the potential energy of the electron in the ground state of the hydrogen atom is $-e^2/a_0$.

Show also that the *most probable* distance of the electron from the nucleus, in the same state, is a_0. [*Hint*: Find the probability of the electron being in a thin spherical shell of radius r, and calculate the value of r for which this is a maximum, keeping the thickness constant.]

2.4. Verify the uncertainty relation (2.152) for any state of the particle in a one-dimensional box (§ 1.5), and also for the ground state of the harmonic oscillator (§ 1.8).

2.5. Show that the operators L_x, L_y, L_z, representing the components of the angular momentum of a particle about the origin, satisfy the commutation relations

$$[L_x, L_y] = \mathrm{i}\hbar L_z, \quad [L_y, L_z] = \mathrm{i}\hbar L_x, \quad [L_z, L_x] = \mathrm{i}\hbar L_y.$$

2.6. Show that the functions $\mathrm{e}^{\mathrm{i}\phi}$, 1, $\mathrm{e}^{-\mathrm{i}\phi}$ form an orthogonal set in the interval $(0, 2\pi)$ of ϕ, and that so do the functions $\sin\phi$, 1, $\cos\phi$, obtained by linear combination of the members of the first set.

2.7. If the operator S is a function of q, the coordinate conjugate to the momentum p, prove that

$$[p, S] = \frac{\hbar}{\mathrm{i}}\frac{\partial S}{\partial q}.$$

2.8. Given three independent degenerate wave functions which are not necessarily orthogonal, construct linear combinations of them which are both normalized and orthogonal.

Problems (Chapter 3)

3.1. Use the variational method to obtain the energy of the ground state of a hydrogen atom, assuming a trial function of the form $e^{-\alpha r}$.

3.2. The potential energy of a perturbed harmonic oscillator is

$$V(x) = \tfrac{1}{2}m\omega_0^2 x^2 + \lambda x^4,$$

where λ is a small constant. Obtain an approximation to the energy of the ground state by means of first-order perturbation theory.

If the perturbing term were λx^3, show that the first-order correction to the ground state energy would vanish, and obtain the first-order correction to the energy of the first excited state.

3.3. The potential energy of an electron is zero within a sphere of radius R, centred at the origin, and it is one rydberg outside this sphere. Use the variational method to obtain an approximation to the energy of the ground state, assuming a trial function of the form $e^{-\alpha r}$.

3.4. A helium-like atom has two electrons and atomic number Z. Write down its Hamiltonian in the atomic units defined in § 3.3. Show, by means of the variational method, that the best approximation to the ground state energy, given by a trial function of the form $e^{-\alpha(r_1+r_2)}$, is $-2(Z-\frac{5}{16})^2$ ryd, and that this is obtained when $\alpha = Z-\frac{5}{16}$.

Verify that the ground-state energy of the hydrogenic atom which remains when one electron is removed completely is $-Z^2$, and hence that the first ionization energy (the energy required to remove one electron) of the helium-like atom is approximately $Z^2-\frac{5}{4}Z+\frac{25}{128}$ ryd. In the case of helium compare the value given by this expression with the observed value, 1.80 ryd.

3.5. The particle in a one-dimensional box, discussed in § 1.5, is subjected to a perturbing field in which the potential energy of the particle is λx, where λ is a small constant (for example, the particle might be an electron, and the applied field a uniform electrostatic one). Show that the first-order perturbation correction to the energy of the state ψ_n is $\lambda L/2$, and that the second-order correction is

$$\frac{32m\lambda^2 L^4}{\hbar^2\pi^6}\sum_{j\neq n}[1-(-1)^{n+j}]^2\,\frac{n^2 j^2}{(j^2-n^2)^5},$$

the sum being over all positive integral values of j except n.

Problems (Chapter 4)

4.1. Using the order of filling one-electron states given in § 4.3, write down the normal configurations of Al (13 electrons,) Fe (26 electrons), Rb (37 electrons), Cd (48 electrons) and Pb (82 electrons), in each case noting which shells are closed.

4.2. Calculate the first ionization energies of He, Li, Be and B, in their ground states, on the assumption that electronic interaction may be neglected. and compare your results with the experimental values of 24.5, 5.4, 9.3 and 8.3 eV respectively.

4.3. Show that the total charge cloud of the electrons in a closed L shell is spherically symmetrical.

4.4. Show that E in equation (4.11) is given by

$$E = \sum_{i=1}^{N} \varepsilon_i - \sum_{i=1}^{N} \int |\psi_i(\boldsymbol{r}_i)|^2 V_i(\boldsymbol{r}_i) \mathrm{d}\boldsymbol{r}_i + \tfrac{1}{2} \sum_{i \neq j}^{N} \sum^{N} \iint \frac{e^2}{r_{ij}} |\psi_i(\boldsymbol{r}_i)|^2 |\psi_j(\boldsymbol{r}_j)|^2 \mathrm{d}\boldsymbol{r}_i \mathrm{d}\boldsymbol{r}_j,$$

when the functions ψ_i are normalized.

4.5. Write down the Hartree equation, in the atomic units defined in § 3.3, for an electron in the ground state of a helium-like atom with two electrons and atomic number Z. Obtain a first approximation to the eigenvalue ε of this equation by assuming the one-electron wave functions to have the form $\exp[-(Z-\frac{5}{16})r]$. Compare $-\varepsilon$ with the approximation to the first ionization energy of this atom obtained in Problem 3.4, and note that the two are very nearly the same when Z is large.
[$-\varepsilon = Z^2 - \frac{5}{4}Z + \frac{75}{256}$, approximately.]

4.6. Show that the one-electron wave functions obtained by the Hartree method for an atom are not orthogonal.

Problems (Chapter 5)

5.1. An electron moves in a central electrostatic field. When a magnetic field is switched on in the positive z-direction the Schrödinger equation is equation (5.9). Treat the term due to the magnetic field as a perturbation and assume that the unperturbed state is a p state with degenerate wave functions

$$R(r) \sin\theta \sin\phi, \quad R(r) \cos\theta, \quad R(r) \sin\theta \cos\phi.$$

Set up the secular equation and solve it, showing that the perturbed energy levels are given by equation (5.11) with $m_l = -1, 0, 1$.

5.2. Write down the determinantal wave function for the ground state of a system consisting of two helium atoms, according to the Heitler-London method. Assume that two of the electrons occupy the 1s atomic orbital ψ_A, centred on nucleus A, with opposite spins, and two the 1s atomic orbital ψ_B, centred on nucleus B. By adding and subtracting rows of the determinant (which leaves it unchanged) show that it is equivalent to a determinant formed from the functions $\psi_A \pm \psi_B$, with appropriate spin factors. Deduce that the Heitler-London and LCAO approximations lead to the same results for this system.

5.3. Prove, for two-electron and three-electron systems, that the *only* antisymmetric wave function of the form (5.22), is the determinant (5.24).

5.4. Consider the normalized determinantal wave function

$$\Phi = \frac{1}{\sqrt{N!}} \begin{vmatrix} \phi_1(\mathbf{x}_1) & \dots & \phi_1(\mathbf{x}_N) \\ \vdots & & \vdots \\ \phi_N(\mathbf{x}_1) & \dots & \phi_N(\mathbf{x}_N) \end{vmatrix},$$

the normalized, orthogonal functions ϕ_i being given by

$$\phi_i(\mathbf{x}) = \psi_i(\mathbf{r})\alpha(\zeta), \quad \text{for} \quad i = 1 \text{ to } n,$$

and

$$\phi_i(\mathbf{x}) = \psi_i(\mathbf{r})\beta(\zeta), \quad \text{for} \quad i = n+1 \text{ to } N.$$

If F is a symmetric operator, independent of spin, prove that

$$\int \Phi^* F \Phi \, d\tau' = \int \Psi^* F \Psi \, d\tau,$$

where

$$\Psi = \frac{1}{\sqrt{n!(N-n)!}} \begin{vmatrix} \psi_1(\mathbf{r}_1) & \dots & \psi_1(\mathbf{r}_N) \\ \vdots & & \vdots \\ \psi_n(\mathbf{r}_1) & \dots & \psi_n(\mathbf{r}_n) \end{vmatrix} \cdot \begin{vmatrix} \psi_{n+1}(\mathbf{r}_{n+1}) & \dots & \psi_{n+1}(\mathbf{r}_N) \\ \vdots & & \vdots \\ \psi_N(\mathbf{r}_{n+1}) & \dots & \psi_N(\mathbf{r}_N) \end{vmatrix},$$

the first determinant being formed from orbitals associated with spin α and the second from orbitals associated with spin β, but spin being otherwise ignored.

Prove also that Ψ is normalized.

Problems (Chapter 6)

6.1. Construct the Hamiltonian operator, similar to (6.1), for an alloy consisting of N_1 atoms with atomic number Z_1 and N_2 atoms with atomic number Z_2. If the atoms are monovalent and divalent respectively, and the ion-cores are small, obtain a modified Hamiltonian, similar to (6.4).

6.2. Verify that for the ground state of a helium atom, in which the two electrons occupy the same orbital, with opposite spins, the Fock equation (6.22) reduces to the Hartree equation (4.18). What is the exchange energy in this case?

6.3. The energy of a metal corresponding to the determinantal wave function Φ of Problem 5.4 is given by equation (6.18). Show that the same energy is obtained from the formula $\int \Psi^* H \Psi \, d\tau$, where Ψ is the product of determinants also given in Problem 5.4.

Problems (Chapter 7)

7.1. Obtain the relation between pressure and volume in a free-electron gas at 0°K, using the Hartree theory [see equation (9.87)]. How is this modified when the Hartree-Fock theory is used?

7.2. A free-electron gas would be ferromagnetic if all the electrons had the same spin, so that in the ground state at 0°K all the orbitals of lowest energy would be occupied by one electron each. Show that, according to the Hartree-Fock theory, the average energy per electron would be

$$\frac{3.51}{r_s^2} - \frac{1.154}{r_s} \text{ ryd.}$$

By comparing this with equation (7.54) show that, according to this theory, a free-electron gas would be ferromagnetic if the atomic radius were greater than about 5.5 B.u. What factor has been omitted which might prevent this?

7.3. Find the average charge density at distance r from a given electron in a ferromagnetic free-electron gas at 0°K, according to the Hartree-Fock theory.

Problems (Chapter 8)

8.1. Find the number of states per atom inside a sphere which just touches the faces of the first Brillouin zone of the simple cubic, body-centred cubic and face-centred cubic lattices. [Ans.: 1.05, 1.48, 1.36.]

8.2. Draw free-electron energy contours in the first and second Brillouin zones for a two-dimensional square lattice, according to the extended and the reduced zone schemes.

8.3. Compare the free-electron energy at the centres of the faces and at the corner points of the first Brillouin zone for each of the cubic lattices.

8.4. Show that, in the application of the tight binding method to a simple cubic lattice given in § 8.10, one of the energy contours on each of the planes $k_1 = 0$, $k_1 = \pi/a$ is a square.

8.5. Show that, according to the tight binding approximation using only atomic s states, the one-electron energies for the body-centred cubic and face-centred cubic lattices are given by

$$\varepsilon(\mathbf{k}) = \varepsilon_0 - \alpha - 8\gamma \cos k_1 a \cos k_2 a \cos k_3 a,$$

$$\varepsilon(\mathbf{k}) = \varepsilon_0 - \alpha - 4\gamma (\cos k_1 a \cos k_2 a + \cos k_2 a \cos k_3 a + \cos k_3 a \cos k_1 a),$$

respectively, where $2a$ is the length of the edge of the cubic cell. Show also that, near $k = 0$, the effective mass is $\hbar^2/8\gamma a^2$ in both cases.

8.6. Show that, when periodic boundary conditions are used, the Hartree self-consistent field in a metal has the period of the lattice.

8.7. The potential energy of a particle in a one-dimensional lattice has the constant value V_0 in regions of width b, which are separated by regions of width a in which the potential energy is zero. Solve the Schrödinger equation in two consecutive regions and, assuming that the wave functions have the Bloch form, prove that

$$\cos k(a+b) = \cos \beta a \cosh \gamma b + [(\gamma^2 - \beta^2)/2\beta\gamma] \sin \beta a \sinh \gamma b,$$

where

$$\beta = (2mE/\hbar^2)^{\frac{1}{2}} \text{ and } \gamma = [2m(V_0 - E)/\hbar^2]^{\frac{1}{2}}.$$

[E is the energy of the state with wave number k.]

If V_0 is allowed to approach infinity and b to approach zero in such a way that bV_0 remains finite, the limiting value of the expression $mabV_0/\hbar^2$ being P, show that

$$\cos ka = (P/\beta a) \sin \beta a + \cos \beta a.$$

Plotting the right hand side as a function of βa, and noting that the left hand side lies between -1 and 1 for real values of k, observe that there are alternately allowed and forbidden energy regions, the latter becoming smaller as the energy increases. [This is the Kronig and Penney model of a one-dimensional lattice.]

Problems (Chapter 9)

9.1. By analogy with equation (8.85) for the faces of a Brillouin zone, obtain the equations of the faces of the atomic polyhedra of the two cubic lattices shown in figure 9.1.

9.2. According to the method of Wigner and Seitz, the Schrödinger equation for the lowest electronic state in *metallic hydrogen* within an atomic sphere, using the atomic units defined in § 3.3, is

$$\frac{\mathrm{d}^2\psi_0}{\mathrm{d}r^2}+\frac{2}{r}\frac{\mathrm{d}\psi_0}{\mathrm{d}r}+\left(\varepsilon_0+\frac{2}{r}\right)\psi_0=0,$$

subject to the boundary condition

$$\frac{\mathrm{d}\psi_0}{\mathrm{d}r}=0 \quad \text{at } r=r_\mathrm{s}.$$

Find ε_0 as a function of r_s, approximately, assuming ψ_0 to be roughly given by

$$\psi_0=\mathrm{e}^{-r}+\mathrm{e}^{r-2r_\mathrm{s}}.$$

[This is not a true solution of the Schrödinger equation, but it satisfies the correct boundary condition and tends to e^{-r} as r_s tends to infinity, as the correct solution should.]

Obtain an approximation to the average energy E per electron by adding to ε_0 the free-electron Fermi energy. Plot E as a function of r_s, and find approximate values of the cohesive energy and equilibrium atomic radius.

9.3. It can be shown that for a metal of valency Z the eigenvalue of equation (9.10) depends upon r_s approximately according to the equation

$$\varepsilon_0(r_\mathrm{s})=Z\left(\frac{A}{r_\mathrm{s}^3}-\frac{3}{r_\mathrm{s}}\right), \quad \text{(atomic units)}$$

for values of r_s near the equilibrium atomic radius, A being a constant. Use this equation in conjunction with equation (9.92), taking α to be unity, to calculate A for metallic magnesium, given that the equilibrium atomic radius is 3.3 B.u. Hence find an approximate value for the compressibility of this metal.

Problems (Chapter 10)

10.1. Using published tables of atomic radii or atomic volumes, calculate $\hbar\omega_p$ for beryllium, magnesium, aluminium and copper. [Ans.: 19, 11, 16, 11 eV.]

10.2. Calculate the band widths of sodium, magnesium and aluminium, according to equation (10.65), with β given by (10.91), and compare them with the calculated and experimental values given in Table 1 of § 7.9.

10.3. Verify equation (10.76) for $(H_{\text{s.r.}})_{0j}$.

10.4. Plot the graph of the correlation energy given by equation (10.93), for r_s between 1 B.u. and 6 B.u., and compare it with that of the Wigner formula (9.82).

10.5. An electron with an energy of several thousand electron volts and momentum $\boldsymbol{p}$ penetrates a thin metallic film. In so doing it excites a single plasmon, losing energy $\hbar\omega$ and being scattered through an angle θ. If $\hbar\boldsymbol{k}$ is the momentum absorbed by the plasmon, show that, to a good approximation,

$$p\theta = \hbar k.$$

Using this expression in the dispersion relation (10.3), obtain the approximate equation

$$\hbar\omega = \hbar\omega_p + \gamma \frac{p^2}{m} \theta^2,$$

where $\gamma = 3\zeta_0/5\hbar\omega_p$, assuming a free-electron gas in the metal. [This relation between energy loss and scattering angle has afforded an experimental test of the plasma theory.]

If the energy of the incident electron is 25 keV, show that for aluminium, with $\hbar\omega_p = 16$ eV, the *maximum* scattering angle, assuming k_c to be given by (10.91), is about 10^{-2} radians.

Problems (Chapter 11)

11.1. Extend the work of § 11.6 to three dimensions.

11.2. The wave function of the electron in a hydrogen atom in the state $n = 2$, $l = 1$, $m_l = 1$ is

$$\psi = Are^{-r/a} \sin\theta\, e^{i\phi},$$

where $a = 2\hbar^2/me^2$ and A is a constant. Using equation (11.34) for the current density, show that the magnetic field at the nucleus due to the orbital motion is $e^7m^2/24\hbar^5c$ gauss. [The field due to a charge $-e$ moving with velocity $\boldsymbol{v}$, at a point whose position vector with respect to the charge is $\boldsymbol{r}$, is $e\boldsymbol{r}\wedge\boldsymbol{v}/cr^3$.]

11.3. For the wave packet given in equation (11.67), show that the maximum probability density decreases to one half its value at $t = 0$ when the packet has travelled a distance $4\pi a^2\sqrt{3}/\lambda$, where λ is the mean wavelength.

11.4. Find the acceleration of an electron in an electric field $\boldsymbol{E}$ when $\varepsilon(\boldsymbol{k})$ is given by equation (8.116).

11.5. Assuming the free-electron model of a metal described in Chapter 7, calculate the matrix element $U_{\boldsymbol{k}'\boldsymbol{k}}$ for the scattering of an electron from an initial state $\boldsymbol{k}$ into a final state $\boldsymbol{k}'$ by a field in which the potential energy of the electron is

$$U = \frac{e^2}{r}\mathrm{e}^{-\lambda r},$$

where λ is a positive constant. [The necessary integration may, to a sufficiently good approximation, be taken throughout the whole of space, rather than throughout the volume v of the metal.]

If $\boldsymbol{k}$ lies on the Fermi surface, show that the probability per unit time of a transition from $\boldsymbol{k}$ to a region of the Fermi surface lying within an element of solid angle $\mathrm{d}\omega$ about the direction of $\boldsymbol{k}'$ is

$$\frac{8\pi^2e^4N(\zeta_0)\mathrm{d}\omega}{\hbar v^2(\lambda^2+|\boldsymbol{k}-\boldsymbol{k}'|^2)^2},$$

where $N(\zeta_0)$ is the density of states in energy at the Fermi surface, according to the free-electron approximation.

INDEX